Robotics and Automated Manufacturing

G000143956

Robotics and Automated Manufacturing

D Sharon · J Harstein · G Yantian
World ORT Union

Pitman Publishing

PITMAN PUBLISHING
128 Long Acre, London WC2E 9AN

Sharan, D.
  Robotics and automated manufacturing.
  1. Robots, Industrial
  I. Title   II. Hartstein, J.   III. Yantian, G.
  629.8'92   TS191.8

  ISBN 0 273 02443 4

Printed at The Bath Press, Avon

Contents

1 Introduction   1

2 Control   7
Open loop and closed loop control   7
Servomechanisms   10
Controlling different types of drive   13
Types of feedback control action   13
Transient response   15
Servo and non-servo controlled robots   17
Adaptive control   23
Off-line programming   24

3 Electronics and Microprocessors   27
Signals   27
Digital circuits   29
Packaged electronics – the integrated circuit   33
Integrated circuit applications   36
Microprocessors   39

4 Computers   47
Mainframes, minis and micros   47
The programmable logic controller   49
Programming languages   50
Compilers and interpreters   53
The three-bus system   54
Input/output management   56
Interrupts and handshaking   60
Timers   61
Advanced computers   62

5 Robot Geometry and Drive Mechanisms   65
Axes of motion and degrees of freedom   66
Robot geometry   68
Hydraulic actuators   74

Pneumatic actuators 80
Electric motors 82
Components of drive systems: gears 92
Belts and chains 101

6 End Effectors, Sensors and Robot Vision 104
End effectors: introduction 104
Types of gripper 106
Tools 116
Programmed end effector changing 120
Sensors: introduction 121
Types of sensor 125
Robot vision 135
Practical vision systems 140

7 Robotics in Industry 149
Work cells 149
Setting up a work cell – a case study 151
Identifying the robot: options and problems 155
Specifying the robot 158
Installation and commissioning 168
Reliability and maintenance 171
Mixed robot-man systems 175

8 Computerised Design and Manufacture 179
Design 179
The computer in draughting and design 183
Computer graphics 184
CAD software 190
Computers in automated manufacturing 196
Integrating the computer into the factory 201
Flexible manufacturing systems (FMS) 208

9 Robots and Economics 215
The production process 215
Financial and management issues 217
The economic benefits of robot installations 222

10 Current and Future Developments 229
Vision systems 230
Programmability 233
Gripper dexterity 234
Size/weight 236
Flexibility 238
Control 239

Communications   242

Appendix I   Optical shaft encoders and the variable transformer   245
Appendix II   Binary numbers, Boolean algebra and logic gates   249
Appendix III   Robot specification sheets   262

Index   269

Preface

Though in strictly economic terms robotics is not the most important wealth creator for the manufacturing industry, it has become the symbol of the technological style of our generation. The reason is that not only do robots encourage us to imagine machines as our competitors, but they also represent the technological motto of our generation: "automate or die". The proliferation of robots – and indeed all other computer-controlled manufacturing and information-handling equipment – is symptomatic of the fundamental change that has taken place in our activities. Whilst, in handling information, we today let machines take care of all the activities which can be automated (i.e. those activities for which an algorithm can be written), in manufacturing we have moved from the automation of a single machine towards the automation of the whole manufacturing process. In other words, we have moved from what we may define as "internal automation" – the automation of a single machine – towards what we define as "external automation" – the automation of the whole manufacturing process, of which the robot is a typical representative.

As the factory becomes a giant computer-controlled complex, with economic, social and organisational consequences, the role of its personnel changes. In the past the worker provided the power as well as the control of the production process. It was power that was at the heart of the first industrial revolution and it is control that is at the heart of the second. Not only do we have to get used to a different role within the manufacturing process, but we need to be able to communicate – and indeed think – in a totally new language. It is this new language that our book is mostly about. Our work in the field of educational robotics during the last six years has brought us to the conclusion that, in addition to its inherent importance, this field has a tremendous potential as a first-class educational environment. It provides the learner, still accustomed to the analogue kind of thinking, with an excellent tool to enable him or her to make the transfer to the digital kind of reasoning essential for today's technology.

Whilst in the past information was handled in an analogue way, today we must be able to transform the information to a computer-comprehensible set of discrete commands as a step-by-step sequence. Today's world requires new disciplines to be learned, new approaches to be taken. We must be able to effectively master the vocabulary, environment and syntax of the new language technology is speaking today. Having adopted this "language approach" to new technologies, our team in ORT developed its concept of "new literacies". A person who is "computer literate" or "robotics literate" must be able to operate in those environments, communicate with the various devices and instruct them in a meaningful way. From the literacy level one can move on to higher-level courses and progress towards increasing levels of competence. Just as one requires a basic degree of alphabetic literacy to be able to make a contribution to and take benefit from society in general, one is doomed to flounder in an industrial society without the basic technological literacy required today. This knowledge, in our view, must be perceived as essential for everybody and not just for experts. To be truly literate in a technological subject one must have had a combination of theoretical instruction and practical experience, such as the one provided by our robotics course. The traditional approach, taken by many when relating to technology, that skill-based training is enough was possible, though wrong, in the past. It is impossible today. This book is designed to start the process by providing the reader with the basic background needed.

Robotics is a multi-disciplinary subject embracing elements of electronics, mechanical engineering, pneumatics, hydraulics, control theory, computer science, electrical machines, as well as economics and sociology, In addition to the ability to program an automatic environment, the student gains appreciation in those fields and understands how modern industrial practice involves the close integration of all individual component subjects. This, in many ways, solves another educational problem typical of modern times, the problem of the totally new way in which technology is "cutting" through traditional disciplines. With the arrival of the subject of robotics – and indeed the educational robot – we are able to provide a powerful demonstration of the importance of integrating the individual learning disciplines. In this book the reader will find reflected the dual nature of robotics – it is an important subject in its own right and, at the same time, an "umbrella" subject for all its component topics.

This book is a result of our work in the field of educational robotics during the last six years. In addition to ORT's fully fledged ROBOTICS AND AUTOMATION course that was developed during the last three years as an open learning course in cooperation with the OPEN TECH unit of the MSC, we felt that there is a need for a book which can reach a broader audience. This book is our response to that need. We wish to express our gratitude to the leading team within the MSC OPEN TECH unit with whom we cooperated during the last three years, and to the WORLD ORT UNION who supported us by providing the encouraging environment without which this work could not have been completed.

D. Sharon, J. Harstein, G. Yantian
London, December 1986

1 Introduction

Figure 1.1 describes the relationship between industrial output and employment in the developed countries between 1950 and 1978 as studied by Rothwell [1980]. There are three distinct phases to this curve: the first, up until 1965, in which industrial output increases linearly with the number of employees; the second, between 1965 and 1973, where in spite of growth in industrial output the number of employees remains constant; and the third, following 1973, through which industrial output still grows in spite of a rather steep decline in the number of employees.

The first phase is typical of the emergence of a new technology, when capital is being invested in setting up new plants, creating new jobs. During the second phase the technology reaches maturity and the increase in production output is reached by improving methods and by making plants more efficient. The third phase is the one where industry, due to severe competition on the one

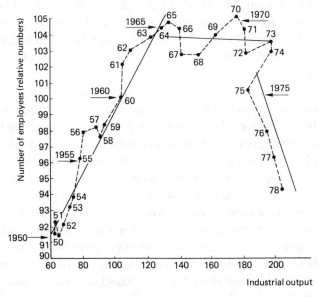

Fig 1.1   Industrial employment vs. industrial output (industrial output as well as the number employed are given in relative numbers compared to 1960)
[From: Rothwell, R. *Technology, Structural Change and Manufacturing Equipment*, IIEP, Dec. 1980].

hand and improved methods on the other, is undergoing a process of "shake-up" – some factories close down unable to compete and others cut their work-force in an attempt to cope with competition.

Looking for explanations, socio-economists came upon work carried out by Kondratieff [1935], in which he analysed the economic development in several leading economies of his time such as the U.S.A., U.K., France and Germany. Kondratieff compared several economic factors like prices, export-import, salaries, output of basic commodities, employment, growth, etc. He reached the conclusion that the economy of the countries he investigated is charac-terised by large waves of 50-60 years. Though Kondratieff himself mentioned a possible relation between the economic waves and technological develop-ments, it was up to other researchers, like Kuznets [1953] and Perez [1983], to build a satisfactory theory to explain this macro behaviour of Western econ-omies (see figure 1.2).

It is the work by Perez which suggests a satisfactory model to explain the large-wave behaviour in terms of technological, social and economic develop-ments. According to Perez, each wave is characterised by a *technological style* – the mixture of technologies and social structures typical of production and industrial output of the time – and by a *key factor* – the underlying basic ingredient fuelling production, at unlimited quantities and cheap in price.

The first Kondratieff wave followed the first industrial revolution during the second half of the 18th century. It was power, or, rather, the ability to convert chemical energy into mechanical work using the steam engine, that was at the heart of this revolution. As a result of this change, weaving and heavy steel industries emerged, built around steam engines and power transmission sys-tems. Concentrated power plants were the focal point of industry and they gave birth to industrial cities, built around factories and coal mines which fuelled this industry.

The second wave was about transportation, characterised by the develop-ment of trains and steamships. During the third, heavy industry emerged. Following the depression of the thirties, the fourth wave came into being. The motor car industry, typified by production lines, became the dominant indus-try. It should be stressed that during each wave the appropriate socio-econ-omic and technological combination was formed where, through the use of current technologies and manufacturing methods, the appropriate goods were produced to be consumed by the people who were employed in their pro-duction. It is this intricate combination of mutually related parameters of technology, production methods, social strata of employees and consumers that form the positive feedback which enables the emergence of a new wave, and it is also this interaction which leads to its decline, when, through improve-ment of methods, an ever smaller number of employees can satisfy the market demand.

Today we are witnessing the emergence of a new wave, the fifth, which will, so it seems, be centred around information processing, and in which auto-mation, robotics, and advanced manufacturing systems are going to play the

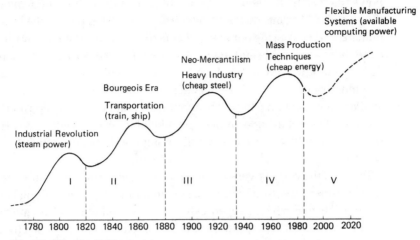

Fig 1.2   Kondratieff waves

	Characteristics of Industry Turn of the Century	Characteristics of Industry Middle of 20th Century	Characteristics of Industry Forecast
Period	Wave III 1875 - 1930	Wave IV 1930 - 1985	Wave V 1984 - (2040)
Technological Style	Heavy industry	Mass production, production lines.	Robotization, FMS, CIM
Development (Key) Factor	Cheap steel and minerals.	Cheap energy, materials concerning energy.	Cheap chips, available computing power.
Typical Industry	Chemistry, electrical motors, construction.	Luxury products, home appliances, cars.	Information-based products and services (informatics, software).
Organisation	⬠	▲	▭
Typical social strata	Industrialists versus workers.	Production engineers, mid-management, directors	Senior working staff and operators.

Fig 1.3   Characteristics of industry during three Kondratieff waves

role of the technological style. Though ideas of automation are not new as such, it is the availability of cheap computing power as the key factor that enables their widespread application to become the technological style of our time. It is important to note that the technological style is not only influencing the way in which goods are being produced, but also what goods are being consumed. Previously dominant areas are no longer at the heart of the socio-economic process, and therefore occupy minority roles in terms of economic influence. While in the past more than 90% of the workforce were busy in production of food, only 3% are needed today.

We can trace the emergence of today's key factors through a brief historical survey. Prior to the first industrial revolution, humans were the source of power as well as the source of control and guidance in producing the goods they needed. During the first industrial revolution, power devices replaced humans and it is during our age that control is also undertaken by the machine. Note that power tools and machines came into their own during later phases only when power could be cheaply converted, distributed and locally implemented through the use of electricity and electro-mechanical devices. A similar phenomenon can be observed with computing power: though in existence for several decades it became a key factor but could revolutionise our production only when made small enough and cheap enough to be widely spread.

Perhaps the earliest version of a modern binary automation system can be traced back to the 14th century when an automated organ using compressed air and a water-driven pegged cylinder produced continuous music without the intervention of a player at the keyboard. The technology used by automatic organ players was later adapted by the weaving industry. Already in these early inventions the binary code was used – the same language used by modern computers today. The other important idea of modern control and automation is also quite an ancient one. The earliest feedback system has been traced back to Ktesibios of Alexandria, who in the third century used a floating valve to control the level of water in one of his clocks.

Using our historical perspective we can see how a number of ideas, central to today's computerised industrial environment, were, in fact, born many years in advance but were forced to wait in the wings until the appropriate technology became available to give them life. It was in 1725 when Basile Bouchon used a paper roll with prepunched holes to push pegs which raised and lowered warp threads for the weaver. In 1784 Oliver Evans established the first automated factory in the USA using power belt-driven conveyors, and in 1792 Eli Whitney introduced new ideas such as standardised parts, division of labour and production lines. In 1801 Joseph Marie Jacquard improved previous ideas to produce the Jacquard loom in which punched cards were used for control. It was the interplay between new ideas and available technologies that enabled the advancement of computing power and automation later on. Whilst mechanical means could not ensure the successful implementation of the idea of The Difference Machine by Babbage, Hollerith was successful in building the electro-mechanical tabulator for the 1890 USA Census.

It was Henry Ford who was able to put together the ideas of production lines, standardisation and labour specialisation to build the first mass production car factory. By 1914 Ford had half a million cars on the road and had effectively established what had become the fourth Kondratieff wave, i.e. mass production and production lines based on the availability of cheap fossil energy, producing cars, luxury products and home appliances. Such practices eventually led directly to automation, the technological style of the fifth Kondratieff wave.

Yet, in spite of theoretical developments in the field of automation, such as those of Wiener in Cybernetics, implementation was still remote, waiting for the key factor to be born and transform the ideas into a viable technological style.

The invention of the transistor by William Shockley at Bell Telephones Laboratories in 1947 and of the printed circuit board, subsequently leading to the development of the integrated circuit by Kilby and Noyce in 1959, provided the means for the implementation of the ideas of Jon von Neumann who had proposed the architecture of the computer earlier in the century. Then in 1969, Ted Hoff designed the microprocessor – the computer on a silicon chip – and this provided technologists with the means for implementing the ideas of automation in a cheap and compact form, making automata a viable option both for production as well as for products.

Machines and production lines for this latest phase thus developed in synchronisation, from the first numerically controlled machine, at MIT in 1947, towards todays automated factory. Through the introduction of automatic machines, manual skills, such as the ability to operate a lathe or a milling machine and ensure that it follows certain desired geometries, became obsolete whilst other needs became evident. The operator has had to analyse information concerning the desired geometries of the manufacturing process and to program the machine to follow them. This pinpoints the crucial change during the last few years. Manual dexterity and hand/eye coordination has given way to logical analysis expressed in a computer language. Whilst in the past the language used by technical staff was inherently analogous by nature, using analog representations of reality, today's computer language is a conceptual one using symbolic notations.

It was during this stage that the idea of the robot was born. Though the first patent for an automatic arm was issued in the UK by Cyril Walter Kenward back in 1957, it was Joseph Engelberger who turned it into a manufacturing tool when the first robot made by Unimation was sold to Ford Motor Company in 1961. The word "robot", coined by the Czech author Karel Capek, is perhaps not a successful one as it bears connotations which are not always positive; to many people, mostly those unfamiliar with the device, it implies some kind of an entity which, in one way or another, is competing with the human race in an inhuman way. However, in reality robots are just another stage in the process of automation whereby automatic manipulators have been created possessing a greater *range* of operation and more *flexibility*. This new development can be regarded as adding another dimension of *external automation* to the existing environment of machinery which uses *internal automation*. This was essential to the formation of manufacturing cells and fully automatic production lines. Basically, however, robots have a lot in common with internal automation – they make use of similar power devices (electrical, hydraulic or pneumatic) and they are controlled by programmable sequencers which can bring the machine at each step to a desired position in space. It is this environment which can well be defined as the *step-by-step* environment that todays' manufacturing is all about.

Several mainstreams can be discerned within todays' automation environment. On the one hand FMS (Flexible Manufacturing Systems) is trying to create a line which can process various kinds of products through adjustments of tools and software. Another approach, perhaps the ultimate in dedicated automation, is the "disposable factory" – a factory totally automated and designed around one single product. There is no doubt that manufacturing is moving to ever-increasing degrees of automation, automated materials storage and transfer, and integration of information flow under what is defined today as CIM (Computerised Integrated Manufacture).

By abandoning hand tools we gave up the idea of powering machines ourselves and by introducing automatic control we let the machine supervise its routine tasks. However, the machine still does not have any authority to make decisions – each step of an operation is dictated by the program. However, by the introduction of sensors and goal-seeking software we are moving today in the direction of granting our machines more autonomy (aspects of this development are dealt with in Chapter 10).

Information processing has become the main tool of manufacturing and information is its prime resource. From processing numerical and schematic data we move today towards the manipulation of figural data. In industry this means using CAD (Computer Aided Design) for design testing and simulation, creating a direct link between the human brain and the finished product (as discussed in Chapter 8).

Perhaps the most significant change, educationally speaking, implied by this environment is the very change in the basic language through which this environment communicates. The language of the new environment, some-times generalised under the term "computerese", is a more conceptual one, yet possesses all three characteristics typical of any language: it has its own vocabulary, it has its own syntax, and it has its own environment to which it relates. A language is not merely a means of communication – it provides us with the fundamental components of our thinking, to enable us to construct and calibrate our ideas out of the influx of stimuli to which we are exposed. We are, therefore, obliged to become adjusted to the idea of building up new thinking ingredients and building blocks needed to be active in the new environment of Robotics and Automation. It is this matter, primarily, with which our book is concerned.

References
R. Rothwell, *Technology, Structural change and Manufacturing Employ-ment*, IIASA CP-80-37, December 1980.
N.D. Kondratieff, The long waves in economic life, *Review of Economic Statistics*, 17 November 1935
S. Kuznets, *Economic change* (W.W. Norton and Co, N.Y., 1953)
C. Perez, Structural change and assimilation of new technologies in the econ-omic and social systems, *Futures*, October 1983

2 Control

Our interest in control is concerned with providing a strategy that enables a computer to direct the movements of a robot and for the robot to inform the computer of the way it has responded. This strategy, known as control theory, is a subject that has been studied by engineers for many years and applied to a wide range of engineering problems. However, before we can go on to understand the workings of mechanical or electrical control systems we must first of all be able to identify the various processes that take place. To help us in this, we shall need to know the conventional terminology and diagrams used.

Open Loop and Closed Loop Control

We can best illustrate the ideas of open loop and closed loop control by the following everyday example. Place something on the table in front of you and move your hand to pick it up. The action involves you in continuously looking at the position of the object and looking at the position of your hand – the difference between these two we shall call the "error". The process of controlling your hand is therefore one in which the brain measures the error and acts in order to reduce the error to zero. Of course, all this happens without you being aware of it. In this exercise you have just demonstrated an example of *closed loop control*. The loop is formed by the chain of information from hand to eye to brain and back to hand. If you were to carry out the same exercise blindfolded, you would be demonstrating an example of *open loop control*, the loop being opened by breaking the feedback of information from hand to eye.

In the control of robots, both open loop and closed loop systems exist. In these systems, the "brain" is a computer which receives its information from numerous sensors positioned in and around the robot.

Representing a Control System with a Block Diagram

Closed Loop Control   A typical control system in which an error is measured and used to correct the process is represented by the block diagram in figure 2.1. The arrows in the diagram indicate the direction in which information flows; in many systems this information is transferred by electronic signals. The boxes represent processes which act on the information in

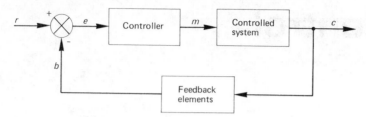

Fig 2.1   Block diagram for closed loop control

some way. In practice they may be a machine, a computer or some electronic circuit. At this point we shall be completely general and treat them only as "black boxes". Let us now work through the diagram, starting from the left.

The small r stands for *reference input*. It is the command which tells the controlled system what the *desired* behaviour is. In many of the systems that we will be considering, r is generated by a computer.

The circle with a cross inside it is called a *summing point*. In the diagram we are looking at, two signals go into the summing point: r and the signal b fed back from the output. The output from the summing point is the error signal e, which is equal to the difference, $r-b$. In other words, the error signal e is the difference between what you want and what you are getting.

Moving on now, the block labelled *controller* looks at the error signal and produces some control signal m. The controller is often a complicated device which can itself be broken down into several blocks. We will have more to say about this later on.

The block labelled *controlled system* is the device being controlled. It may, in the case of a robot, be an electric motor.

The control system is now completed by feeding the controlled output c back to the summing point. On its way, the quantity c will normally pass through a block (labelled *feedback elements*) whose function is to convert c into a form suitable to be fed into the summing point. For example, c may be the position of a motor and b may be a voltage; the function of the feedback elements would then be to convert mechanical position to volts.

The system we have just described forms an important class of closed loop control systems. The "loop" is the closed path along which information flows from the input to the output and back to the input again.

Open Loop Control   We could represent an open loop control system by the block diagram in figure 2.2. Certainly it is quite possible to successfully carry out the exercise of picking up an object if you are blindfolded but the success of the operation will depend on two important factors. Firstly, after deciding where to move your hand, you must be able to carry out the operation accurately. Secondly, once the operation begins, the object either should not move at all or should move only in a way that has been previously determined or could be predicted.

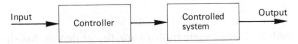

Fig 2.2 Block diagram for open loop control

In practice there are many examples of open loop control. A toaster normally operates in this way. The input is the colour of toast required and the output is the colour of toast produced. The results are usually successful because the manufacturer has calibrated the device. However, the action of the toaster may become inaccurate if any unforeseen changes occur such as deterioration of the heating element or the use of unusually dry or unusually thick slices of bread. We can conclude that open loop control is simpler (and therefore less expensive) but is only suitable for situations which are entirely predictable and independent of outside influences.

Before moving on to examine control systems in more detail you should be aware that when deciding whether a system is closed loop or open loop it is necessary to carefully identify the **system boundary**. Returning to the example of a blindfolded person picking up an object, it is clear that *within* the person's body the muscles are being controlled by the brain in a closed loop system. Similarly, almost all industrial robots are equipped with internal sensors which enable their movement to be controlled in a closed loop way. However, many of the operations carried out by these robots may be performed under open loop control so that the robot is in effect working "blindfolded". This is possible because of the high degree of precision and repeatability that can be achieved. We can represent this diagrammatically (figure 2.3) by showing that within a complete control system, some of the boxes may themselves contain control loops.

Before designating a system as closed loop or open loop we should therefore take care to define where we are drawing the line round the system. This concept of systems within systems is important because it leads us on to the idea of a hierarchy of automation in which the small computers controlling robots are themselves being controlled by larger computers, and so on.

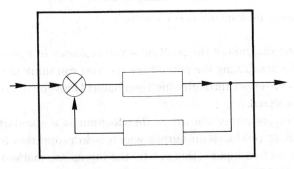

Fig 2.3 An open loop system may contain closed loop systems within it

Servomechanisms

In Chapter 5 we shall look at electric motors and linear drives. Needless to say, both motors and linear drives are only of limited use in robots unless the angle through which they turn or the distance through which they move can be controlled. This is where the servomechanism comes in. The block diagram in figure 2.4 shows the arrangement for a **position servo** used to control the amount of rotation of an electric motor.

The main feature of the block diagram is the **servo amplifier.** This is a power amplifier which produces the appropriate voltage needed to drive the motor to the desired position. The *actual* position of the motor shaft is measured by a potentiometer. Together with the necessary electronics, the potentiometer produces a voltage which is the feedback signal b. The error signal is then produced by some more electronics in the summing point which produces a voltage e equal to the difference between the requirement r and what is actually being achieved b.

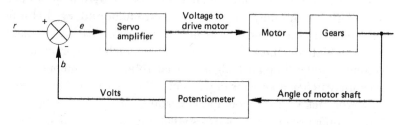

Fig 2.4   Block diagram of a position servo

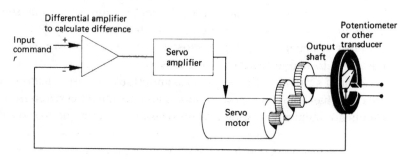

Fig 2.5   More realistic diagram of a position servo

A more realistic diagram of the position servo is shown in figure 2.5. Here you can see the gears driving the potentiometer. You can think of the potentiometer simply as a device through which mechanical movement is translated into an electrical signal.

The *differential amplifier* shown in the diagram is a standard type of electronic circuit. It produces an output which is in proportion to the *difference* between its two inputs (this is why the inputs are marked plus and minus).

Now you have an idea of how a position servo works, the **speed servo** shown in figures 2.6 and 2.7 should be straightforward. The only basic difference between the speed servo and the position servo is in the way that the mechanical output is converted into an electrical feedback signal. In the case of the speed servo, a device known as a tachometer (or tachogenerator) is built into the motor and produces a voltage which increases in proportion to its speed. In practical systems, both the speed and position of a motor need to be controlled so servomotors are made which contain all the necessary mechanisms. Gears, potentiometer and tachometer are built neatly into a single servo motor unit.

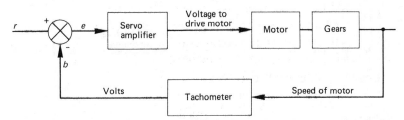

Fig 2.6   Block diagram of a speed servo

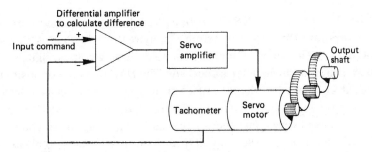

Fig 2.7   More realistic diagram of a speed servo

In many applications the servo motor is controlled by a *microprocessor* (see Chapter 3). Since almost all microprocessors used in automation are digital whereas electric motors are inherently analog devices, we can therefore identify two problems involved with incorporating microprocessors into the control system:

1   Converting the digital pulses from the output of the microprocessor into suitable voltage levels which can be used to power the motors.

2   Converting the voltage levels produced by the potentiometer and tachometer into pulses which are suitable for use as input to the microprocessor.

The first of the problems, converting digital pulses to voltage levels, is solved by use of a *digital-to-analog converter* or DAC for short. The second of the problems, converting voltage levels to digital pulses, requires the opposite sort of device called an *analog-to-digital converter* (ADC).

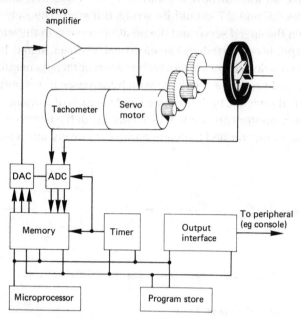

Fig 2.8   A computer incorporated into a servo system

The diagram in figure 2.8 shows one possible way that a microprocessor can be incorporated into a servo system. Compare this with figures 2.7 and 2.5. The ADC does the job of changing continuously varying voltage signals into digital pulses suitable for the microprocessor. The DAC does the opposite job of the ADC. It converts the digital pulses from the microprocessor into voltages which, when amplified, can be used to drive the motors. ADCs and DACs are able to work at very high speeds – the fastest can respond to changes at more than ten million times a second. At these high speeds, the step-by-step action of the microprocessor is, to all intents and purposes, continuous.

The ADC is, in some systems, dispensed with by the use of an *optical shaft encoder.* You can think of this device as a sort of "mechanical" analog-to-digital converter. Instead of using a potentiometer to convert angular

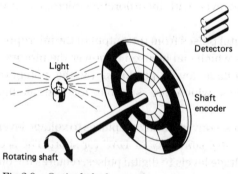

Fig 2.9   Optical shaft encoder

position to voltage and then using an ADC to convert the voltage to a digital signal, the optical shaft encoder (shown in figure 2.9) provides a digital output which can be directly translated into the angular position of the motor shaft. The details of how these encoders work is given in Appendix I.

Controlling Different Types of Drive

Linear drives are controlled by servos in a similar way to motors. The control signal from the servo amplifier is used to operate the hydraulic or pneumatic transfer valve which controls the flow of fluid to the cylinder. As the piston-actuating rod moves, its position is measured and converted into an electrical feedback signal by a potentiometer with a linear track. These types of potentiometer can be used to measure movements of up to one metre. In some arrangements, gears are used to convert linear movement into rotational movement. The gear shaft can then be linked to the more common rotational type of potentiometer.

Variable transformers (explained in Appendix I) are another type of sensor used to convert linear movement into an electrical feedback signal. These types of transducer can be used only to detect movements of up to a few centimetres but are more sensitive, more accurate and more reliable than potentiometers.

Sensing the *speed* of linear drives is a less-important requirement than sensing the speed of rotary drives. The reason for this is that rotary drives are normally incorporated into jointed-arm type robots where the movements are complicated and require the careful coordination of speed and position as in paint spraying or welding. Linear drives, on the other hand, are normally used in applications such as loading, stacking or positioning components where control of the speed is not usually necessary. Generally speaking then, speed sensors are not fitted to linear drives. However, when a microprocessor forms part of the control loop it is possible to calculate the speed simply by sampling the position every fraction of a second and performing a simple calculation (dividing the distance moved by the time taken).

Types of Feedback Control Action

One of the key factors in determining the behaviour of a control system is the way in which the error signal is dealt with. There are four distinct possibilities here which we will now consider separately. Practical control systems, as we shall see, incorporate a mixture of each type.

On-Off (or "Bang-Bang") Control   This is the simplest form of closed loop control. As the name implies, the system is either switched fully on or fully off according to the size of the error signal. A common example of this is found in the thermostatic control of a room heater. The heating is on when the room temperature falls below a certain lower limit and off when the temperature rises above a higher limit. In this case there is very little to be gained from a more sophisticated type of control. The sluggish time response of the system effectively smooths out any sudden changes in the output. In certain situations, on-off control may even be necessary because the device being controlled can only be turned either on or off. A simple rocket motor may have to be controlled in this way. In industry we might use on-off control to open or close certain types of valve controlling the flow of gases or liquids. This is in fact done in the case of pick-and-place robots, discussed later.

Proportional Control   In order to achieve better control of a process it seems sensible to take account not only of whether there is an error but also of how big the error is. Proportional control does this by applying a control action in proportion to the size of the error. In practice this means that a large corrective action will be applied when there is a large error and that the corrective action will be reduced as the target is approached more closely. This is of course familiar to us from the way we control our own body. We move our arm faster when it is a long way from an object, slowing down as we approach it.

When used alone, proportional control can never produce an output which exactly matches the required input. It will always result in some **steady state error**. This is because the control action results from measuring the size of the error so can therefore never reach the point when the error is zero.

Integral Control   Integral control is never used alone, but in conjunction with proportional control it can reduce or eliminate the steady state error. Integral control works by taking account not only of the size of the error but also of the *time* for which the error has existed. This is expressed mathematically using the integral function in calculus. In non-mathematical terms it can be understood with the help of figure 2.10, which shows a graph of how an error signal might be changing with time. The corrective action produced by integral control depends on the area under this graph (shown shaded). You can see from this that even if the error stays constant, the area under the graph

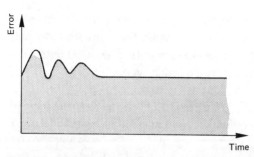

Fig 2.10   Integral control produces a control action in proportion to the area shown shaded

increases with the passing of time and so a corrective control action will be applied. Integral control therefore takes account of how long the error has existed and therefore can be said to look back in time.

Rate Control (Derivative Control) Rate control measures the rate at which the error is changing ("derivative", the alternative name, is the mathematical term for rate of change). A rapidly changing error at one instant of time will indicate that the error is going to change by a large amount in the next instant of time. In effect, then, rate control is predictive. Just as integral control can be said to look back in time, so rate control can be said to look forward. Rate control is therefore useful in improving the time response of a control system especially in cases where the desired output is subject to rapid changes.

Combining Proportional, Derivative and Integral Control Each of the ways of treating the error discussed above are normally combined into a single system to produce a **PDI** (proportional, derivative and integral) **controller**. PD and PI controllers are also found. The relative effect of each of the P, D, and I can be adjusted to produce a controller with the optimum characteristics for the system concerned.

In evaluating the effectiveness of a control system, it is necessary to test for good *transient response* and good *steady state response*. Transient response applies to how the system behaves in the short time following a change in input. Steady state response is relevant to how the system behaves in the longer period when all the short-term effects can be considered to have died away.

Transient Response

One important way of evaluating the transient response of a system is to observe the effect of a "step change" in input, or **step input**, as illustrated in figure 2.11. In practice this might be done by commanding a robot arm to move, instantaneously, to a new position. Figure 2.12 shows some possible responses to the step input which we will consider.

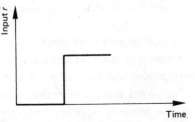

Fig 2.11   Step input to the control system

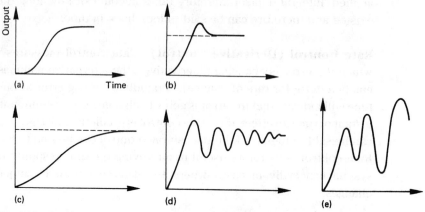

Fig 2.12   Possible transient responses to a step input

In judging the various possible responses to a step input it must be realised that *no* physical system can follow such an input faithfully. To do so would imply that a mass can be accelerated instantaneously and this in turn would imply (according to the principles of basic physics) the existence of an infinite force. In practice then, we look for a control system response which is "optimal", that is one which produces the best response. The difficulty here is in deciding on what is "best". In an ideal situation the control system should produce the required output in the minimum time without overshoot and with no steady state error. In practice the optimal response coupled with the cost (never a factor that can be neglected in engineering) may lead to conflicting requirements.

The curve in figure 2.12*a* shows a control system response which achieves the required output with the minimum of delay and without overshoot. If a faster response is required, this can be achieved at the expense of allowing a small overshoot as shown in figure 2.12*b*. A poorer response time, shown in figure 2.12*c*, could also be acceptable in some applications and this may result in a less expensive system. The transient responses illustrated in figures 2.12*a* to 2.12*c* are all said to be **stable**. That is to say, after a length of time the system settles into a new position. The response shown in figure 2.12*d* is also stable but not acceptable because it is **oscillatory**. Figure 2.12*e* shows the response of an **unstable** system. This can be particularly serious because it can result in damage to the equipment.

In practice, the transient response is affected by the mechanics of the robot. The weight of the robot's arm and whether or not it is carrying a heavy load will affect how quickly it responds to the motor which is driving it. For example, if the motor only has to drive a very light load, it is possible that a control signal sent to the motor will cause the arm to move too quickly and overshoot. This will then produce a new error in the opposite direction. If, on the other hand, the load is very heavy, then a larger control signal may need to be sent in order to compensate for the fact that the heavy load will move more sluggishly. This is the effect of **inertia**, which is the basic tendency of a body to resist change of direction or motion when a force is applied.

In addition to the problems caused by inertia, there are also problems caused by **hysteresis**. Hysteresis literally means "lagging behind" and occurs when there is slackness in gears and mechanical linkages. In these situations, the motor may move without producing any effect on the robot until the slackness has been taken up.

In order to make the servomechanism produce the best results, it is therefore necessary to "tune" it by adjusting the gains of the amplifiers and sometimes to incorporate some more sophisticated improvements. The differential amplifier, shown in the block diagrams in figures 2.5 and 2.7, has the function of amplifying the difference between the input requirement (what you want) and the feedback signal (what you are getting). If the gain of the amplifier is too high then the large error signal may cause overshoot; in the case of a position servo this would mean the motor going too much in the other direction, producing a new error. This new error would in turn be over-corrected and so on. The overall effect would be that the position of the motor would swing either side of the required position until eventually the error became negligible. This results in the oscillatory behaviour referred to above in figure 2.12*d*. It is rather like the behaviour of a saloon-bar door, that you sometimes see in westerns, when the door is suddenly pushed open and then flaps backwards and forwards until it settles down. In extreme cases, if the gain of the amplifier is made too high, the system never settles down, but instead the error becomes increasingly bigger. This is a cause of instability.

One of the problems in setting-up a servo controller is to make sure the gain is at the best possible value. The setting at which unstable behaviour just disappears is known as the **critical gain** . Reducing the gain a long way below this value makes the system more stable but has the undesirable effect of producing a weaker control action. Since few systems are stable under all possible conditions, in practice designers are mainly concerned with the **relative stability** of a system. This can be measured according to variety of different mathematical criteria which in effect give an indication of the range of conditions for which the output is stable.

Servo and Non-servo Controlled Robots

In industry, there are two categories of robot which are described, according to the method used to control them, as being either servo controlled or non-servo controlled. Each type has different characteristics and requires different signals to be sent to the actuators (motors or fluidic drives, etc.). Servo-controlled robots can be divided into two further categories: *point-to-point control* and *continuous path control*. Each of these behave in a different way and are used for different types of operation.

Non-servo controlled robots have at times been criticised as not being "true" robots although they are almost always included in statistics relating to the use of robots in industry. Names such as limited sequence robot, pick-and-place robot, and end-point robot are all terms which are used to refer to them.

The essential feature of a **non-servo controlled robot** is that each axis can move only between fixed limits called **hardware stops** or *end stops*. Usually there are only two hardware stops per axis although some robots of this type have a limited number of intermediate stops. Each axis is operated in turn by the controller (or sequencer) which causes the joint to move between the hardware stops. Almost all non-servo controlled robots are hydraulically or pneumatically operated and the joint is decelerated as the hardware stop is approached by means of a valve or a simple shock absorber. From this you will see that the controller only needs to supply to the actuator either full power or no power. Non-servo controlled robots are therefore operated by a closed loop on/off control system.

Because of the nature of the control mechanism (that is, suddenly applying full power to an axis), robots of this type are generally small and are used only for relatively light loads. The inertia of a large mass would be difficult to get moving and once moving, would be difficult to stop. A typical non-servo controlled robot is shown in figure 2.13.

Programming a non-servo controlled robot is carried out by a procedure which involves both software and hardware operations:

(*a*) The controller is programmed to operate each axis in the required sequence.

(*b*) The hardware stops are physically adjusted for each axis.

Flexibility is incorporated into the program by using sensors on and around the robot which can cause the program to branch between different sequences. Let's look at a simple example to illustrate how a non-servo controlled robot is operated.

Figure 2.14 shows a non-servo controlled hydraulic robot being used to lift items from one point and place them to the side. This is how signals from the controller and sensors are sent to produce the required operation.

1   A signal is sent from the controller to open a valve and cause (say) the base of the robot to rotate.

2   The valve opens fully and the axis rotates until the hardware stop is reached.

3   A limit switch is activated and a signal is sent to the controller telling it that the hardware stop has been reached.

4   The controller sends a signal to close the valve.

5   Steps 1 to 4 are repeated for each axis that is required to move in the operation sequence.

If you look at figure 2.14 again you will notice two photoelectric sensors – one to detect parts arriving and one to detect the presence of an empty box.

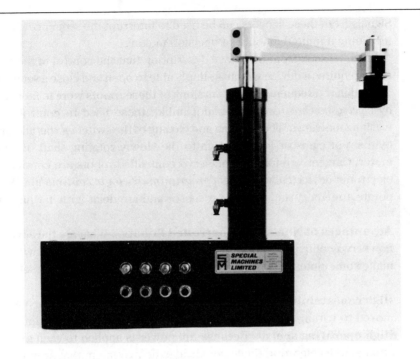

TECHNICAL DATA

Drive and Control	Pneumatic	Vertical Lift	40 mm.
Number of Movements	Two	Radial Travel	52°
Load	5 kg Max.	Jaw Movement	0.5 to 8 mm.
Working Pressure	5 to 7 Bar	Air Consumption	0,10 L/Cycle
Positional Accuracy		Actual Load Time	2.5 Seconds
Standard Unit	± 0.1 mm.	Total Cycle Time	5 Seconds
Positional Accuracy with			
Positive Stop Attachment	± 0.03 mm.		

OPTIONAL EQUIPMENT

1) Positive Stop Attachment
2) Variable Hydraulic Damping Unit
3) Variable Stroke Unit
4) Jaw Type Pick-Up Head
5) Various Jaw Configurations
6) Vacuum Pick-Up Head

SUGGESTED USES

Loading and Unloading:-

Conveyor Systems
Assembly Machines
Machine Tools
In areas with hostile or dangerous environments

Fig 2.13   A series 200 non-servo controlled robot (Courtesy: Special Machines Ltd.)

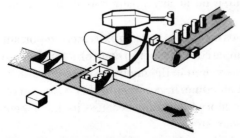

Fig 2.14   A pick-and-place operation

Signals from these sensors can be used to interrupt the sequence if necessary, providing a limited amount of decision making.

It can be seen from the above description that the control of these types of robot requires a device which is simply able to open and close a set of switches in the desired sequence. Early versions of these robots were in fact controlled by *electro-mechanical devices* not unlike those used to control automatic washing machines. The opening and closing of the switches was accomplished by a set of cams or levers set on to the slowly rotating shaft of an electric motor. Current versions of non-servo controlled robots are controlled by an electronic device called a *PLC (programmable logic controller)*. PLCs incorporate a memory and a microprocessor and are dealt with in Chapter 3.

Advantages of Non-servo Controlled Robots   What are the advantages of non-servo controlled robots? (Perhaps, before reading on, you would like to make some notes of any advantages that you can think of yourself.)

High repeatability   Because of the use of hardware stops, each axis can be moved to within a fraction of a millimetre of its required position.

High operating speed   Because full power is applied to each axis, acceleration and deceleration times are always the maximum that are mechanically possible.

Low cost   This applies not only to the initial cost of the equipment but also to the cost of programming (software is often expensive) and to the cost of maintenance.

Servo Control

Servo controlled robots are what everyone in industry would think of as "true" robots. In contrast to a non-servo controlled robot, motion of this type of robot is characterised by smooth and continuous control of speed and acceleration for every axis of the robot. The mass of the robot and the mass of the load that it moves are factors which are allowed for in determining the amount of power to apply. Large massive robots operating with heavy loads can therefore be moved under complete control.

The points at which each axis comes to rest are determined not by hardware stops but by *software stops*. A software stop is written into the controller's program and can of course be at any position that falls within the work envelope of the robot.

The use of software stops makes possible an extremely important advantage of servo control when compared to non-servo control: a servo controlled robot can have several programs stored in the memory of the controller and any of these can be executed at any time. In contrast to this, a non-servo controlled robot can have only one stored program because its movement is always constrained by the hardware stops.

On the negative side, the use of software stops makes high repeatability difficult to obtain. Typically the repeatability of a servo controlled robot is within one or two millimetres rather than a fraction of a millimetre. Improving on this figure involves higher quality internal sensors, more sophisticated controllers, and carefully designed motors (or valves for fluidic drives). The net result is that all of these factors add up to higher expense and in the end lower reliability when compared to non-servo controlled robots.

Point-to-Point Servo Control

The feature of **point-to-point servo control** is that only a limited number of points on the end effector's path are entered into the memory of the computer. If, for example, it is required for the end effector to move from point A to point B, then the robot is first driven to point A by operating controls on a *teach-box* (or *teach-pendant*). The positions of each axis at this point are then read from the internal sensors and recorded as data in the memory of the controller. The same operation is then repeated for point B and for any other points that are to be learnt. Teaching by this method is known in industry as **lead-through**.

When the robot program is run, the end effector moves sequentially to each of the positions taught to it. To make this possible, the controller will normally drive each of the actuators at a speed such that each axis arrives at its final position at the same time. This may mean that the base has to rotate at its maximum speed while the wrist is rotating very slowly. The actual command signals sent from the controller to actuators are calculated by a special program and therefore bear no relation to the speed and path through which the axes were driven during the teach mode. The exact paths taken by the end effector between points cannot therefore be easily predicted.

Despite the apparent disadvantages of point-to-point control, it is neverthe-less very widely used for industrial robots. Decision-making and branching to different sequences is easily incorporated into a point-to-point program, and a further advantage is that the amount of memory required is relatively small since only data for a limited number of points needs to be stored.

Continuous Path Control

You can probably think of many situations where the exact path taken by the end effector is quite critical. Seam welding (welding along a continuous line) is a particular example where not only the path of the end effector needs to be continuously controlled but also the speed at which it moves. This operation is in complete contrast to the situation in which the end effector is required only to pick up an object at one position and set it down at another.

Programming of a **continuous path robot** is normally carried out by a method called **walk-through**. Here, a skilled person holds the end effector of the robot and performs exactly the operation that the robot is to learn. Whilst the robot is being taught, the controller continuously samples the output from each of the robot's internal sensors and stores the data. The sampling is typically done between 50 and 100 times per second (that is, 50 to 100 hertz). This of course means that a large amount of data has to be stored by the controller, making it necessary to provide either a floppy disc or magnetic tape.

When the robot is running, the controller causes the taught movements to be accurately reproduced. Although the resulting continuous path motion is in fact made up of a very large number of closely spaced points, it would be wrong to think of it simply as point-to-point control with a large number of points. The important difference is that in continuous path control, the robot moves smoothly between the points due to its inertia. No "decisions" are made by the controller (and no decisions are necessary) about moving the axes between each point. In contrast to this, with point-to-point, the controller "decides" how to move the axes between each point.

Just as we looked at an example of the way in which signals are sent from the controller on a non-servo controlled robot, we now look at the equivalent procedure for servo control. The following outline is of course simplified, but will illustrate the main points:

1   The position of each axis (sensed by the internal sensors) is read by the controller.
2   The required position of the axes (for the first step) is read from memory by the controller.
3   The data in steps 1 and 2 are compared and error signals are generated.
4   The error signals are amplified and the resulting *command signals* are sent to the actuators.
5   The actuators cause the axes to move and signals from the internal sensors are fed back to the controller.
6   The feedback signals are compared to the required positions of the axes and new command signals are generated until the error signals are reduced to zero.
7   The next step in the program sequence is read by the controller and the process is repeated.

This is now a convenient point to collect together our facts and set out a list of the most important features of servo controlled robots:

● The end effector can be positioned anywhere within the work envelope of the robot.
● Velocity and acceleration of each axis can be controlled at every point in the motion.
● Many programs can be stored and executed without the need for any mechanical adjustments.
● Sequences which require fast movements of each axis can be carried out smoothly. This is done by regarding the error signal as being zero once it has fallen below some certain minimum value.

Adaptive Control

Adaptive control is a term which has been used in traditional control theory for many many years, but which has taken on a new meaning in the field of robotics. Here we shall only use the term in the way used by the manufacturers of industrial robots.

In order to appreciate what is meant by **adaptive control**, consider the following situation. It is required to use a robot to remove the irregular edge left on a metal casting after it has been removed from the mould. A continuous path robot can be programmed to do this job by moving a grinding tool along the edge of the part. However, since no two parts will be identical (the object of the exercise is after all to remove the *irregular* edge) the controller cannot follow the path exactly as it was taught – it must adapt its program to follow the edge of the particular part it is working on. This is what is meant by adaptive control.

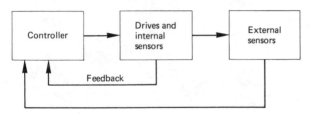

Fig 2.15   External sensors feed information to the controller for adaptive control

So now that we know what is meant by adaptive control, how is it made to work? Figure 2.15 shows by means of a block diagram what is involved. External sensors, which may be incorporated into the hand of the robot, detect deviations from the basic path that has been taught. Signals are then sent to the controller to adapt the path appropriately. For example, in the system used by the ASEA robot shown in figure 2.16, the sensor sends one of four digital signals (0, 1, 2, or 3) to the controller:

0   programmed path OK, no correction needed
1   correct the path in the negative direction
2   correct the path in the positive direction
3   alarm signal – call a human!

The example of adaptive control given here is called **curve adaptivity** in order to distinguish it from point adaptivity. **Point adaptivity** enables a robot to search for a point which may not be in exactly the same place for every job. An example of this might be locating the corner of a workpiece or finding the beginning of a seam to be welded. Curve adaptivity is generally a more complex operation because it involves two aspects: contouring and velocity control.

Fig 2.16   An ASEA robot with adaptive control

Contouring refers to following and adapting to the curve. *Velocity control* is an added degree of sophistication which allows the controller to adapt the speed at which the end effector moves. This is important in the operation shown in figure 2.16 because, to be effective, the grinding tool must move more slowly over the large irregularities than over the small ones.

The use of adaptive control therefore makes it possible to use continuous path robots for jobs that could otherwise only be done by people. This is one (small) step in the direction of controllers with "artificial intelligence" – a subject in its own right, which we will return to in Chapter 10.

Off-line Programming

It is clear from what has been said so far that the control of a robot requires a large number of electronic devices and that for a servo-controlled robot, a microprocessor or computer plays an essential part. However, for the operations we have so far described, the user of the robot would not need to be aware of the presence of a computer and would certainly not be required to deal with a computer of the desk-top type seen in so many of todays offices.

Indeed, as far as the user is concerned, programming these robots means nothing more than teaching them by the methods of lead-through or walk-through. The programming of a robot in this way is termed an **on-line** operaton. On-line simply means programming while the computer is connected to the robot and the computer behaves in a way that does not even require the operator to be aware of its existence. Increasingly, however, manufacturers of robots are being asked to provide **off-line** programming facilities in which the movements of the robot can be programmed without the presence of the robot itself. In off-line programming, the operator does indeed sit down at a keyboard in front of a desk-top computer and writes a program for the movements of the robot.

Although on-line teach and repeat schemes are suitable for a wide variety of applications, especially where a robot will perform a single task for a long run of workpieces, there are nevertheless a large number of reasons for sometimes wishing to adopt the off-line approach:

● If a robot can be programmed off-line, then while the program is being written the robot remains free to carry out useful work. For a small company engaged in batch production of goods this requirement can often mean the difference between profit and loss. Without off-line programming a second identical robot would need to be employed simply for the teaching phase, the learned programs then being transferred to the main robot.

● Some tasks are better calculated than taught. For example, palletizing is a common task for robots. In such a task the robot places items at fixed positions on a horizontal tray called a pallet (rather like placing biscuits on a baking tray). It is more efficient for the robot's computer to calculate each new position from the dimensions of the pallet than for the operator to manually teach all the required positions.

● If a task can be defined independently of the robot hardware then it should be feasible to have this task carried out by a variety of different robots. In practice this is difficult to achieve but it would mean that when upgrading or replacing robots a manufacturer would not have to undergo the expensive task of reprogramming. This feature is known as **portability**.

● Many industrial Numerically Controlled (NC) machines are already programmed in this way with programs derived from Computer Aided Design (CAD) systems. If robot programs could be incorporated into this scheme then the goal of total integration would be closer at hand. (Chapter 8 deals with this topic at greater length.)

In the overall process of control the computer can now be seen to be used in one of two ways. Firstly, it may be used as a device which is to all intents and purposes invisible to the operator. Here, its function is to take charge of the processes required to control the movements of the robot. As we shall see in Chapter 3, some of these processes could be accomplished with *hard-wired* (that is, non-programmable) electronic *circuitry*. However, the ability of the computer to be programmed (and re-programmed) is the essential feature that separates the robot from its relatively inflexible predecessor, the numerically controlled machine.

Secondly, and nowadays with increasing importance, the computer may be used to control not only the mechanical movements of the robot but also the entire automated process. Here, it is programmed in such a way that the robot is only one of a number of machines and processes under its control. When used in this way, the computer forms the cornerstone of the automated process. In the chapters that follow, we shall deal in greater depth with the operation of the computer itself.

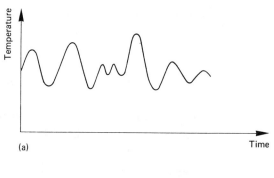

(a)   Time

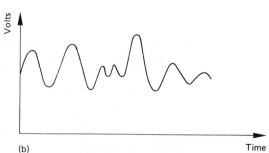

(b)   Time

Fig 3.1   An analog voltage signal (b) varies in proportion to the changing temperature (a)

3 Electronics and Microprocessors

Electricity has two distinct uses. Firstly it is used as a means of transferring energy to provide us with heat, light and mechanical power. Secondly, it is used as a means of transferring information, making possible such devices as amplifiers, computers, radio and television. It is the second application we are concerned with here, and it is this that is referred to as **electronics**. Without the development of electronics, a robot could be nothing more than just another machine powered by electricity like those of the earlier part of this century. It is electronics that has made possible the advances into automation and it is electronics that continues to take us towards the making of increasingly "intelligent" machines.

In order to appreciate what electronic devices can do and how they operate, we first of all need to look at how electricity can be used to transfer information or provide a *signal*. We can then go on to understand electronic circuits simply in terms of how they use, generate or alter electrical signals.

Signals

To use electricity to produce a signal there are really only two things we can do with it: either we can switch it on and off or we can alter the amount of it (that is change the current or voltage). As you will see shortly, the type of signal in which the electricity is switched on and off is called a *digital signal*. The other type, in which the voltage or current changes, is called an *analog signal*. We will look first at an example of an analog signal.

Imagine you have a device which produces a small but measurable voltage when exposed to heat. The greater the heat, the higher the voltage produced. If the temperature is changing with time then the voltage will change in a similar way, as shown in figures 3.1a and 3.1b. The changing voltage, which can be seen to vary in proportion to the changing temperature is called an analog voltage signal (derived from the Greek word *analogos* meaning proportionate). Analog signals, which are continuously changing voltages or currents, arise naturally from the fact that changes normally take place continuously rather than in sudden steps. Their greatest disadvantage, as we shall explain shortly, is that they are prone to distortion.

Digital signals, in one form or another, have been known and understood for many years. Possibly the earliest use of digital signals was that of morse code, in which combinations of pulses were used as a code to represent letters of the alphabet. In principle, digital signal techniques used today are not very different from those used a hundred years ago. The great advance has been brought about by the ability of modern electronic devices to generate and deal with millions of pulses per second.

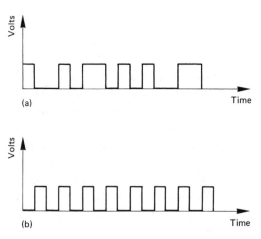

Fig 3.2   (a) A digital signal containing information;
            (b) Timing pulses produced by a clock

The shape of a **digital signal**, of the type most commonly used in electronics, is shown in figure 3.2. It consists of a train of pulses, each of the same height and lasting for the same length of time. In order that two or more pulses (or spaces) in succession can be distinguished from one single pulse (or space), the arrival of the signal must be synchronised to a timing device. The timing device responsible for this function is called a **clock** and forms an essential part of most digital electronic devices. In practice, the timing is complicated by the fact that the pulses have sloping edges rather than the square edges shown in figure 3.2. However, at this stage we need not concern ourselves with this level of detail.

To transmit a digital signal, we produce the pulses by generating two distinctly different voltages between the wires. In a typical digital signal, ON might be represented by 5 volts, and OFF by zero volts. Usually we need to send more than a single bit of information and there are two methods by which this can be achieved.

One method is to use several wires, each of which carries an electrical signal corresponding to a different bit in the message. This is called **parallel transmission**.

Alternatively, the individual bits which constitute the message can be sent, one by one, down a single pair of wires. This is **serial transmission**.

To see how information can be encoded by a digital signal, take an example similar to that for the analog signal in which temperature is the information. The simplest code would be one in which the arrival of a pulse indicates a high temperature (above some agreed threshold), and the absence of a pulse, a low temperature. This, of course, would be of limited practical use, so an improvement would be to use a group of two pulses to code the information. Using this method we could have four possible combinations as follows:

1,1   very hot (two pulses in succession)
1,0   hot (a pulse followed by a space)
0,1   warm (a space followed by a pulse)
0,0   cold (two spaces in succession)

A further improvement could be obtained by using groups of 4 pulses. This allows 16 possible combinations, representing 16 levels of temperature. With groups of 8, the number of combinations is increased even further, to 256 (that is, 2 to the power of eight).

It appears from this that a digital signal is only an approximation to the truth since, unlike an analog signal, it cannot represent the continuous range of possible values. However, in practice, the approximation can be made very good indeed. By increasing the number of pulses in a group from 8 to just 16, the number of levels that can be represented increases from 256 to 65 536 (that is, 2 to the power of 16). In computers, a single pulse is called a *bit* (because it represents a BInary digiT) and a group of eight pulses or bits is called a *byte*. The two states of the signal can be referred to as

ON and OFF
high and *low*
1 (one) and 0 (nought)
true and *false*.

We will return to these points later when we discuss microprocessors.

Digital Circuits

A **digital circuit** uses or produces digital signals. We can divide digital circuits into three categories:

1. Circuits with digital signals as both inputs and outputs.
2. Circuits which have digital inputs and analog outputs.
3. Circuits which have analog inputs and digital outputs.

The first category is comprised of **logic circuits**; these circuits process digital information. Many different types of logic circuit exist to perform various mathematical and logical operations on digital signals. They can, for example, be made to add or subtract binary numbers, check whether two binary numbers are the same, or store digital information for retrieval at a later time. Appendix II deals with binary numbers and the rules of Boolean algebra, for performing the operations of digital logic.

The two other categories of digital circuits given above are involved with *converting* analog signals to digital signals and vice-versa. We have already mentioned that a quantity such as a voltage can be represented as accurately as we wish by a digital signal. You will also remember that an analog signal is simply a voltage that varies with time. In order to convert an analog signal into a digital signal, we must measure the voltage of the analog signal at regular intervals and convert these measurements into a digital code. A circuit which performs this function is called an **analog-to-digital converter** (ADC for short).

The process involved in converting an analog signal into a digital form suitable for transmission requires three steps:

1. The analog signal is sampled at regular, short intervals of time.
2. The sample values are coded using binary digits.
3. For every sample, the codes are transmitted as ON or OFF pulses.

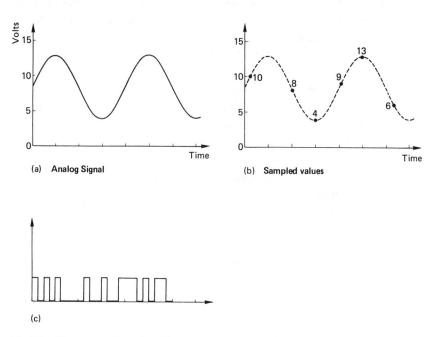

Fig 3.3   How an analog signal is converted into a digital signal

To see how analog-to-digital conversion may be carried out, take the example of the analog signal shown in figure 3.3*a*. The result of sampling the signal is to obtain a series of numbers each representing the size of the analog signal at the moment it was sampled, as shown in figure 3.3*b*. It is, of course, extremely important to sample the signal sufficiently often to ensure that no large changes are missed. Theory shows that sampling must be done at least twice as fast as the signal is changing, and in practice a signal may be sampled many millions of times a second.

Having obtained sample values of the analog signal, the next step is to convert them into a digital *code*. You will notice that in this example all the

Binary Code	Sequence of pulses	Number represented
0000		0
0001		1
0010		2
0011		3
0100		4
0101		5
0110		6
0111		7
1000		8
1001		9
1010		10
1011		11
1100		12
1101		13
1110		14
1111		15

Table 3.1

numbers are within the range 0 to 15, that is 16 possible numbers in all including 0. Now recall from above that 16 levels can be coded by using a group of 4 pulses. Table 3.1 shows the possible combinations of 1s and 0s together with the patterns of pulses they represent. The code used in this example is in fact *binary code* (see Appendix II). Note that, although there is no separation between two or more consecutive pulses (they appear as a single wide pulse), they can still be distinguished because the device that receives them will have a clock which tells it the duration of a single pulse.

Using the information contained in Table 3.1 you should now be able to see how the digital signal in figure 3.3c has been constructed. Each of the numbers appearing in figure 3.3b has been coded using a train of four pulses. The resulting continuous train of pulses contains, in coded form, all the values sampled from the original analog signal. By reversing the process, it is also possible to convert the digital signal back to an analog signal.

We can use a suitable ADC to take any type of analog signal, whether it represents speech, music or the output from the sensor of a robot, and convert it into a digital signal. At this point you may well ask: "why do we need analog-to-digital conversion?" Why do we take a perfectly good analog signal and take the trouble to convert it into ones and zeros? The three most important answers to this question are as follows:
- Sometimes we have no choice. Digital computers, which account for almost all computers in general use, can only deal with and process digital signals. For computer processing it may therefore may be necessary to convert what was originally an analog signal into digital form. Analog-to-digital converters are able to do this conversion. Similarly, it may be necessary to use the output of a digital computer to drive a device such as a motor, which requires an analog input. This will require the use of a **digital-to-analog converter**.

- Highly accurate devices for dealing with analog signals are difficult and expensive to produce. Since all the information carried by an analog signal is contained in the voltage (or current) level, any unwanted changes in this level will result in the information being changed. Digital signals, on the other hand, are immune to this problem because the voltage level of a pulse carries no information – the pulse is either there or not there. Information can therefore only be lost from a digital signal if whole pulses are lost. It is far easier (and less costly) to build electronic devices that simply count pulses than it is to build devices where the voltage or current level is accurately controlled to within thousandths of a volt.
- In any electrical device, unwanted random fluctuations in voltage called **noise** always occur. When noise is added to an analog signal, the result is as shown in figure 3.4a. The effect of noise on an analog signal becomes serious when the level of the noise is comparable to the level of the signal, as shown in figure 3.4b.

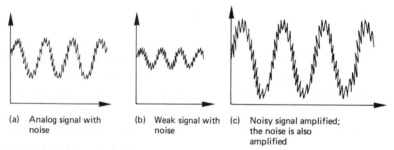

(a) Analog signal with noise

(b) Weak signal with noise

(c) Noisy signal amplified; the noise is also amplified

Fig 3.4   Effect of noise on analog signals

This situation can occur after transmission of a signal over a long distance. Note that the noise itself is not weakened since it is introduced at all points during transmission, including the point at which the signal is received. The result is that the information contained in an analog signal can be seriously corrupted or even lost entirely. Amplifying a weak and noisy signal has the undesirable effect of amplifying the noise by the same amount, as shown in figure 3.4c.

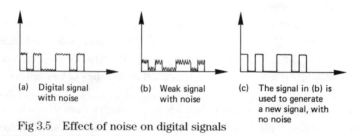

(a) Digital signal with noise

(b) Weak signal with noise

(c) The signal in (b) is used to generate a new signal, with no noise

Fig 3.5   Effect of noise on digital signals

Although the use of filters can reduce the problem mentioned above, only the use of a digital signal can solve the problem of noise entirely. Figure 3.5a shows a digital signal with noise and figure 3.5b shows the weakened signal. In order to restore the original signal, it is only necessary to detect the sharp changes in level occurring at the start and end of each pulse and to use this information to generate the "clean" signal shown in figure 3.5c.

Packaged Electronics – The Integrated Circuit

Today, complex circuits are seldom built on a commercial scale by connecting together individual electronic components. Instead, integrated circuits are used which are themselves often no bigger than a single transistor. Integrated circuits have in effect become the "components" of modern electronics. Figure 3.6 shows the appearance of some typical integrated circuits. These small rectangular pieces of plastic, which vary in size from between around one and five centimetres in length, contain the equivalent of thousands of electronic components. Yet even this description doesn't do justice to their small size. About ninety nine per cent of what you see of the ICs in figure 3.6 consists of just the plastic casing and the terminals. The entire electronic circuit is contained on a thin chip of silicon no more than a few square millimetres in area.

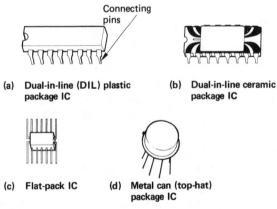

(a) Dual-in-line (DIL) plastic package IC

(b) Dual-in-line ceramic package IC

(c) Flat-pack IC

(d) Metal can (top-hat) package IC

Fig 3.6   Typical integrated circuit devices

The Advantages of Integrated Circuits

In order to understand why the integrated circuit was invented it is necessary to look at the history leading up to its development. Prior to the development of the transistor, the most important component in electronics was the valve (or vacuum tube). The valve performed a similar function to the transistor but occupied around one hundred times the volume. Circuits using valves were built by constructing an aluminium chassis fitted with sockets. Individual sockets were then connected together and linked to resistors, capacitors and other components mounted on boards of insulating material. Although this method of construction was seen as adequate for devices such as radios it had a major disadvantage for the building of digital computers. The digital computer relies not on the action of amplifying, which can be accomplished with ten or so valves, but on the action of *switching*. Even the most modest computer requires thousands of switching circuits and the first large digital computer, built in 1956, contained 18 000 valves!

The announcement of the *transistor* in 1947 came as a major breakthrough. Not only was the transistor a fraction of the size of a valve, but it also consumed far less electrical power and could be directly soldered to a circuit board alongside other components. By 1957 transistors were being produced at the rate of 30 million per year and the construction of transistorized equipment was becoming routine. It was also at about this time that the need to build more powerful computers now containing not thousands but millions of switching circuits posed a new problem.

The method of mounting individual components on a board was time consuming and the space occupied by the board meant that powerful computers were becoming too large. Various methods were proposed for miniaturization until it was realised that all the basic components could be made from the same material – silicon. This opened the way for an entire circuit to be made on a single piece of silicon with the elimination of all soldered connections.

In February 1959 a patent was filed for the first integrated circuit. Since that date, thousands of millions of pounds have been channelled into their development – but not solely for the sake of miniaturization. So what are the other advantages that have caused the development of integrated circuits to attract so much money, time and effort? We can identify four advantages of integrated circuits (IC) that may be equally important; these are *size, cost, reliability,* and *speed*.

Size   Early ICs had the equivalent of up to 10 transistors on a chip and by the late 1960s people were talking of LSI (Large-Scale Integration), which made it possible to implement a few thousand transistors on a chip. Today we regularly speak of VLSI (Very-Large-Scale Integration), and now SLSI (Super-Large-Scale Integration) has already arrived.

Although there are no strict definitions of LSI, VLSI, etc., the classifications generally used in the microelectronics industry are as follows:

SSI (Small-Scale Integration)	1 to 10 transistors per chip
MSI (Medium-Scale Integration)	from 10 to around 500 transistors
LSI (Large-Scale Integration)	from 100 to around 20 000 transistors
VLSI (Very-Large-Scale Integration)	from 10 000 to around 100 000 transistors
SLSI (Super-Large-Scale Integration)	more than 100 000 transistors

Cost The reduction in cost of electronics has been one of the most dramatic effects of integrated circuit technology. Today, a complex integrated circuit containing the equivalent of tens of thousands of transistors costs about the same as a single transistor bought several years ago. Effectively, the cost of a transistor has been reduced by a factor of about ten thousand! This important advantage of integrated circuit technology is due to the fact that, once the technique has been established, it costs little more in time and materials to manufacture a single IC than it does to manufacture a single transistor. So, the more components that can be squeezed onto a chip the cheaper is the cost per component. The two graphs in figure 3.7 illustrate how the price per component has come down as the number of components per chip has gone up over the last twenty years.

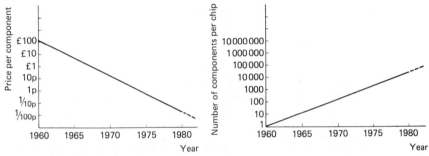

Fig 3.7   Illustrating the decrease in the price per component as the number of components per chip has increased over the last 20 years

Reliability Today, electronic equipment rarely goes wrong. How have integrated circuits contributed to this increased reliability?

Electronic equipment fails either because of failure or damage to a component, or because of a mechanical fault – a badly soldered joint or a faulty contact in a switch for example. The first significant increase in reliability came when valves were replaced by transistors. A valve is rather like an electric light bulb in that it contains a filament of wire that is heated by an electric current. Over the course of several hundred hours of use, the metal from which the filament is made slowly evaporates until a point is reached when the filament is so weak that any small vibration, or just the shock of switching on an electric current, causes it to break. Inevitably then, a valve has only a limited life, however carefully it is used. The early valve computers of the 1950s which contained several thousand valves spent as much time having valves replaced as they did working.

The introduction of transistors brought an increase in reliability of several thousand times. In fact, so far as anyone knows, the life of a transistor is unlimited in normal use. The failure of a transistor is often due to a fault elsewhere in the circuit, resulting in a larger-than-normal current or voltage. As well as benefiting from the reliability of transistors, integrated circuits further increase reliability by reducing the chance of mechanical failure which can result from faulty connections or faulty switches. An integrated circuit can contain thousands of components all made on a single piece of silicon with soldered joints completely eliminated. In addition, the use of complicated mechanical switches has also been eliminated by replacing them with electronic switching circuits. Previously such circuits could not have been built at an economical cost.

In the field of computers, the use of integrated circuit technology has led to an increase in reliability of several million times. Europe's first commercial computer, the Ferranti Mark I Star built in 1950, contained 4000 valves, 10 000 metres of connecting wire, and 100 000 soldered joints. By contrast, Europe's first microprocessor, the Ferranti F100 with one hundred times the computing power of the Mark I Star, contained the equivalent of 70 000 components yet had only 2 metres of metallic interconnections.

Speed   Speed of operation is probably not a factor that most people would immediately think of when dealing with electronic devices. Yet, in the design of computers, speed of operation can be crucial.

The time taken by a computer to execute an individual instruction depends on two factors. Firstly, it depends on the time required for a transistor to switch on or off. Secondly, it depends on the time taken for a signal to move from one part of the computer to another. The design of the integrated circuit reduces the delay resulting from both of these factors. Delay in switching time is reduced by the extremely small size of the transistors. This has the effect of reducing the unwanted capacitance that is responsible for slowing down the switching time by storing electrical charge. At the same time, the microscopic distances between components shorten the distance travelled by the signals.

Over the last decade, the operating speed of integrated circuits, which is measured in millionths of a second, has improved by a factor of about one hundred. This has been achieved by a combination of packing components closer together and the use of new technologies for fabrication.

Integrated Circuit Applications

Integrated circuits are now produced for almost every imaginable application, the different types available numbering several thousand. Here, we will only point out a few important types of IC in order to give a general overview of their possible applications.

All electronic circuits, including integrated circuits, divide naturally into two groups: digital and analog. Digital ICs have of course had the greatest impact because of their importance in computers. As we shall see later, they are used for microprocessors and memory, the essential components of computers of the type used in industry today. Broadly speaking we could say that digital ICs are at the heart of the intelligent aspect of the operations performed in the automated factory. Analog ICs, on the other hand, provide the essential bridge between the intelligence and the actual operation of equipment. Amplifiers, in the form of analog ICs, are required to boost small signals from sensors (see Chapter 6) and to enable electro-mechanical relays and powerful electric motors to be switched on and off by small signals sent from computers.

Digital Integrated Circuits

One of the earliest types of digital integrated circuit available was the **logic gate**. The function of logic gates themselves is explained in Appendix II, but here it will be sufficient to regard them simply as the building blocks of computers. In the early seventies, digital ICs appeared with several logic gates on a chip. The development of MSI made it possible to combine the functions of several of these ICs on a single chip, enabling complicated devices such as desk-top calculators and digital clocks to be designed using ten or so integrated circuits. Circuits designed in this way are referred to as **hardwired logic**. Nowadays, of course, LSI has made it possible to combine the functions of several MSI integrated circuits on a single chip, but there is still a need for integrated circuits containing logic gates which can be configured into a system for some specialized application. Hardwired logic offers a simple solution where the application does not justify the development of a microprocessor-based system or the manufacture of a custom-designed integrated circuit.

Customised chips are at the other extreme to hardwired logic. A manufacturer wishing to mass-produce a particular electronic instrument, for example an electronic thermometer, may have a chip designed to personal specifications. The resulting instrument will have the advantage of being compact and will become economical to produce if sold in sufficient quantities.

Between the extremes of hardwired logic and custom chips, there is a halfway house called a **semi-custom chip**. A finished semi-custom chip contains a large number of logic gates connected together according to the customer's specification but the production of the chip is halted just before the final stage of making the metallic interconnections. The result is a chip consisting of isolated logic gates as shown in figure 3.8. When an order is received from a customer, the production of the chip is completed by making the metallic interconnections between the logic gates according to the specifications required. The final result is a logic circuit with the appearance shown in figure 3.9, cheaper than a custom chip and more compact than hardwired logic.

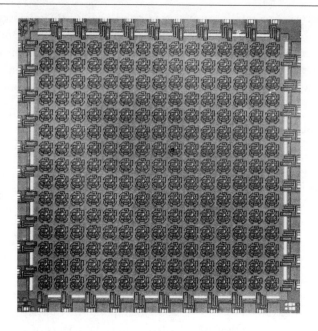

Fig 3.8   A semi-custom chip before completion

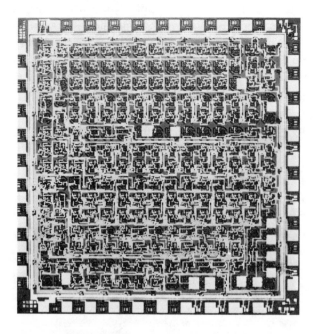

Fig 3.9   A finished semi-custom chip

Microprocessors

Integrated circuit logic gates are valuable components to the robotics engineer. Such circuits, as well as being of small size, low cost and high efficiency, can be combined in numerous ways to provide powerful circuitry capable of processing information to enable complicated decision making to be carried out with speed and accuracy. However, combinations of logic gates made by connecting together integrated circuits can only perform the single function for which they are designed. In the early seventies, the technique of large-scale integration made possible the development of the **microprocessor**, which is based on logic gates but is capable of being *programmed* to perform almost any conceivable arithmetic or logical operation.

To attempt to understand microprocessors in terms of circuit diagrams would be of little use to anybody since they are extremely complex devices. It is therefore usual to discuss a microprocessor from two points of view: the *physical view* and the *logical view*. The physical view is concerned with the appearance of the device – identifying its terminals, what voltages and currents can be connected to it, etc. The logical view describes the internal working of the device, showing block diagrams of the various units within it and how they function together. We shall look first at the logical view.

THE LOGICAL VIEW

The diagram in figure 3.10 shows how the microprocessor is connected to other devices to form a system. Note that the microprocessor is not a *microcomputer*. The system of which it forms a part may be called a microcomputer if it comprises units which enable the microprocessor to be easily programmed by the user. In what follows, we will treat each of the units shown in the diagram as "black boxes", without considering how they work in any great detail.

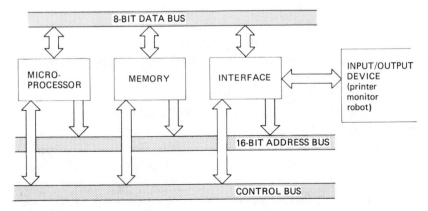

Fig 3.10   How the microprocessor is connected to other devices to form a system

Memory We can visualize the memory as rows of compartments each able to store a BInary digiT or **bit** which is either 1 or 0. Combinations of these 1s and 0s are used as codes to represent any type of information from letters of the alphabet to pure numbers (using the binary system).

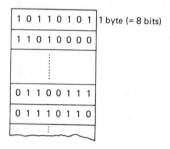

Fig 3.11   Memory organised into bytes

The "compartments" in the memory are organised into groups of eight as shown in figure 3.11. Each group of eight bits is called a **byte**. Each byte has an identifying number called its **address** which the microprocessor uses to locate the particular byte that it requires.

In reality, the memory we are referring to is contained in one or more integrated circuits and the 1s and 0s are held in bistable circuits (see Appendix II), which are either ON (1) or OFF (0). Two main classes of integrated circuit memory may be used:

1 ROM (which stands for Read-Only Memory). In this type of memory the transistor switches are wired to be either ON or OFF at the time of manufacture and can never subsequently be altered. ROM therefore stores data permanently which can only be read – hence the name.

2 RAM (which stands for Random Access Memory). In RAM type memory the bistable circuits can be set to ON or OFF by the microprocessor. The microprocessor can therefore both read the contents of the memory and also write to the memory to store new results. An important point to note about RAM is that, when the electricity supply is switched off and then later restored, all of the bistables reset themselves to some random state. Data stored in RAM will therefore be lost whenever power is switched off. The contents of RAM, if required for later use, must be recorded onto magnetic tape or magnetic disc from which it can be loaded back into RAM when required.

The Interface Interfaces (there may be more than one) form the important link that allow the microprocessor to communicate with the outside world. Devices that may be connected to an interface include the keyboard for entering instructions or data, a monitor or printer for viewing the results produced by the microprocessor, or, of particular interest to us, a robot.

An interface usually has several different lines of communication to the outside world. Each of these is called a **port** and each port has its own port address rather like a memory address. A single interface can therefore be used to deal with more than one type of input or output. The subject of interfaces is dealt with in greater detail in Chapter 4.

The Microprocessor itself Having looked at the system surrounding the microprocessor we can now turn our attention to the microprocessor itself. As you will see from figure 3.10, the microprocessor communicates with the other devices in the system by means of three **buses**. These buses are simply lines of electrical conductors. The *address bus* and *data bus* may both be 8-bit consisting of a group of 8 parallel conductors, or 16-bit consisting of a group of 16 parallel conductors. The *control bus* consists normally of between 10 and 20 parallel conductors.

As a simplified example of how the whole system works, imagine that the microprocessor is executing a program to move a robotic arm. The sequence of instructions is stored in the memory as a binary code. The operations performed by the microprocessor are as follows:

1 The microprocessor sends a signal on the control bus indicating that it wants to read from the memory. It then sends on the address bus the address of the memory location where the first instruction is stored.
2 The instruction stored in the memory is sent to the microprocessor along the data bus.
3 The microprocessor acts on the instruction.
4 The microprocessor sends a signal on the control bus indicating that it wants to write (send data) to the interface. It then sends an address on the address bus which is the address of the port within the interface device.
5 The data for moving the robot is sent from the microprocessor to the interface device along the data bus.
6 The interface sends the signal, in suitable form, to the robot.

The example that we have looked at illustrates in general terms the purpose of the three buses. We will return to a more detailed examination of their working in Chapter 4.

The Standard Microprocessor Architecture

The block diagram representing the design and internal layout of a microprocessor is called the **architecture** of the device. Today, the majority of microprocessors use the same basic architecture which has come to be known as the "standard" architecture and is shown in figure 3.12.

The two main components of the microprocessor are the **ALU** (arithmetic-logical unit) and the **control unit**. The shifter enables multiplication and division by 2 as explained earlier and the other units, including the accumula-

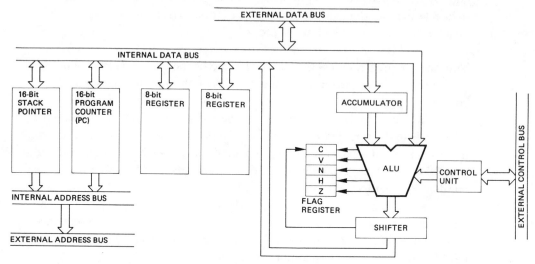

Fig 3.12   Standard microprocessor architecture

tor, are called **registers** and are basically small blocks of memory reserved for special purposes. The number of bits that can be held by a register is called the **word length** and is usually 4, 8 or 16. Microprocessors with a 16-bit *internal* data bus are known as *16-bit microprocessors* and are both faster and more powerful than 8-bit types. A 16-bit (2 byte) word length is usually found on a 16-bit microprocessor and an 8-bit (1 byte) word length on an 8-bit micro-processor. For computers or control applications, 8-bit microprocessors are the minimum requirement.

In order to illustrate how the microprocessor works internally let us suppose that it is going to be used for the arithmetic operation of adding two numbers together. We will assume that the two numbers concerned, together with the instruction to add them, have been stored in the RAM connected to the microprocessor. The operation could be carried out as follows:

1   Take the first number from the RAM and store it in the accumulator (actually a very small memory) inside the microprocessor.
2   Take the second number from the RAM and use the ALU to add it to the contents of the accumulator.
3   Store the result back into the accumulator.

Of course, the microprocessor cannot do anything unless it is given a list of instructions of what to do. This list of instructions is in fact the **program** and is stored in the memory (RAM or ROM) in the form of codes called operation codes or **opcodes** represented by binary numbers. The program to carry out the three steps above might be as follows (the example actually applies to the Motorola 6800 microprocessor):

Memory address	Opcode contained in memory	Meaning of opcode
5		
6	1 0 0 1 0 1 1 0	Get the first number and store it in the accumulator.
7	0 0 0 0 1 0 0 0	This is the address where the first number will be found.
8	1 0 0 1 1 0 1 1	Add the second number to the number now in the accumulator and put the total back into the accumulator.
9	0 0 0 0 1 0 0 1	This is the address where the second number will be found.

Even a simple example such as this causes us to think of many questions about how the microprocessor actually works. We will now attempt to answer these questions, at least in part.

Q. How does the microprocessor know where in the memory to look for the instructions?

A. A special register (small internal memory) called the **program counter** or PC (see figure 3.12) keeps track of the address of each instruction. As an instruction is dealt with, the program counter is automatically updated by the correct amount, enabling the microprocessor to "remember where it has got up to".

Q. Opcodes such as 10010110 appear to us to be meaningless. How does the microprocessor make sense of them?

A. Opcodes are first sent to the control unit where they are decoded. The control unit itself contains a small program called a **microprogram** for decoding instructions. In the majority of microprocessors available, the microprogram is written by the manufacturers and can never be altered. Manufacturers supply a list of the opcodes that can be used with their microprocessor.

Q. Apart from actually writing the result on a printer or performing another calculation, can we make use of it in any other way, perhaps to influence the next step to be taken by the program?

A. A special piece of memory called the **flag register** (or *program status register* or *condition code register*) automatically keeps a note of useful or "interesting" conditions occurring as a result of the ALUs operation. This register holds (depending on the model) up to eight binary digits which are each set to 0 or 1 in response to certain conditions. Programmers refer to these digits as *flags*. Five essential flags are shown in figure 3.12 and their purpose is as follows. (Note: In what follows, *set* refers to a flag being 1 and *reset* refers to a flag being 0.)

C (Carry) flag   This is set when the result of an addition produces a carry. For example

$$
\begin{array}{r}
1\ 1\ 1\ 1\ 0\ 0\ 0\ 1\\
+\quad 1\ 0\ 0\ 0\ 0\ 0\ 0\ 0\\
\hline
=\quad 1\quad 0\ 1\ 1\ 1\ 0\ 0\ 0\ 1
\end{array}
$$

↑

(carry)

The 1 to be carried is stored as the C flag.

The C flag is also set when the shifter causes a 1 to *spill-out* as a result of shifting a row of digits to the left or right.

V (oVerflow) flag   With certain types of computer arithmetic, a carry can affect not only the size of a number but also whether it is considered as positive or negative. The V flag is set when an addition operation affects a number in this way.

N (Negative) flag   On some microprocessors this is called the S (Sign) flag. With arithmetic involving positive and negative numbers, if the N flag is set it indicates that the number in the accumulator is negative, and if reset it indicates that the number is positive.

H (Half-carry) flag   A common type of computer arithmetic used when exact results are required is called BCD (binary coded decimal). In BCD, the 8 bits stored in the accumulator are interpreted as two separate 4-bit codes. A programmer can set the H flag to tell the microprocessor that the accumulator is holding a BCD number.

Z (Zero) flag   Whenever the result of an arithmetic operation is zero, the Z flag is set. This enables the result to be tested, possibly forming the basis for making a logical decision on what to do next.

Q. When the microprocessor is doing a more complicated operation, does it have anywhere to "jot down" intermediate results?

A. For a microprocessor, sending data to the RAM along the external data bus takes a relatively long time (two or three microseconds). It therefore has available a small amount of internal memory, which works around a hundred times faster, for storing numbers that it needs to work with during a calculation. In an 8-bit microprocessor the **general-purpose registers** are usually each able to store 8-bits. A number of these registers are normally *paired* enabling them to store 16-bits.

The Stack Pointer   We have so far dealt with all of the elements contained in figure 3.12 with the exception of an important register called the stack pointer, which we will now explain.

A long program is normally broken down into sections, each of which produces its own results. These results sometimes have to be kept for later use while another section of the program is being dealt with. A special *area of memory*, called the **stack** (in most microprocessors this is external RAM but in a few it is internal registers), is used to hold results while the microprocessor is performing another calculation. The stack builds up rather like a stack of paper might build up on your desk if you were doing the same job yourself. The top of the stack contains the most recent result and the bottom of the stack contains the oldest result.

The job of the stack pointer is to hold the memory address where the last data item was stored in the stack. The stack pointer is automatically updated whenever data is put into the stack (an operation called PUSH) or taken out of the stack (an operation called POP). Data cannot be pushed or popped from anywhere other than the top of the stack and this gives rise to it being described as LIFO which stands for Last In First Out.

THE PHYSICAL VIEW

Externally a microprocessor looks similar to any other integrated circuit, except that it has rather more pins. Most microprocessors in fact have either 40 or 42 pins although a few types have 48 or 64.

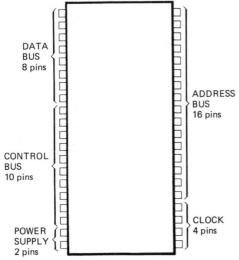

Fig 3.13   Physical view of a 40-pin microprocessor

Figure 3.13 shows the typical pin connections to a 40-pin microprocessor. A total of 16 pins, labelled A0 to A15, are allocated for connection to the external address bus. A further 8 pins, D0 to D7, are allocated to the external data bus. The power supply requires at least 2 pins and probably 4 more are needed to connect a quartz crystal to operate the internal clock (or clocks). The remaining 10 pins form the control bus.

Earlier it was pointed out that 16-bit microprocessors, which are faster and more powerful, have a 16-bit *internal* data bus. For greatest efficiency, a 16-bit microprocessor should therefore have a 16-bit external data bus (requiring 16 pins). However, in practice this is often not the case. The external data bus cannot be increased beyond 8 without going to at least a 48-pin package since the control bus requires a minimum of 10 pins and the address bus 16 pins. At present, manufacturing constraints make a 16-pin data bus an expensive option and the result is that many so-called 16-bit microprocessors have only an 8-bit external data bus. The necessary 16 bits of data are taken in two operations by electronically switching the internal connections to the pins – a technique called **multiplexing**.

True 16-bit microprocessors, with 48 or 64 pin packages, are of course faster in operation.

4 Computers

As you learn more about automation you will begin to appreciate that the role of the computer goes beyond the control of robots discusssed in Chapter 2. The computer is today involved in all aspects of the manufacturing process and it is therefore important to know something of the way computers work, how they are programmed and how they can be connected both to different devices and to each other.

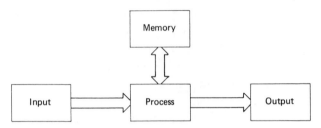

Fig 4.1   The von Neumann architecture of a computer

Almost all computers in current use are designed according to the basic configuration shown in figure 4.1. The blocks in this diagram depict the so called *logical* arrangement of the computer rather than the individual physical devices themselves. The arrangement is called the *von Neumann* architecture, after the famous mathematician who worked on its theory. The block labelled *process* refers to the central processing unit, or CPU, consisting of the ALU and control unit (see Chapter 3). In microcomputers, which have now become so common, the job of the CPU is done by a microprocessor. The memory, as we have seen in Chapter 3, contains the program instructions and data. It is an essential feature of computers, in contrast to simple calculators and controllers, that they can be programmed and re-programmed to carry out any task required by the user.

Mainframes, Minis and Micros

Depending on their size, complexity and of course cost, computers fall into categories of mainframe computers, minicomputers and microcomputers. Increasingly, however, as microcomputers become more powerful, the distinction between them and minicomputers is becoming blurred.

Mainframes: These are the largest type of computer. Three main features of their design distinguish them from minis and micros.

1 A very large number of general-purpose registers in the CPU, typically up to 64. These general-purpose registers are small memories which are used by the CPU to store intermediate results during calculations. A large number of these registers reduces the necessity for frequent transfers of small amounts of data to and from the main memory. The result is much faster operation.

2 The ability to input and output data at very high rates, permitting the use of mass storage devices in the form of large high-speed magnetic disc systems. This allows mainframe computers to deal with vast amounts of data.

3 Tens of megabytes of main memory making possible the use of large programs.

In addition, mainframe computers use a word length of at least 32 bits. Recall from Chapter 3 that the word length is the maximum number of bits that can be dealt with by the CPU in a single operation. The word length has a direct effect on the speed of a computer since it makes possible the use of a larger number of instructions by the control unit. Of equal importance, it enables numbers consisting of many digits to be dealt with in a single operation. This greatly increases the speed at which arithmetic can be done as well as permitting faster handling of long memory addresses. However, long word lengths are now becoming available also on the latest microcomputers.

Mainframe computers are seldom directly involved in control applications. Their chief use is in performing long calculations involving a large amount of data.

Minis and Micros: The **minicomputer** was originally designed as a low-cost, scaled-down version of the mainframe. To reduce cost and complexity, a simplified architecture was used, with typically 16 general-purpose registers in the CPU. Size and cost was further reduced by use of a smaller selection of *peripherals*, that is, equipment such as disc drives, printers and other external devices. The main memory was limited to only several hundred kilobytes.

The **microcomputer** is designed around a microprocessor and today it is chiefly distinguished from the minicomputer by its overall cost and by the size of the system of which it forms a part. The microcomputer is self-contained with its own keyboard, monitor and perhaps one or two magnetic disc drives for additional storage. The minicomputer is also often based on a microprocessor but this forms only the nucleus of a complete system comprising additional memory with the option of larger-capacity disc storage.

In what follows we shall mainly be referring to microcomputers or minis based on microprocessors since it is these which are used for the tasks of control in the automated factory. In a large installation, several microcomputers may be used, each being **dedicated** to a particular machine. A minicomputer may be then be used to act as a superviser, co-ordinating the overall operation.

The Programmable Logic Controller

Here, we should mention the programmable logic controller (PLC), also known as the programmable controller (PC), which is another device based on the microprocessor and may be regarded as a type of computer configured specifically for the purpose of control. A typical PLC unit is shown in figure 4.2.

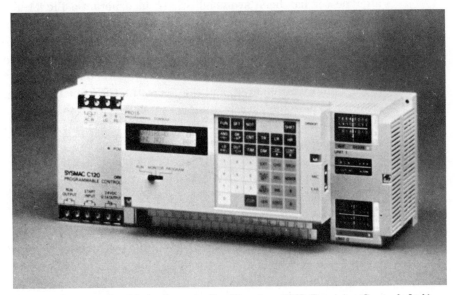

Fig 4.2   A programmable logic controller (Courtesy: IMD Precision Controls Ltd.)

The programming console is only required for inputting programs, carried out by entering a sequence of instructions directly from the keypad. One console can therefore serve a number of PLCs. The PLC unit itself acts basically as a sequencer. It responds to various sensors connected to its inputs, makes logical decisions according to instructions programmed into its memory and sets outputs as required by the program. More advanced PLCs, however, are also able to simulate control procedures such as proportional control, PI, PD or PID control (see Chapter 2). Typical applications of the PLC are too numerous to list but we can summarise the types of equipment with which they are most frequently associated as follows:

Industrial equipment, such as motors, pumps and valves

Furnaces and driers

Process control equipment

Materials and product handling

Packaging machinery

Assembly machines and transfer lines

Non-servo robot control.

For the above applications, there are several advantages in using PLCs rather than computers. Firstly, they are programmed in a very simple language called **ladder logic.** This language takes the form of a sequence of easily learned instructions entered directly from the appropriately labelled keys on the console. Secondly, the inputs and outputs of a PLC can be directly connected to a large range of devices such as switches, relays and sensors whereas the outputs of a computer require additional interfacing equipment in the form of I/O ports (dealt with later in this chapter). Thirdly, the PLC is fitted with a PROM (programmable read only memory) which retains the program after power has been switched off. To incorporate a PROM in a standard computer would require some modification to be carried out.

In order to classify PLCs, we need to choose some criterion. A useful one is the maximum number of input/output (I/O) ports. This can give information about the PLCs power, because the more I/O ports that can be controlled, the more memory is required, and the faster the CPU must be. Using this as a criterion, a possible classification is as follows:

Micro scale – up to 64 I/O ports
Small scale – between 64 and 128 I/O ports
Medium scale – between 128 and 512 I/O ports
Large scale – from 512 I/O ports and above.

Programming Languages

In the last chapter we saw an example of the instructions required to make a computer add two numbers together; this was an example of a program written in **machine code.** Machine code is in fact the only programming language that the computer can understand directly. Of course, writing a program of any significant length in this way would involve an enormous amount of work, not to mention the fact that mistakes would be difficult to locate and correct. Even more importantly, machine code programs can only be written by a person who has an intimate understanding of how the CPU carries out its instructions. Fortunately then, it was realised early on in the development of computers that the computer itself could do the job of translating instructions given as familiar English-sounding words and converting these into the necessary machine code. Thereafter the user would be able to write a program using only the English-sounding instructions. This is the principle of a computer language.

Such computer languages can be divided into two categories, according to their complexity: low-level languages and high-level languages. *Low-level languages* are those in which each instruction given in the programming language is translated into just one machine code instruction. *High-level languages* are those in which one instruction in the programming language may be translated into a whole string of machine code instructions. As we shall explain shortly, despite the name, a low-level language has essential advantages in certain applications.

Low-level Languages   A low-level language helps the job of the programmer by allowing the use of names to represent the machine code instructions. The names which are used are **mnemonics**, that is to say they are in the form of words or letters which serve as a reminder as to the purpose of the code they represent. Numbers such as data or addresses of memory locations are represented by their hexadecimal equivalents (see Appendix II). For example, the mnenomic representing the code to "add a number into the accumulator" would be ADDA or something similar. Mnenomics such as this are more easily remembered than codes such as 00001001.

The process of converting the list of mnenomics and hexadecimal numbers into machine code is called assembly and is carried out by a program called an **assembler**. In fact, most assemblers do more than simply convert mnenomics and hexadecimal into machine code. They also perform the arithmetic needed to calculate memory addresses and do many other operations which simplify the task of writing a program.

Even with the aid of *assembly language*, the programmer still has to understand a great deal about the internal workings of the computer. You may recall from Chapter 3 that even the simple operation of adding together two numbers requires a knowledge of how the accumulator works and how the memory is organised. Assembly language cuts down the work of writing a program, but does not free the programmer from having to understand the computer.

High-level Languages   When a program is written in a high-level language, a single instruction can lead to the generation of many machine code instructions. The result is that the programer who uses a high-level language does not need to understand the innermost workings of the computer. Adding two numbers together, for example, would typically be done in a high-level language by an instruction of the form 3 + 4. This instruction would eventually be converted into the several machine code instructions before being sent to the CPU. The advantages of this are quite easy to see. Programs become not only easier to write but also easier for others to read and correct. The choice of a language will usually depend on the application. For example, a program to handle business accounts or stock control might well be written in COBOL, whereas a program to control a robot might be written in AML. Each language, and the range of commands it provides, is tailored to the requirements of its intended application. Scientific languages such as FORTRAN and ALGOL provide the programmer with a large selection of commands for performing mathematical calculations, whereas commercial languages such as COBOL provide commands which allow the programmer to easily produce figures in tabulated form.

VAL, AML, RAIL and many others are examples of high-level languages used in automation. These provide the programmer with commands such as MOVE, UP, DOWN, etc. for controlling equipment and contain many features not found in languages in more general use. These features include:

1 A sensor interface to provide a way of receiving data from a number of sensors within the system, analysing this information and acting upon it.

2 Special control structures which provide the facility to make logical decisions based on the inputs from sensors. A hypothetical example might be

IF no obstructions THEN Move Hand UP 30cm

If we were programming on-line we might well know that the intended path was clear or else we could guide the arm around any obstructions; when we write an off-line program we have to consider a range of possibilities that could occur at run time and the action to be taken in each case.

3 A machine interface to enable the programmer to include the facility of communicating with other equipment in the factory. Thus a robot engaged in feeding work to a lathe will need to be able to know, for example:

When the lathe is ready to accept work.

When the lathe cycle is complete.

When the tool needs to be exchanged.

If a fault occurs.

To carry out this communication, the factory equipment must, of course, be fitted with appropriate signalling facilities (which could be analog or digital) but, unless the program has the facilities to deal with these signals, then this process of integration cannot be implemented.

4 Geometry transformations which allow the programmer to specify the position of a point by its X,Y,Z coordinates and then translate this into the angles of joints appropriate to the design of the robot. For example, if a robot with six revolute joints (see Chapter 5) is being programmed, then the operator could not possibly be expected to calculate the angles of each joint necessary to place the end effector at some particular position. The programming language performs this calculation from the simpler X,Y,Z coordinates supplied by the operator.

5 User support modules to make the program "user friendly". Features may include:

HELP facilities – where the user can interrupt programming to obtain more information about the correct use of commands available.

TUTORIAL dialogue – where the program guides and prompts an inexperienced user as to what action to take. It should be possible to switch off this facility once the user has gained experience.

SCREEN EDITING – which enables the user to simply alter the program by entering commands from the keyboard and seeing their effect on the screen.

DEBUGGING AIDS – A program will not usually work first time, and a good software package will provide a means of testing programs and applying changes as required.

Compilers and Interpreters

A program written in a high-level language is converted into machine code instructions either by a compiler or by an interpreter. We will deal with the compiler first.

A **compiler** is itself a machine code program, but one which is bought from the supplier of the computer and need not be the concern of the user. The input to the compiler is the high-level program written by the user and is called *source code*. The output of the compiler is the translation into machine code and is called *object code*. Source code only needs to be compiled once and the resulting object code can be stored and re-used as often as required. However, object code is unintelligible to the user and any changes required must be made to the original source code. The edited version then has to be re-compiled.

There are two disadvantages to compilers. The first is that the use of a compiler requires a computer with a large amount of memory. This memory may be either in the form of RAM or in the form of magnetic disc. The second disadvantage is that the translation from source code to object code will generally result in many more machine code instructions than would have been required if the program were originally written in machine code. This is because a machine code programmer can often structure a program to make the most efficient use of the CPU. Where the amount of memory is a limiting factor it may therefore be necessary to program in assembly language rather than a high-level language.

As remarked above, one of the disadvantages of a compiler is the memory it requires. If a compiler is to be used, then there must be sufficient memory available for the compiler itself, for the source code and for the object code that is produced. While this is not a problem on a mainframe, it requires minis and micros to be provided with additional memory in the form of magnetic disc. To get around this problem, the interpreter was invented.

Unlike a compiler, an **interpreter** translates source code line by line, passing each line to the CPU as it is dealt with. Object code is not available to be stored and re-used. While this procedure saves a great deal of memory space, the process of interpreting takes a comparatively long time. Whereas a program, once compiled, may be executed in a few fractions of a second, the same program may take tens of seconds if it has to be interpreted as it is being executed. Nevertheless, interpreters are the only economical solution for small microcomputers. The majority of microcomputers are supplied with an interpreter, for at least one high-level language, built into a ROM. When necessary, programs can be compiled on a larger machine or written directly in assembly language in order to bypass the need for interpreting.

In Chapter 3 we explained the operation of the microprocessor, which forms the brain of computers, by showing how it is able to manipulate numbers. Indeed, until a few years ago, computers were regarded as machines for doing calculations or "working things out". We shall now begin to explain how the computer is able, through the manipulation of numbers, to control all kinds of equipment from printers to robots.

The Three-bus System

As you have learned in Chapter 3, the computer has memory (ROM and RAM) in which is stored not only the program but also the results of calculations and many other items all of which we can refer to as data. Of course, whatever this data happens to represent, it is nothing more than groups of bits (binary digits), and the use to which the data is put depends on where in the memory it has been stored. Different areas of the memory are used by the computer for different purposes. So, for example, a certain area of the memory holds the data for the monitor screen (each of the thousands of points forming the image on the screen correspond to a bit in the memory); if this same data were to be placed in the area of memory used for storing the program, then the computer would attempt to treat it as a program, which of course would only result in error messages. Data may therefore represent either instructions or signals to be sent to control external devices. Whatever the data is used for, it is moved around the computer on a system of buses.

The standard computer is organized around the **three-bus system** referred to in the previous chapter. The three buses are the data bus, the address bus and the control bus.

The Data Bus The data bus is used to carry a computer word in the system. Each wire in the data bus carries a binary signal (a 0 or a 1) so that an 8-bit data bus can either handle eight separate signals, such as the information from eight separate switches, or it can carry a single group of 8 bits. The eight wires in the data bus are numbered as follows:

D_0 first data bus wire (least significant bit)
D_1 second data bus wire
$\vdots$
D_7 most significant data bus wire

In general, the larger the data bus, the more powerful the computer in terms of its computing capability and speed.

The Address Bus A typical 8-bit microcomputer computer has an address bus with 16 wires or lines; a 16-bit microcomputer typically has an address bus with 20 wires. The function of the signals on the address bus is to help to switch on or **enable** (select) a specific memory location. Once the location has been enabled, the computer can either read data from the location or can write (store) data in it. The sixteen lines on the address bus in an 8-bit microcomputer are numbered as follows (remember from Chapter 3 that an 8-bit microcomputer refers to one having an 8-bit internal data bus):

A_0 least significant address bus line

A_1 second address bus line

$\vdots$

A_{15} most significant address bus line

The binary value on the 16-bit address bus can therefore have any value in the range

0000000000000000 to 1111111111111111

that is   0 to 65 535

This gives a total of 65 536 addressable locations (including location zero which is the first available location).

When a particular memory location is enabled and its address placed on the address bus, all the remaining memory locations are disabled (or deselected). By this simple means, the computer can talk to one (and only one) location at a time. Moreover, this mechanism prevents several locations in the memory trying to "talk" to the CPU simultaneously. (Imagine the chaos if several locations try to put data onto the data bus simultaneously!).

The Control Bus   To illustrate the function of the control bus, we will look at one of the wires in the bus of a microprocessor-based computer. Every microprocessor has one or sometimes two lines whose function it is to tell the support devices in the system whether the CPU needs to read from an input device or whether it needs to write data to an output device. This line is known as the READ/WRITE control line; for simplicity, most manufacturers simply call this the R/W line. Note that, in computer jargon, a line is said to be "driven low" when it has a logic 0 on it and "driven high" when it has logic 1 on it.

When the CPU puts a logic 1 on the R/W line, it tells the computer system that it is about to READ or input data from the location whose address it has placed on the address bus. When the CPU puts a logic 0 on this line, it tells the system that it is about to WRITE or output data to the location whose address is on the address bus. The fact that the WRITE operation is selected when the R/W line is *low* is indicated by a horizontal bar drawn above the W, thus R/$\overline{\text{W}}$.

Coordination of the Computer   A simplified description of the process of **reading data** from a typical data bus is given below.

  1   The CPU drives the R/$\overline{\text{W}}$ line high, indicating that it is in its reading phase.

  2   The address of the required location is placed on the address bus (this enables the address).

  3   Once the location is enabled, data is put on the data bus.

  4   The CPU reads the data.

This general principle applies to all microprocessors. The speed at which the above sequence takes place depends to a large extent on the clock frequency, and typically it takes less than about 600 nanoseconds for the CPU to gain access to the data. (600 nanoseconds is 600 thousandths of one millionth of one second – you can see the need for accurate synchronization.)

A simplified description of the process of **writing data** or storing data in a memory location is given below:

    1 The R/$\overline{\text{W}}$ line is driven low to indicate that the CPU is in its writing phase.

    2 The CPU puts the address of the location on the address bus (this enables the location).

    3 Data is placed on the data bus and is written into or stored in the location.

Input/Output Management

Memory-Mapped I/O Addressing So far we have talked in terms of an address referring to a memory location. In many computer systems a small number of addresses do not refer to memory locations at all. Instead, they refer to addresses of input/output ports (see below) which may be connected to various external devices. When this system is used, the ports are said to be memory-mapped.

The advantage of memory-mapped I/O is that any programming instructions that work with data in the memory can just as easily be used to work with data from external equipment. No special instructions are necessary and no additional control signal is needed to distinguish memory from input/output. This makes for less complicated programming methods. The main disadvantage of memory-mapped I/O is that it reduces the amount of memory that can be used because it takes up some of the available addresses.

Isolated I/O Addressing Isolated I/O addressing (an alternative name given to this method is accumulator I/O addressing) is another method of sending data to and from external input/output devices. This may be used instead of or as well as memory-mapped addressing. In this method a signal on the control bus is used to select or deselect the I/O section as required. Since there are relatively few I/O ports, the I/O addresses can be shorter than the memory addresses. For example, eight bits are sufficient for 256 I/O addresses. Shorter addresses mean simpler decoding in the computer.

Input/Output Ports The CPU itself works on very small voltages at currents which are tiny fractions of an amp. Input/output devices, on the other hand, may be anything from another chip to an electric motor or a simple mechanical switch. Connection of external devices is therefore made through an electronic buffer known as an input port or output port. These ports act to interface the CPU to the outside world. There are many types of I/O port, some being as complex as the CPU itself. An I/O port may be either a serial I/O port or a parallel I/O port

Many I/O devices can use either serial or parallel ports, subject only to them being equipped with the appropriate circuitry. A **serial I/O port** handles signals which are transmitted along a single cable in the form of a succession of logic 1s and 0s (Morse code is an everyday example of serial data transmission). The computer itself, however, deals with parallel data, that is it handles data represented by groups of several bits, typically 8 or 16, transmitted or received simultaneously along the data bus. The primary function of the serial I/O port is to convert the serial data into parallel data (and vice versa). A popular serial I/O interface or port is a **UART** (universal asynchronous receiver/transmitter).

A **parallel I/O port** is one which is able to handle data directly in its parallel form. Parallel data transmission is of course faster than serial data transmission because several bits are sent simultaneously. The disadvantage is that it requires multi-stranded cables and is not generally used for transmission of data over distances greater than a few metres at most.

Basic Parallel I/O Ports   A simplified diagram of a parallel input port and a parallel output port is shown in figure 4.3. Each comprises two series-connected banks of switches (these "switches" are, in reality, electronic circuits but are referred to and drawn as switches for the sake of simplicity). The output port also contains an 8-bit register or latch whose function is described below.

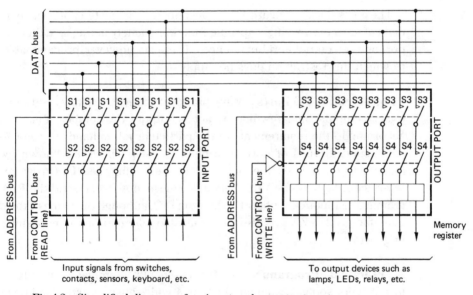

Fig 4.3   Simplified diagram of an input and an output port

To read data from an input device, it is necessary for the computer to enable the input port. It does so by two operations: firstly, by putting the address of the port on the address bus (this enables or closes the set of switches S1 in the input port); and, secondly, by applying a logic 1 to the R/$\overline{\text{W}}$ line of the control bus (thus telling the system it is reading data); the latter action enables or closes the bank of switches S2 in the input port. The net result is that only the selected input port is enabled. All other ports and memories are disabled. At this time, the input device is given access to the data bus, allowing the CPU to read the data from it.

The input port is disabled either when the address on the address bus is changed (disabling the bank of switches S1) or when a logic 0 is placed on the R/W̄ line of the control bus (disabling switches S2).

The computer can output data to an output device by enabling the output port in figure 4.3; this occurs when all the switches in the port (bank S3 and bank S4) are closed. To do this the CPU puts the correct address on the address bus (enabling the bank of switches S3) and simultaneously puts a logic 0 on the R/W̄ line of the control bus to enable the bank of switches S4. The output device can then read the data on the data bus.

Now, the computer works at a very high speed, and it only applies data to the data bus for about one half of a microsecond (or even less in some cases!). Many of the devices which may be connected to the computer work at comparatively slow speeds and therefore would not respond to signals which come and go within millionths of a second. If data is to be used, for example, to illuminate a light, then that data needs to be **latched** or held by the output port for as long as it is required. For this reason many output ports contain a memory register called a latch whose function is to retain a signal after receiving it.

The ports shown in figure 4.3 are described as dedicated ports since they are dedicated to performing a specific function, namely acting as either an input port or as an output port but not both. There are however, progammable ports to which this restriction does not apply.

Programmable I/O Ports   Many practical applications may need a few lines to act as inputs and a few lines to act as outputs, the number of each varying according to the requirements of the particular job in hand. To cater for this need, special types of port have been devised. These are known by their manufacturers' names, the most widely used being the **PIA** (Programmable Interface Adaptor), the **VIA** (Versatile Interface Adaptor), and the **PIO** (Programmable Input/Output port). The term PIO, although the name of the device manufactured by Zilog, is also widely used to refer to programmable interfaces in general.

A Practical Programmable Interface   Programmable interfaces are usually very sophisticated and include a wide range of extra facilities which improve the capabilities of the computer. Typically they are housed in a chip which is physically as large as a microprocessor chip (usually a 40-pin dual-in-line pack [DIP]). Typical facilities, some or all of which may be included are
Several programmable I/O ports.
One or more programmable timers.
A small amount of random access memory (RAM).
A small amount of read-only memory (ROM).
Interrupt facilities (described later).

Controlling a Programmable I/O Port   When using a PIO, it is necessary to program each of the lines to suit the particular application (you cannot assume that the PIO "knows" your own problem!). We shall use the Versatile Interface Adaptor (VIA) as our example; the principles involved apply to most other PIOs.

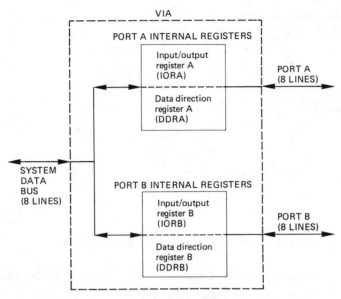

Fig 4.4   A versatile interface adaptor (VIA)

The VIA has sixteen 8-bit registers which can be used to control it. (The VIA is a device which is versatile and is sometimes a little complex in operation, but a simple application can be dealt with using only a few of these registers.) A simplified block diagram of the VIA is given in figure 4.4. Pay particular attention to the four registers shown in the figure as follows:

IORB   I/O Register for port B
IORA   I/O Register for port A
DDRB   Data Direction Register B
DDRA   Data Direction Register A

The function of the two data direction registers DDRA and DDRB is to specify which of the eight lines in each port is to act as an input line and which as an output line. You specify this by storing a direction word (a group of eight bits) in the appropriate data direction register, each bit in the word being defined as follows:

1 *in a bit position makes that line an output line*
0 *in a bit position makes that line an input line.*

If then you store the binary word 00001111 in the DDRA, port A functions such that the first four lines are input lines and the next four lines are output lines.

The function of the two I/O registers IORA and IORB is to store the data which is either being input to the CPU or being output from it.

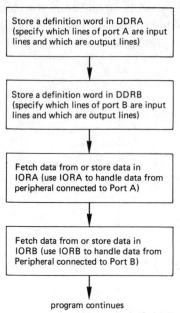

Fig 4.5   Part of a flowchart to control peripherals using a VIA

The operating condition of each of the ports should be established at an early point in the program. Figure 4.5 shows the sequence of operations for the start of a program which controls peripherals using a VIA. You should carefully note that the data direction word must be stored in the data direction register before using the I/O registers to handle data.

Interrupts and Handshaking

An **interrupt** is an electronic signal applied to the CPU. Its function is to cause operation on the main program to be suspended (interrupted) so that the CPU can attend to something which is more urgent. There are two types of interrupt: a maskable interrupt and a non-maskable interrupt. These terms are explained below. The interrupt signal itself is produced by the electronic hardware and may be either a logic 1 or a logic 0, depending on the way in which the CPU is engineered.

A **maskable interrupt** is one which can, if it is so decided by the programmer, be "masked out" or ignored. An analogy of this in real life might be that you are working in a room and can choose either to lock the door (thus preventing interruptions) or to leave the door open, allowing anyone to walk in and interrupt you.

In a computer system the source of a maskable interrupt signal may, for example, be from the computer keyboard. Whenever a key is pressed on the keyboard, a special circuit will generate an interrupt signal. This signal is sent to the CPU which can then either accept the interrupt and read the key or, if the programmer has used the facility to mask the interrupt, ignore the key.

A **non-maskable interrupt** is one which cannot be ignored. An analogy of this in real life might be when you are working in a room where the door cannot be locked. Any external device which is to be given the very highest priority, such as an emergency stop button, can be connected via the non-maskable interrupt of the CPU.

Operation of an Interrupt   When the CPU receives an interrupt signal it completes the instruction it is presently processing in the main program and then attends to the interrupt. At this stage all operations on the main program areas are suspended. The computer then turns its attention to the interrupt routine. This is another program stored elsewhere in the memory, specially written to deal with the interrupt. On completion of the interrupt handling routine, control is returned to the main program once more. The CPU continues with the main program from the point where the interrupt was requested.

Handshaking   Many peripherals such as keyboards and printers operate at a speed which is much slower than that of the CPU. Furthermore, these devices transmit or receive data at irregular time intervals, or asynchronously. The problem of coordinating asynchronous devices is overcome by a technique known as handshaking. There are two types of handshake, namely an input handshake and an output handshake.

The steps involved in a **data input handshake** are:
1   The peripheral tells the CPU that data is available at one of its ports.
2   The CPU reads the data.
3   The CPU sends an *input acknowledgement* signal to the peripheral to say that it has received the data.

The steps involved in a **data output handshake** are:
1   The CPU tells the peripheral that data is available.
2   When the peripheral is ready to receive the data (remember that some peripherals such as printers are relatively slow in operation), it sends a *peripheral ready* signal to the CPU.
3   The CPU sends the data to the peripheral.

Timers

Timers may be needed either to introduce a period of delay during the execution of a program or, as is often the requirement in automated processes, to periodically interrupt a program in order to collect data from various sensors (see Chapter 6). Reading sensors in this way is known as **polling** them. The timing may be done in one of two ways: by means of *software*, using a program that loops round a time-wasting sequence in order to produce a delay, or by means of electronic *hardware* in the form of a programmable timer.

Hardware timers are able to operate independently of the program being executed by the CPU and therefore maintain their timekeeping accuracy regardless of what other demands are being made of the computer. In some microcomputers, a timer is used to control the reading of the keyboard. In this technique an interrupt signal is generated by the timer typically every fiftieth of a second. On receiving the interrrupt signal, the CPU executes a program which scans the keyboard to detect whether a key has been presssed. This is an alternative method to that described earlier in which the pressing of a key generates the interrupt. Note that the interrupts produced by the timer are relatively infrequent compared to the millions of operations per second carried out by the CPU.

Many programmable interfaces contain a hardware timer. This comprises a counter that stores a value previously programmed into it. The stored value is decremented (reduced in value) during each clock cycle of the main computer clock, thereby providing a highly accurate method of timing. A logic signal, which can be used to interrupt the computer, is generated when the value in the timer reaches zero.

The features of software and hardware timers can be summarised as follows:

Software timer
- No additional hardware is needed.
- When the computer is handling a software timing program, it is not possible to run any other programs and still maintain accurate timekeeping.

Hardware timer
- The computer is free to run other programs while the timer is running.
- Additional hardware is needed.

Advanced Computers

The current computer technology is adequate for performing calculations and for the control of machines but lacks the basic functions for non-numeric processing of speech, text, vision and pattern recognition, and for the demands of artificial intelligence such as inference, association and learning. To provide for these more advanced and higher-level functions, the design philosophy of the current computer technology has had to be studied and evaluated. During recent years, VLSI integrated circuit techniques have substantially reduced hardware costs, so computer systems can use as much hardware as required. This has paved the way for the development of a new architectures using several processors simultaneously.

The speed and versatility of the traditional von Neumann architecture using a single processor is limited by two factors. One is the distance between the processor and the memory, the so-called *communication path*. The electronic signals move between processor and memory at about one half the speed of light and so their journey to and fro limits the maximum speed at which processes can be carried out. The most obvious way around this difficulty is to shorten the communication path. This approach is however limited by the fact that the small amount of heat generated by each of the chips becomes difficult to get rid of when the chips are packed closely together. This becomes an increasingly serious problem as the number of chips is increased. In a few of the largest and most powerful computers this problem has to be dealt with by pumping a liquid coolant around them. The second limitation of the von Neumann architecture is the need to do one thing at a time in a prescribed order, or sequentially. It is the necessity for **sequential processing** which imposes the greatest limitation on processing power.

There are several new techniques to get several jobs done at once, providing an alternative to the von Neuman type of sequential processing. Two different ideas (or combinations of them) have been tried: pipelining and parallel processing.

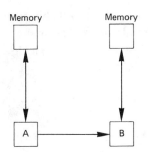

Fig 4.6   Pipelining: processor A passes its output to processor B; one-way communication only

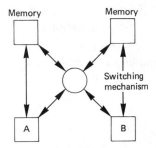

Fig 4.7   Multiprocessing: processors A and B chatter and share memory

In the **pipeline system** shown in figure 4.6 the processing is shared among several processors, each of which deals with a particular part of the computer's memory and carries out a particular part of a program. Output of one processor is passed (or *piped*) to the next one. This can be thought of as working rather like a production line in a factory. Pipelined processors speed up operations dramatically.

The second non von Neumann technique, **parallel processing**, is potentially even more exciting, although more difficult to achieve. The idea is to use a multiprocessor system, as shown in figure 4.7, not just to parcel out a job in such a way that different processors can work on different bits of the program, but to allow different processors to work simultaneously, doing different operations on the same data.

(The term *multiprocessor* should not be confused with *multiprocessing* which refers to the technique of running several programs simultaneously on a conventional computer.)

The snags with multiprocessors are two-fold. The first snag is that you have to make sure that different processors know which one of them is to get a particular bit of information from the computer's memory. The second snag is in writing the required software. Ideally you would want a computer that employed ten processors operating in parallel to be ten times faster. In fact, using conventional programming languages, it has been found that the maximum speed-up that can be achieved is only about four times. The solution is to develop special parallel programming languages.

The Transputer   The transputer (transfer computer) is an entirely new device designed to overcome the problems of both lack of speed and lack of flexibility of the conventional computer. A prototype transputer has already been launched and it is seen as an essential component in tomorrow's electronics. In this device, which has been described as "the computer on a chip", a single chip contains the processor, memory and communications for parallel processing. A special parallel processing language, called Occam, has also been developed to go with it.

Speed is assured by the fact that the transputer is a 32-bit device (able to process 32 individual bits of information simultaneously) running at 10 million instructions per second (10 mips). Currently available 32-bit single chip microcomputers are rated at around 1.2 mips.

5 Robot Geometry and Drive Mechanisms

Having learnt the theory of how a robot is controlled and programmed, we now turn our attention to the mechanical structure. Robots, although ideally able to be programmed to do any job, are in fact usually designed with some particular job in mind. For example, a robot which resembles a human arm, like that shown in figure 5.1a, would be quite suitable for paint spraying because of its manoeuvrability but would not be suitable for welding a long straight line several metres long because of its limited reach. The design of a robot arm therefore has to take into account whether it is to be able to cover a large area, perform intricate movements, lift heavy loads or move with great speed, or of course a combination of these things.

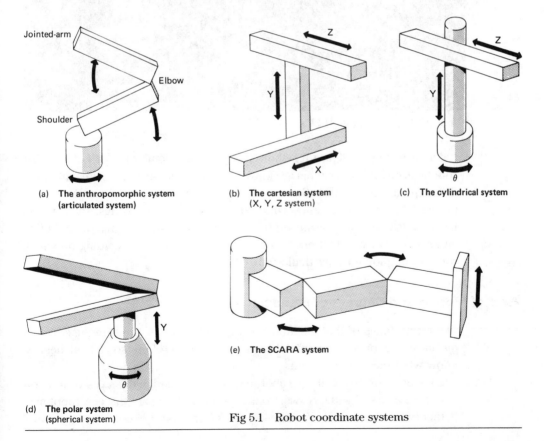

(a) **The anthropomorphic system**
   (articulated system)

(b) **The cartesian system**
   (X, Y, Z system)

(c) **The cylindrical system**

(d) **The polar system**
   (spherical system)

(e) **The SCARA system**

Fig 5.1   Robot coordinate systems

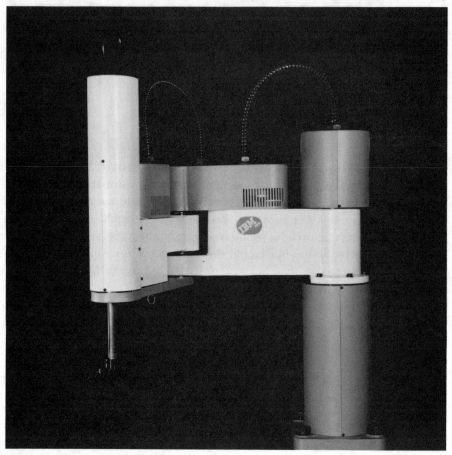

A SCARA robot – the IBM 7545

The drawings in figure 5.1 show the five most common ways of building robotic arms. These systems are known as anthropomorphic, cartesian, cylindrical, polar and SCARA. Some of these systems are also known by one or more of the alternative names which are shown on the drawings. Each system has its advantages and disadvantages with regard to strength, manoeuvrability and speed, and we shall need to be aware of this before deciding on which robot to employ for a particular job.

Axes of Motion and Degrees of Freedom

The terms "axes of motion" and "degrees of freedom" are often used when discussing robot geometry and the specifications of robots, so you will need to know what these terms mean.

Look at the drawing of the robot in figure 5.2 in which the **axes of motion** have been marked with arrows. Count the axes – there are three. A robot may in theory have any number of axes and it is clear that the more axes there are,

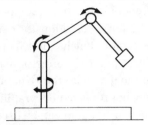

Fig 5.2   Robot with three axes of motion and three degrees of freedom

the more manoeuvrable the robot is; at the same time however, the more complicated it will be to program. The axes of motion need not necessarily be rotations as they are in figure 5.2. They could be motions along a straight line as shown, for example, by the straight arrows on the robots in figure 5.1. Axes that allow *rotation* are often referred to in manufacturers' specifications as **revolute joints**, and those which allow movement in a *straight line* as **prismatic joints**.

The number of **degrees of freedom** is a term which is often confused in robotics with *axes of motion*. But, to the engineer, the term "degrees of freedom" has its own important meaning. It is the number of *independent* directions in which the end effector (tool or gripper) of the robot can move.

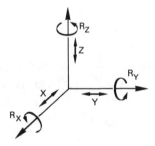

Fig 5.3   The six degrees of freedom possible for a solid object

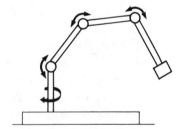

Fig 5.4   Robot with four axes of motion and three degrees of freedom

Any solid object has a maximum of six degrees of freedom – these are shown on the diagram in figure 5.3. Three of them, labelled X, Y and Z, represent movements along a line, and the other three, R_x, R_y and R_z, represent rotations.

As an example, the robot shown in figure 5.2 has three axes of motion. To work out how many degrees of freedom it has, you will have to focus your attention on the end of the arm. By various combinations of movements in the three axes of motion, it is possible to position the end effector anywhere along the X axis, anywhere along the Y axis or anywhere along the Z axis. This robot therefore has THREE degrees of freedom. In this case, the number of degrees of freedom and the number of axes of motion happens to be the same. Now look at the robot in figure 5.4. We have added an extra axis of motion but this does not affect the number of degrees of freedom. The tool or gripper can only move along the X, Y and Z axes as before. In this case, adding the extra axis of motion has made the robot more manoeuvrable but has not increased the number of degrees of freedom. A robot with a fixed end effector may have up to three degrees of freedom. Adding additional axes to the structure cannot increase this number beyond three but may improve manoeuvrability. Within the limits of the robot's reach, three degrees of freedom can be used to place the end-effector as a whole in any position – but not at any angle.

Adding Degrees of Freedom – the Wrist

The end effector is not often fitted directly onto the end of the robotic arm. Usually, some form of mechanical wrist is used to allow it to be placed at different angles. In this way, the number of degrees of freedom can be increased up to a maximum of six.

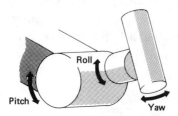

Fig 5.5   A robot wrist with three degrees of freedom

Figure 5.5 shows a typical **robot wrist**. Like your own wrist, the robot's wrist can swivel, bend upwards or downwards and bend from side to side. In all, the wrist has three degrees of freedom (R_x, R_y and R_z in figure 5.3). In the diagram, we have labelled these movements roll, pitch and yaw, which are the technical terms used by engineers.

If a wrist with three degrees of freedom, R_x, R_y and R_z, is fitted to the end of a robotic arm which itself has three degrees of freedom, X, Y, and Z, then the complete assembly will have a total of six degrees of freedom. For some purposes, six degrees of freedom are not necessary, and a wrist having only one or two degrees of freedom can be used instead. Manufacturers offer various optional wrists which can be attached to the basic robotic arm that they supply.

Robot Geometry

The three degrees of freedom, X,Y, and Z, can be obtained by configuring a robot structure in many different ways. In fact, mathematical analysis of the problem shows that there are 37 possible configurations. However, only the five configurations shown in figure 5.1 are used in practice and we shall now look at each of these in turn.

Anthropomorphic Geometry The name "anthropomorphic" suggests some likeness to human beings. The anthropomorphic arm shown in figure 5.1a is like a human arm in the way that the sections are jointed together, but the resemblance seems to end there! The names "shoulder" and "elbow" are often used to refer to two of the joints as shown in the diagram and we have already referred to a wrist which can be attached to the end of the arm. If an arm more flexible than the one shown in figure 5.1a is needed, then additional sections may be used. For example, the anthropomorphic arm shown in figure 5.4 has four sections.

The anthropomorphic-type arm is quite clearly the most manoeuvrable and is often the choice for paint spraying. Compared to the other types of arm however, it is slow moving, and it is also difficult to move the end of the arm in a straight line. Compared to the cartesian arm, it cannot cover a very large area.

Cartesian Geometry The cartesian arm can move in three independent directions (see figure 5.1b) labelled X, Y, and Z. In some cases, the cartesian arm is suspended from an overhead gantry forming the X-axis (see figure 5.6). This arrangement releases valuable floor space making it possible for the arm to cover an area of several square metres.

The arm itself has three axes of motion and three degrees of freedom. Motion along the X axis allows the arm to move along the workpiece. Motion along the Y axis allows the arm to move towards and away from the workpiece, while the Z axis allows movement upwards and downwards. Notice that each of the three movements is at 90 degrees to the other two. With this type of system, the end of the arm can move over the surface of an imaginary rectangle. We would say that this arm has a rectangular **work envelope**. The

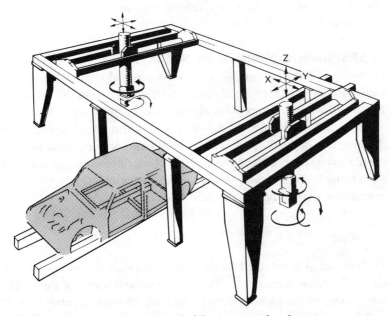

Fig 5.6   A cartesian arm suspended from an overhead gantry

shape and size of the work envelope is obviously an important factor to be considered when designing a robotic arm and we will return to this point later.

At first sight, a cartesian arm may seem much less useful than the more manoeuvrable anthropomorphic (jointed arm) type. It does however have its advantages and it is often used where a large area has to be covered, but intricate movements are not necessary.

Cylindrical Geometry   The cylindrical system is similar to the cartesian system except that this time there is no movement along the X axis. Instead, the arm can rotate on a central support (see figure 5.1c). The angle of rotation is usually referred to by the Greek letter θ (theta).

How many axes of motion and how many degrees of freedom does this robot have? Looking again at figure 5.1c you can see that cylindrical geometry provides three axes of motion (Y, Z, and θ). The end effector has three degrees of freedom since it can move along the X, Y and Z axes of figure 5.3.

The work envelope of this type of arm is cylindrical, meaning that the end of the arm can reach parts of the surfaces of imaginary cylinders drawn around the central support. The cylindrical-type robot arm is capable of moving much faster than the cartesian type and may, for example, be used in loading or unloading conveyor systems.

Polar Geometry   Polar geometry robotic arms have the same Y and θ axes as the cylindrical type, but in this case the arm is pivoted so that it can rotate in the vertical plane instead of moving up and down along the Z axis (see figure 5.1d). The work envelope is part of the surface of a sphere and this system is sometimes also called *spherical geometry*. This type of arm can move faster in the vertical direction than a cylindrical-type arm, but of course the range of movement is much more restricted.

SCARA Geometry   The word SCARA stands for Selective Compliant Assembly Robot Arm and the design has been adopted by several companies who manufacture this type of robot under licence from the original inventors. The SCARA robot (figure 5.1e) appears rather different to the other types of robot in that all the revolute joints in the arm rotate about vertical axes. Examination of the diagram will show that the complete arrangement (excluding the wrist) nevertheless has three degrees of freedom. SCARA robots such as the IBM 7545 (see page 66) are now being increasingly used for assembly operations, particularly in the field of electronics.

The Work Envelope

We have already referred to the work envelope in discussing the different types of robotic arms above. The exact size and shape of the work envelope will be one of the main factors in deciding whether a robot is suitable for a particular job.

Think for a moment about the work envelope of your own arm. Standing in one place, you can extend your arm upwards, downwards and to either side. It doesn't reach very far backwards because the joints only move through limited angles and some areas cannot be reached because the rest of your body gets in the way. You can visualize a sort of imaginary chamber or "envelope" which surrounds your arm; the end of your arm can reach anything placed within this envelope but anything outside the envelope is inaccessible. The shape of this work envelope would not be particularly easy to draw, but it is roughly some portion of a sphere – not unlike an apple with a large bite taken out of it.

The size and shape of the work envelope of robotic arms vary enormously, depending on their design, so we will examine two specific examples of different types of industrial robot.

Figure 5.7 shows a TALON V polar geometry robot with three axes of motion. The manufacturers describe the main use of this robot as "machine load/unload, component transfer and matrix packing". In the manufacturer's data sheet and drawing for this robot, the length of the arm ranges from 2.85 metres when fully extended to 1.83 metres when fully retracted. The arm can swing upwards from the horizontal through an angle of 10 degrees or down-

Fig 5.7   The TALON V polar coordinate arm (Courtesy: ATM Engineering Ltd.)

wards from the horizontal through an angle of 30 degrees. Finally, the whole arm can rotate through an angle of 340 degrees, which is almost a complete circle. From this information we can draw out the shape of the work envelope, which is shown in figure 5.8.

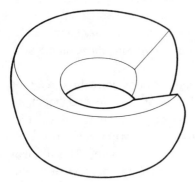

Fig 5.8   The work envelope for the
TALON V robot

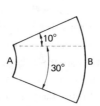

Fig 5.9a   A vertical
section

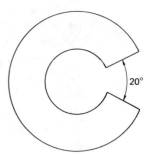

Fig 5.9b   A horizontal
section

A little imagination is needed here because we are trying to represent a three-dimensional shape on a flat (two-dimensional) piece of paper. Usually, if you look at manufacturers' data, you will see the work envelope represented in the way shown in figures 5.9a and 5.9b. Figure 5.9a shows a vertical section through the work envelope, that is what we would see if we cut through it with a knife vertically, and figure 5.9b shows a horizontal section. Other polar robots may have much larger or much smaller work envelopes, although all will be the same general shape.

As our second example, we will look at an ASEA Industrial Robot. This robot, together with its work envelope, is shown in figure 5.10. Figure 5.11 shows a vertical section through the envelope giving more detailed information.

Comparing the work envelopes of the two robots from the views given in figures 5.9 and 5.11, we see that there is an area just in front of both robots where the envelope is, roughly speaking, the same. Both the polar arm and the anthropomorphic arm are able to move from point A to point B. Let us examine this a little more closely. In order for the polar arm to move from A to B it is only necessary to operate one of its drives and the arm extends from A to B in a straight line. Now let us imagine the anthropomorphic arm trying to move along a similar path from A to B. This is in fact quite a complicated manoeuvre for the anthropomorphic arm because it involves the carefully coordinated movement of several joints – really a job for a computer to calculate! Clearly there will be some situations where the manoeuvrability of the anthropomorphic arm is not an advantage.

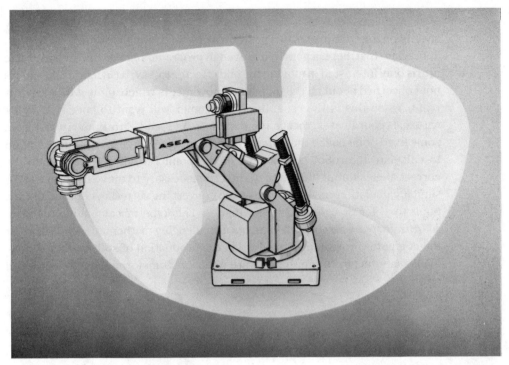

Fig 5.10   An ASEA industrial robot showing work envelope (Courtesy: ASEA Robotics)

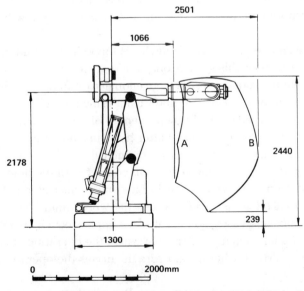

Fig 5.11   Vertical section through the work envelope of the ASEA robot (Courtesy: ASEA Robotics)

For certain applications it may be required to program the robot "off line" by specifying the coordinates of a position in a written computer program. We can appreciate that, here, a person involved in programming the anthropomorphic arm is only interested in moving the end effector to, say, B (in figure 5.11) and is not concerned about all the individual movements which allow it to reach this point. When this is the case, the programmer will want to specify B by its cartesian coordinates, that is the distances X, Y and Z to B, measured from some fixed point called the origin. The computer can then use this information to calculate the robot coordinates of the point B: that is, to calculate the correct angles for all the joints of the arm necessary to move the arm to B. A similar calculation can be carried out to convert the cartesian coordinates of a point to polar or cylindrical coordinates. This type of calculation, called a *coordinate transformation*, presents a challenging mathematical problem for the computer programmer involved in the production of software for robots. Many manufacturers supply software to enable transformations to be carried out.

Hydraulic Actuators

Actuator is the term used for the mechanism that drives the robotic arm. This may be an electric motor or a hydraulic or pneumatic cylinder. Hydraulic and pneumatic actuators are generally suited to driving prismatic joints since they produce linear motion directly. They are often referred to as *linear actuators*. Electric motors, which produce rotation, are more suited to driving revolute joints. However, as we shall see later, various gear mechanisms may be used to convert linear motion to rotary or vice versa. We shall deal first with hydraulic actuators.

A common example of a hydraulic device is found in the braking system of most modern cars. Using this system, only moderate force applied to the brake pedal is sufficient to produce a force large enough to stop the car. How is such an enormous force produced? The underlying principle of all hydraulic systems was first discovered by the French scientist Blaise Pascal in 1653. The SI unit of pressure, the pascal, is named after him. He stated that

If external pressure is applied to a confined fluid, then the pressure is transferred without loss to all surfaces in contact with the fluid.

This statement is now known as Pascal's Law and is illustrated in figure 5.12.

Note that Pascal's Law is careful to use the word "fluid". The word fluid covers both liquids and gases, so Pascal's Law applies equally whether a gas, let us say air, or a liquid is used. Drives in which the operating fluid is air are called pneumatic drives, whereas in hydraulic drives the operating fluid is a *liquid*.

The diagram in figure 5.13 shows how Pascal's Law is put to use in a hydraulic drive mechanism. A liquid is confined in a cylinder between the two

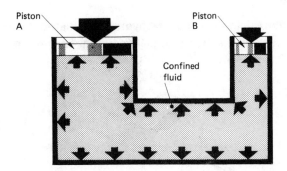

Piston A

Piston B

Confined fluid

Fig 5.12   Pascal's law

pistons, A and B. Now, suppose you apply a force of 3 kilograms (kg) to B which has a surface area of, say, 1 square centimetre (cm^2). There will be a pressure in the liquid of 3 kg per cm^2 (or, in SI units, 300 000 pascals). According to Pascal's Law, this is also the pressure on the surface of piston A. If piston A has a large surface area, say 20 cm^2, the force on piston A would therefore be 60 kg (because 60 kg divided by 20 cm^2 gives 3 kg per cm^2, the pressure in the fluid). It appears that we have succeeded in multiplying the input force by twenty times at no extra cost! In fact, if we examine the system more closely we will see that, because a liquid is incompressible (that is, its volume does not change when under pressure), then if piston B is moved through a distance of, say, 20 cm, piston A will only move through one twentieth of this distance, that is 1 cm. We can summarize this by saying that

Force × Distance moved at input = Force × Distance moved at output

That is, we can use a small force acting through a large distance to produce a large force acting through a small distance, or vice versa.

This follows from Pascal's Law and the fact that the total volume of liquid remains constant. The quantity "force × distance" is actually a measure of the mechanical work done, or the *energy*, and is measured in units of joules. In fact, we could have said instead, that (neglecting friction)

Mechanical work put in = Mechanical work got out

This is reassuring, because one of the fundamental laws of nature is that energy cannot be created or destroyed!

Returning to our example of the car braking system, we can now appreciate how it works. When the brake pedal is pressed it travels a few centimetres, but the pistons which operate the brakes in the wheels move only one or two millimetres – the small force applied to the brake pedal has been used to produce a much larger force at the brakes.

Wherever large forces are required we can expect to find hydraulic devices. Mechanical diggers on building sites, pit props in coal mines and jacks for lifting cars all use the principle of hydraulics.

Now let us look in more detail at a practical hydraulic actuator. Referring again to figure 5.13, suppose that piston A is to be the output. The pressure required

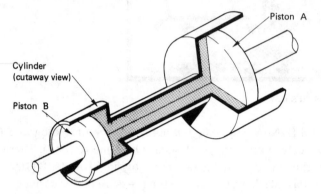

Fig 5.13   Applying Pascal's law

to move A can be provided by pumping the liquid with a suitable electric pump, instead of by actually pushing on B. If this is done, the relationship between the input and output forces mentioned above still holds. In this case it means that a pump of relatively low power can be used to produce large forces at the output.

The Spring Return Piston   Having got this far, we are now ready to look at a hydraulic actuator of the type that could be used on a robot. Let us start with the simplest type, the spring return piston shown in figure 5.14.

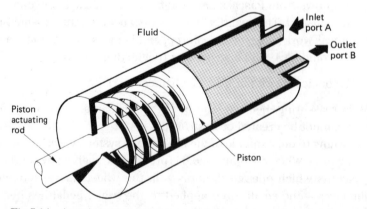

Fig 5.14   A spring return piston

With the inlet port A open and the outlet port B closed, hydraulic fluid can be pumped under pressure into the cylinder. As the cylinder fills, the piston is forced back and the spring becomes compressed. If at any time both ports are closed, then the piston can be held in its position. If port B is opened (port A closed), the spring will cause the piston to return. Fluid in the cylinder will be expelled through port B and return to a storage reservoir.

Is there a disadvantage to this simple type of system? Well, the chief disadvantage is that the return of the piston is limited in power by the strength of the spring; at the same time, if a strong spring is used, then unnecessary power has to be expended in compressing the spring when moving the piston outwards.

The Double Acting Cylinder If we are prepared to have a more complicated arrangement of valves then the system shown in figure 5.15, called a

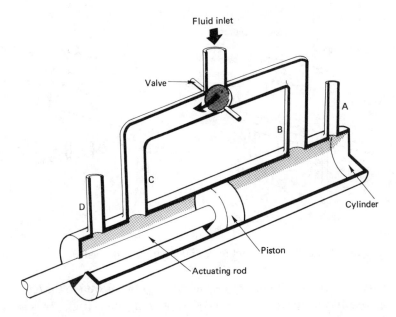

Fig 5.15   A double acting cylinder

double acting cylinder, dispenses with the need for a spring. Here, movement of the piston in both directions can be controlled by pumping liquid into the cylinder. Selecting port B as the inlet (A closed and D open) will move the piston outwards. Selecting C as the inlet (D closed and A open) will move the piston inwards.

The Hydraulic Transfer Valve A practical arrangement of the double acting cylinder, allowing very precise control, uses a hydraulic transfer valve called a *spool valve* and is shown in figure 5.16. The complete system consists of a high-pressure pump, a reservoir, an electrically operated spool valve, and the hydraulic piston and cylinder. With the spool valve in the position shown in the diagram, the piston would be unable to move, since no fluid can enter or

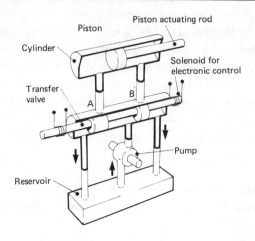

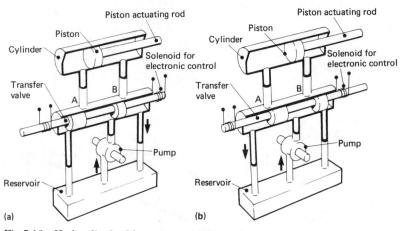

Fig 5.16   Hydraulic double acting cylinder with transfer valve

leave the cylinder. Imagine that the valve is now moved to the *left* as shown in figure 5.16*a*, so that ports A and B are both fully open. High-pressure fluid from the pump would then enter the cylinder through A, forcing the piston outwards. Fluid behind the piston would be expelled through port B and returned to the reservoir. By a similar argument, if the valve were instead moved to the right, as in figure 5.16*b*, fluid would enter through B and leave through A, and the piston would move inwards. By moving the valve so that ports A and B are only partly open, it is possible to produce very fine movements in the position of the piston. The movements of the valve are in fact produced by a low-current solenoid which is under the control of a computer.

Some More Practical Details   So far we have only dealt with the principles involved. We ought also to consider some of the more practical details.

What type of fluid? Water might at first seem a good idea because it is cheap and plentiful. A little thought though, and we see that water is liable to cause corrosion of the cylinders and to freeze solid in cold weather. In addition, water, particularly warm water, evaporates rather easily producing a vapour. A hydraulic system in which there were pockets of vapour would not operate normally because a vapour is compressible. For the same reason, precautions must be taken to prevent air, which is also compressible, from entering the system. The liquid usually used is a type of oil, since oil is non-corrosive, has a low freezing point, and does not noticeably evaporate. It is also important that the liquid is not a type that will absorb moisture from the atmosphere otherwise it would eventually become corrosive. For robots operating where there is a high fire risk, it may be desirable to use a non-inflammable liquid instead of oil.

Fluid is transferred to and from the cylinders either by flexible plastic tubing or by steel pipes, which can withstand high pressures. Care must be taken to ensure that all connections are, and remain, leakproof. It is obviously important that liquid does not leak out of the system. It is equally important that air does not leak in.

The piston has to move along the cylinder freely, but at the same time, liquid must not escape past the sides of the piston, otherwise pressure would be lost. A rubber seal is therefore fitted around the piston and also where the rod of the piston enters the cylinder. Any dirt or grit in the liquid is liable to damage these rubber seals so care must be taken during maintenance to prevent dirt being introduced.

The Hydraulic Accumulator   In some applications a robot may be required to produce a very large force for a very short time. For such a short burst of energy it would not be economical to provide an immensely powerful pump which would be working at only a fraction of its capacity for most of the time. What is needed is a method to store up energy during light work and to release this stored energy when an extra heavy demand is made. A hydraulic accumulator does this. The accumulator shown in figure 5.17 is spring-operated. When demand on the pump is low, liquid is pumped into the accumulator cylinder and is held under pressure by the force of the spring. A supply of high-pressure hydraulic fluid is then available from the accumulator to assist the pump whenever a heavy demand is made of it. Other types of accumulator use a weight or pressurized gas instead of a spring.

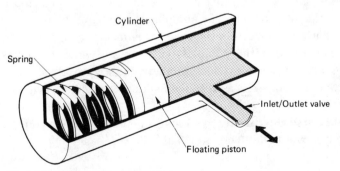

Fig 5.17   A hydraulic accumulator

Advantages of Hydraulic Systems   Before proceeding to pneumatic actuators we will list some of the advantages of the hydraulic mechanism:

- A hydraulic drive can produce an enormous range of forces without the need for gears, simply by controlling the flow of fluid.
- Movement of the piston can be smooth and fast.
- Position of the piston can be controlled precisely by a low-current electrically-operated valve.
- There are no sparks to worry about as there are with an electric motor, so the system is safe for use in explosive atmospheres (such as in paint spraying) or near inflammable materials.

Pneumatic Actuators

Everything that we have said before about the relationship between force and area is still true when air is used instead of a liquid. Unlike a liquid, when air is put under pressure its volume changes. We say that air is compressible. So, in order to build up the pressure required to operate the piston, extra work has to be done by the pump to compress the air. This means that pneumatic drives are less efficient.

Remember that when discussing hydraulic drives we said

Mechanical work put in = Mechanical work got out

When considering pneumatic drives we have to take account of the fact that *some* of the mechanical work put in is used to compress the air. This work appears as heating of the air, so we will have to modify our earlier statement and say that (neglecting friction)

Mechanical work put in = Mechanical work got out + Heat

If you have ever used a bicycle pump you may have noticed that it becomes hot as it is used. The heat is produced by the mechanical work done in compressing the air. *Heat represents wasted energy.*

The system for pumping air into a pneumatic cylinder is much simpler than the hydraulic pumping system. This is mainly because there is no point in recirculating used air. Air expelled from the cylinder is released to the atmosphere through a valve. Sudden changes in pressure are prevented by having an "air receiver", that is a pressurized tank connected to the high-pressure side of the pump. The pump then only has to be powerful enough to ensure that the pressure in the receiver is maintained. A pressure-sensitive switch ensures that the pump is only working when the pressure in the receiver falls below some predetermined value. Figure 5.18 shows a pneumatic drive system. Compare this with the hydraulic system shown in figure 5.16.

Advantages of Pneumatic Systems   Pneumatic systems offer a number of advantages over hydraulic systems as follows:

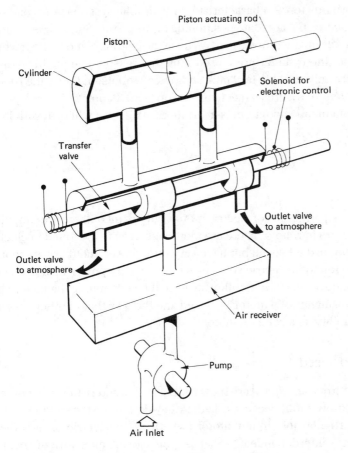

Fig 5.18   A pneumatic system with transfer valve

● A pneumatic system is generally less expensive than an equivalent hydraulic system. Many factories have compressed air available and one large compressor pump can serve several robots.

● Whereas a leak in a hydraulic system will require prompt attention to prevent loss of liquid and the introduction of air into the cylinders, a small amount of air leakage from a pneumatic system can usually be tolerated.

● The compressibility of air can also be an advantage in some applications. Think about the automatic doors of buses and trains which are operated pneumatically. If you are unfortunate enough to be caught in the doors you won't be crushed. In addition, a pressure relief valve can be incorporated to release the pressure when a certain force is exceeded. This principle can be used in the gripper of a robot to protect the robot both from damaging itself and from damaging the equipment with which it is working.

● Finally, the fact that air is light means that a mass of air can be accelerated quickly. Therefore pneumatic drives are faster to respond than their hydraulic counterparts.

The main disadvantage of pneumatic actuators is that they cannot produce the enormous forces characteristic of hydraulic systems. A second disadvantage concerns the accurate positioning of the piston. Since air is compressible, heavy loads on the robot arm may cause the pistons to move, even when all the valves on the cylinder are closed. For this reason, pneumatic actuators are generally only suitable for "pick and place" robots. In these, the robot moves until an axis hits a preset mechanical stop (see Chapter 2). The other important use of pneumatic actuators is in grippers, which we will deal with in the next chapter.

Electric Motors

There are many types of electric motor, but not all of them are suitable for use as actuators in robots. There are motors such as those found in clocks which rotate at constant speed but have very little power and there are motors such as those found in electric vehicles which are very powerful and able to rotate at varying speed. In what follows we shall be examining the factors by which the performance of a motor is judged and the way that these factors influence its suitability as a robot actuator.

Power, Torque and Speed

Power, torque and speed are the three basic characteristics of a motor that you should know about because together they determine the suitability of a motor for a particular job. In any motor (whether it is electric or not) these three things are interdependent – that is, you cannot alter any of them without affecting one of the others.

Power In everyday language we use phrases like "this is powerful", "high power", "low power", and so on. In fact, to most people, the word "power" does not have any definite meaning. Here, we shall be using "power" to mean something definite.

In the case of electric motors, we need to distinguish between electrical power and mechanical power. Both may be measured in the same units, watts (W). Electrical power is a measure of the electricity that a motor uses (and that eventually has to be paid for). Of greater interest to us is the mechanical power produced by the motor. If it were possible to build a motor that was 100 per cent efficient, then each 1 watt of electricity used by the motor would be changed into 1 watt of mechanical power. In practice, electric motors are little more than 50 per cent efficient, meaning that little more than half the electrical power used is converted into mechanical power. The rest generally ends up as heat and noise.

The unit of horsepower (hp) is still widely used to measure mechanical power although it is increasingly being replaced by the metric unit of the watt.

Conversion of horsepower to watts is straightforward and simply involves multiplying the number of horsepower by 746, since

   1 hp = 745.7 W

for which 746 is a sufficiently accurate number for most purposes.

Taken by itself, mechanical power is not the best indicator of the "strength" of an electric motor in terms of how much turning-force it produces.

Torque If you were considering a motor for some particular purpose you would certainly want to know how "strong" it is or how much *turning-force* it is able to produce. The technical term for turning-force is **torque**. In the metric system, torque is measured in units of newton-metres (abbreviated N m). Just to give you a feel for the size of these units, a household electric drill would produce a torque of around 1 newton metre.

The unit of torque is always: force × distance. This follows from the definition of torque which is:

The force multiplied by the shortest distance measured from the axis of rotation to the line along which the force acts.

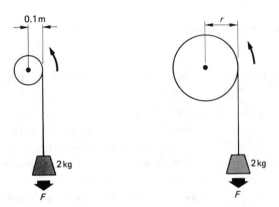

Fig 5.19a (*left*)   A torque of 2 Nm is required to raise the weight using the pulley

Fig 5.19b (*right*)   A larger torque is needed to raise this weight, but it moves a greater distance for each revolution of the pulley

The drawing in figure 5.19a shows in practice what is meant by torque. Following from the definition, the weight attached to the pulley produces a torque of $F \times r$. In the metric system, force is measured in units of newtons (N). A mass of one kilogram produces a force of approximately 10 newtons. However, engineers sometimes state forces in units of kilograms (kg), pounds (lb) or ounces (oz). Where this is done, it is correct to write an f after the unit: kgf, lbf or ozf, in order to distinguish between units of mass and units of force. Torque may therefore be given as newton-metres (N m), pounds force-feet (lbf ft), or sometimes ounce force-inches (ozf in).

Returning to figure 5.19a, since the force F is 2 kg (or 20 newtons) and r is 0.1 metre then

   Torque = 20 × 0.1 = 2 N m

This is the torque that a motor would have to produce in order to turn the pulley and raise the weight. Notice that if a pulley of larger diameter were used, then the torque would be greater (figure 5.19b), but on the other hand, each revolution of the pulley would raise the weight through a greater distance. So there is a relationship between torque and speed, which we will say more about in a moment.

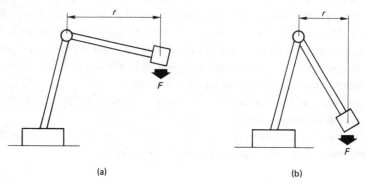

Fig 5.20   The torque decreases as the load moves inwards towards the axis of the motor

When motors are incorporated into robots, the torque will change as the arm of the robot moves. Figure 5.20 shows how the torque can change from a high value (figure 5.20a) to a low value (figure 5.20b) as the distance from the load to the axis of the motor is reduced. Don't forget that even if the gripper of the robot is empty, the weight of the arm itself will produce a torque.

Torque should not be confused with power. In everyday language you might make the mistake of saying "this motor is powerful" when what you really mean to say is "this motor produces a high torque". Power and torque are two different things but there is a link between them.

Speed   The speed at which a motor rotates, usually measured in rpm (revolutions per minute) is the link between power and torque. An example of this is seen in the familiar behaviour of a car. In low gear the engine is able to produce a large turning-force at the wheels enabling the car to climb steep hills slowly (the torque is high but the wheels rotate slowly). In high gear the car can cruise along a level road at a high speed (the wheels rotate quickly but the torque is low). In fact, you have the choice of high torque at low speed or low torque at high speed. Notice that it is wrong to say that low gear gives you more power – it does not; low gear gives you more torque. To be more precise, assuming that the power is fixed, *if you double the speed you halve the torque*, and vice-versa. This is a fundamental relationship between torque and speed and applies irrespective of the type of motor or what ever else is producing the rotation.

You can work out the torque T in newton metres if you know the mechanical power P in watts and the number of revolutions per minute R, from the formula

$$T \approx \frac{10\,P}{R} \text{ newton metres, approximately}$$

[The approximation arises from rounding down the number π (pi) used in converting revolutions per minute to a velocity.]

We can illustrate the relationship between speed and torque with another familiar example. Let us say we have an electric drill of 240 watts mechanical power, which rotates at 2400 rpm. At this speed it produces a torque of 1 newton metre. If the speed is halved to 1200 rpm but with the power still at 240 W (this can be done using gears), then the torque will be doubled to 2 newton metres.

Here we have chosen a straightforward example. In practice, electric motors are not very straightforward at all. The complication with all electric motors is that the power they work at is affected by the speed at which they turn. This means that if you use a motor to turn something (in other words apply a load) then this may cause the motor to run more slowly, which will cause it to draw a different amount of current which in turn will affect the power it uses. The relationship between speed and torque is therefore not a simple one. Different types of motor behave in different ways in this respect and the relationship between speed and torque is an important factor that has to be considered when choosing a motor.

How Should a Motor Behave?   Earlier we noted the difference in requirements between a clock motor and a motor used to drive an electric car. Think about the requirements of a motor designed to be incorporated into a robot. Here is what it should be able to do:

1 The motor should be able to provide a maximum torque sufficient to permit the robot to lift the heaviest object it may be expected to work with.

2 The motor should be able to rotate over a range of speeds considered necessary by the designer.

3 The motor should be controllable in such a way that it can produce any value of torque at any speed provided these fall within the ranges mentioned in 1 and 2.

The amount of power used by a motor is not normally a limitation unless it is intended to be battery operated.

The Different Types of Motor

There are three principal types of electric motor which behave in quite different ways and are used for different purposes. These are:

AC motors, operated by alternating current electricity.

DC motors, operated by direct current electricity

Stepper motors, operated by pulses of electricity.

Each of these types of motor come in many different forms.

In principle, any type of electric motor could be used for a robot, if it is possible to electronically control the speed and power so that it behaves in the required way. In practice, mainly DC motors and stepper motors are currently used for robots. Although it is possible to devise electronic controllers for AC motors, it is generally considered to be unnecessarily complicated. A further limitation of AC motors is that most types cannot withstand overloads of more than about twice their rated torque. DC motors can withstand overloads of several times their rated torque.

DC Motors

A cutaway view of a **DC motor** is shown in figure 5.21. Every motor has two basic parts:

  1 A stationary, fixed part called the *stator*. This produces a magnetic field either with a coil (that is, an electromagnet) or with a permanent magnet.
  2 A rotating part called the *rotor* (or armature). This carries a coil through which electric current passes.

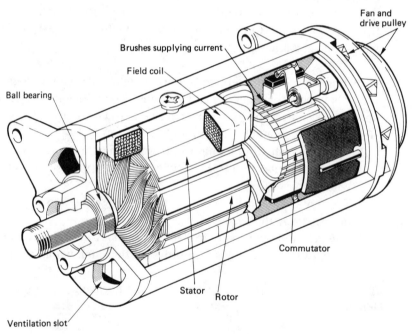

Fig 5.21   Cutaway view of a DC motor

The motor shown in figure 5.21 looks rather complicated, so in order to see how it works we shall refer to the series of simplified diagrams in figure 5.22. For simplicity, the rotor coil is represented by a single loop of wire.

Current is led into the coil through the brushes which are held in contact with the *commutator* by the pressure of a spring. In the position shown in figure 5.22a, the current produces a magnetic field through the coil which

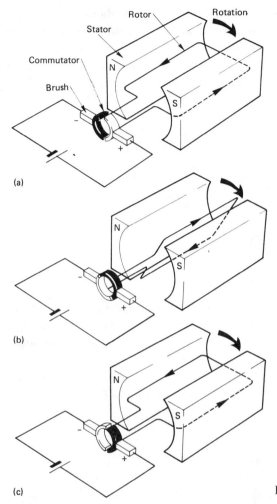

Rotor

Rotation

Stator

Commutator

Brush

N

S

(a)

N

S

(b)

N

S

(c)

Fig 5.22   Principle of a DC motor

repels the magnetic field of the stator magnet and causes the coil to rotate in the direction shown by the arrow. If the current were to continue flowing in the direction shown in figure 5.22a, the coil would come to rest in the vertical position after rotating through 90 degrees. Now you will see the purpose of the commutator. The momentum of the coil enables it to pass through the vertical position and, as it reaches the position shown in figure 5.22b, the commutator causes the direction of the current through the coil to reverse. The current now produces a magnetic repulsion which turns the coil through a further 90 degrees to the position shown in figure 5.22c, where the cycle repeats.

For simplicity we have described a commutator with only two segments connected to a single coil. In a practical motor, such as the one shown in figure 5.21, there will be many coils and a commutator consisting of many segments. This produces a smoother rotation and greater torque. There will also be many magnetic poles rather than just the two shown in the diagram and these poles may be electromagnets rather than permanent magnets.

Construction of Motors   The types of motor are known by different names according to the electrical arrangement inside them and according to their physical construction. We shall deal first with the physical construction.

There are three basic ways of building electric motors and these are known as the *standard motor*, the *bell motor* and the *disc motor*. Examples of each type are shown in figures 5.23, 5.24 and 5.25.

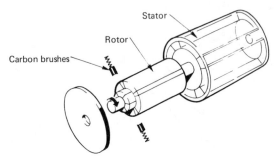

Fig 5.23   Standard motor construction

Look at figure 5.23 which shows the **standard construction** (the type shown in figure 5.21). It is the sort of motor you would expect to find in a vacuum cleaner or washing machine. The rotor carries coils wound on an iron core and is surrounded by the stator.

The **bell motor**, shown in figure 5.24, is like the standard motor turned inside-out. The rotor is a bell-shaped cylinder which surrounds the stator.

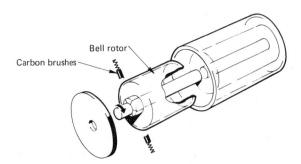

Fig 5.24   Bell motor construction

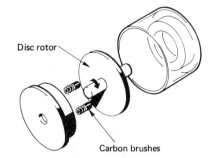

Fig 5.25   Disc motor construction

Figure 5.25 shows the **disc motor**. The rotor is in the form of a flat disc. This type of construction is much less bulky than either of the other two types.

Electrically, DC motors differ in the way that the magnetic field is produced in the stator. In all motors, the torque produced is affected by the speed at which the motor is rotating and this **speed/torque characteristic** is determined by the type of motor. There are four types but it is not possible to distinguish between them from their outward appearance.

Permanent Magnet Motors As the name implies, the magnetic field in the stator is produced by a permanent magnet. The magnetic field is therefore limited in strength and this limits the torque that these motors can produce. The speed/torque characteristic is similar to that of a shunt-wound motor (see below).

Series-wound Motors (Universal Motors) Series-wound motors are important because they work equally well on either AC or DC electricity. For this reason they are also called universal motors and are the type found in household vacuum cleaners, electric drills, fans and so on.

Since the rotor and stator coils are connected in series (figure 5.26), whatever current flows through the stator must also flow through the rotor. It therefore makes no difference that the AC current is continuously changing direction – the current in the stator will always flow in the same direction relative to the current in the rotor. The speed/torque characteristic is almost the same whether the motor is running on AC or DC.

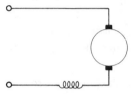

Fig 5.26   Series-wound motor

The series-wound motor is characterised by the fact that it rotates very slowly when a heavy load is applied (high torque) but dangerously fast with only a light load. At the same time, however, at low speed the torque is very high. This makes series-wound motors very suitable for use in hoists for lifting heavy loads. The graph in figure 5.27 shows how the speed varies with applied torque for a particular value of applied voltage. Increasing or decreasing the applied voltage causes the motor to rotate faster or slower, but the relationship between speed and torque follows basically the same-shaped graph.

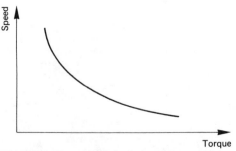

Fig 5.27   Characteristic for series-wound motor

Shunt-wound Motors   Another way of connecting the coil on the stator is in parallel with the rotor coil. This method of connection is referred to as shunt-wound. Figure 5.28 shows how the rotor and stator coils are connected in a shunt-wound motor. The speed/torque characteristic is shown in figure 5.29.

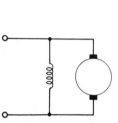

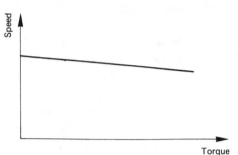

Fig 5.28   Shunt-wound motor   Fig 5.29   Characteristic for shunt-wound motor

Compare this graph with the one in figure 5.27. Unlike the series-wound motor, the speed of a shunt-wound motor varies very little with torque. Increasing the load causes the motor to compensate by drawing more power from the supply. This makes shunt-wound motors suitable for driving many types of machine tools. The speed can be varied by adjusting the voltage applied to the rotor.

Compound-wound Motors   Compound-wound motors are a sort of cross between series-wound and shunt-wound motors. The magnetic field in the stator is produced by two separate coils. Figure 5.30 shows how these two coils are connected.

The speed/torque characteristic for compound-wound motors is shown in figure 5.31 and depends on whether the motor is *differentially-compounded* (curve A) or *cumulatively-compounded* (curve B). Differentially-compounded motors are used in some applications in industry but have the disadvantage that the speed can become dangerously high if the maximum load (that is, the maximum torque) is exceeded. The behaviour of cumulatively-compounded motors falls somewhere between that of series-wound motors and shunt-wound motors. The exact behaviour depends on the size of each of the two field coils.

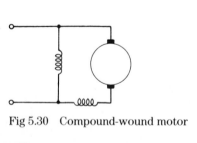

Fig 5.30   Compound-wound motor

Fig 5.31   Characteristic for compound-wound motor

Stepper Motors

If a voltage is applied to a DC or AC motor, then the motor will rotate continuously. **Stepper motors** differ in that they operate on pulses of electricity. Each time a pulse is sent to the electronic controller, the motor *steps*, that is rotates through a small angle. The size of the step depends on the design of the motor and can be as small as 1.5 degrees or as large as 30 degrees. The motor is made to rotate faster or slower by sending more or fewer pulses per second. Pulses can usually be sent up to a maximum rate of around 2000 per second. Figure 5.32 shows a typical stepper motor.

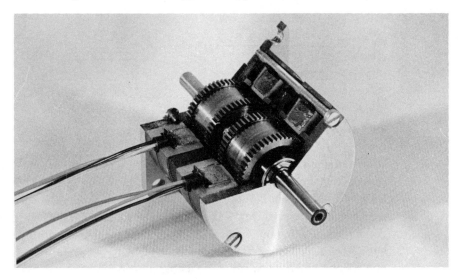

Fig 5.32   Typical small stepper motor

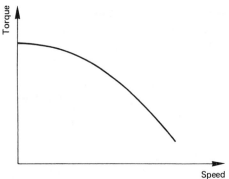

Fig 5.33   Characteristic for a stepper motor

A typical torque/speed characteristic for a stepper motor is shown in figure 5.33. Notice that the graph shows speed along the horizontal axis (the characteristics for other types of motor showed speed along the vertical axis). This is the normal way to plot the stepper motor characteristic because it is the torque that depends on the speed and not vice-versa; the stepper motor either runs at the required speed or doesn't run at all. In other types of motor a load (torque) is applied and the characteristic indicates how fast the motor will run with that load.

Returning to figure 5.33, you will notice that as the speed is increased, the torque falls to a very low value. Actually the situation is not quite as bad as it appears, because it is possible to compensate for the drop in torque by increasing the supply voltage.

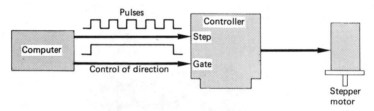

Fig 5.34   Principle of computer-controlled stepper motor

In robot applications, the pulses needed to work the stepper motor are produced by a computer. The arrangement is shown in figure 5.34. The controller is needed to generate the correct pattern of signals at the correct level of power needed to operate the coils within the motor. As far as the computer is concerned, sending one pulse to the controller causes the motor to move one step. The direction of rotation is controlled by a second terminal on the controller, shown on the diagram as the *gate*. As long as the computer maintains a voltage at the gate, the motor will rotate in a clockwise direction, otherwise it will rotate in an anticlockwise direction. Controlling a stepper motor with a computer is therefore a simple matter.

An advantage of stepper motors is that the computer can at any time know the position of the motor shaft by keeping count of the number of pulses that have been sent to the controller. However, a problem can arise if a heavy load causes the motor to turn without it receiving pulse or prevents the motor from turning when a pulse is sent. When this happens, the motor shaft will no longer be where the computer "thinks" it is.

Components of Drive Systems: Gears

Having looked at how actuators work, we shall now turn our attention to the mechanical devices used to transmit the power from the actuators to the joints of the robot. We shall begin with the most common of these devices, **gears**.

In common terminology the word "gears" is often used to include chain drives as in the phrase "the gears on a ten speed bicycle". Here, when we use the term *gear* it will be in its more precise form where the teeth of the gearwheels mesh directly to form the drive.

Terminology of Gears   Illustrated in figure 5.35 is a typical spur-wheel and pinion drive. A pinion is a small gearwheel. Shown on the illustration are the terms used in specifying the dimensions of a gearwheel, the most important for our purposes being pitch and pitch circle diameter (PCD). The *pitch circle diameter* is the effective diameter of the gearwheel used for design calculations. The *pitch* is the distance between the centre of one tooth and the centre of the next tooth measured along the pitch circle diameter.

When two gears are correctly meshed the pitch circle diameters should just be touching. That is, the distance between the centres of the two gearwheels should be

$$\frac{\text{PCD gear 1}}{2} + \frac{\text{PCD gear 2}}{2}$$

The shape of each tooth on a gearwheel must be very precise if the gears are to run smoothly and not jam. The tooth shape on one gearwheel must therefore match the tooth shape on the other. This shape is a precise mathematical curve.

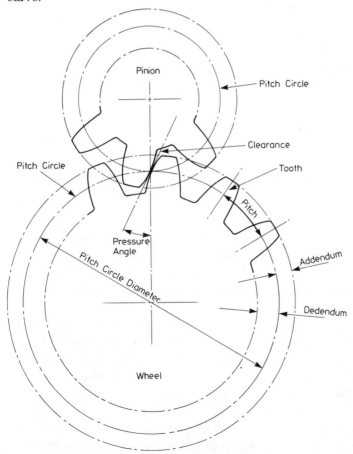

Fig 5.35   Typical spur-wheel and pinion drive

Gear Ratios   The gear ratio (transmission ratio) of a pair of gears is simply the ratio of the number of complete revolutions of the input gearwheel to the number of complete revolutions of the output gearwheel.

From this it follows that the gear ratio obtained when using a pair of gears is simply the ratio of the number of teeth on each gearwheel. Note that while the gears are turning, the gearwheel with the greater number of teeth will make fewer revolutions than the smaller gearwheel. Using the definition of gear ratio given above, it can be seen that if the input gearwheel has 20 teeth and the output gearwheel 100 teeth then the gear ratio is 100 to 20, that is 5 to 1. If on the other hand the 100 tooth wheel were the input and the 20 tooth wheel the output then the ratio would be the other way around, that is 1 to 5.

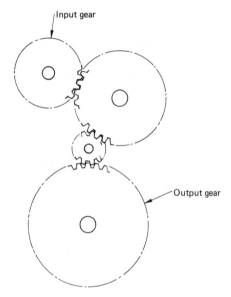

Fig 5.36   Gear train

What happens when there are more than two gearwheels (say four) and we want to find out the overall ratio? This depends on how the gears are arranged. If they are as in figure 5.36 then the overall ratio is still given by the number of teeth on the output gearwheel divided by the number of teeth on the input gearwheel as before.

A more common arrangement is shown in figure 5.37. Here gearwheels 2 and 3 are fixed together so that every time gearwheel 2 makes a revolution so does gearwheel 3. The overall ratio of the gear system is the ratio between gearwheels 1 and 2 multiplied by the ratio between gearwheels 3 and 4. That is

$$\frac{\text{Teeth in gear 4}}{\text{Teeth in gear 3}} + \frac{\text{Teeth in gear 2}}{\text{Teeth in gear 1}}$$

If gearwheel 4 were not the output but fastened to a fifth which in turn drove a sixth gearwheel as in figure 5.38, then the calculation to find the overall ratio would be extended:

$$\frac{\text{Teeth gear 6}}{\text{Teeth gear 5}} \times \frac{\text{Teeth gear 4}}{\text{Teeth gear 3}} \times \frac{\text{Teeth gear 2}}{\text{Teeth gear 1}}$$

From this you should see that no matter how complicated the gear system, to find the overall ratio all one has to do is multiply together all the individual ratios.

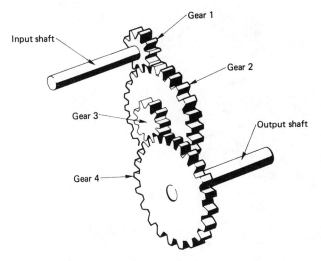

Fig 5.37   Two-stage reduction gearing

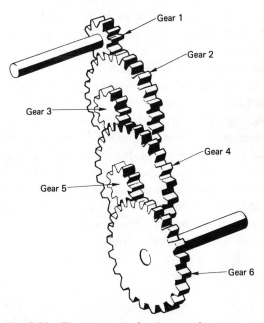

Fig 5.38   Three-stage reduction gearing

Backlash   Backlash arises because when two gears are in mesh there must be some clearance between the teeth in order to prevent the gears jamming. This clearance is illustrated in figure 5.39. The clearance allows one gearwheel to turn slightly without affecting the position of the other.

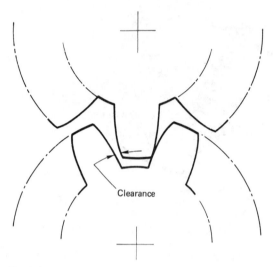

Fig 5.39   Clearance of gears

The *backlash* in a system of gearwheels is the angle through which the output gear can move without the input gear moving. Note which way round this is. What is important is the error in the angular position of the output shaft.

Backlash is cumulative. Every time one gearwheel meshes with another some backlash is introduced into the gear system and the overall backlash is simply the sum of the backlashes for each pair of gearwheels. Backlash is always a bad thing but is extremely undesirable in a robot drive system and many different ways have been used to minimize its effects. One obvious way is to use very high precision gears with very small clearance, but this unfortunately makes the gearing prohibitively expensive. Another way is to reduce to a minimum the number of gears in mesh, and an increasingly popular way of doing this is to use a harmonic drive gear system which we will look at shortly.

Torque Conversion   Earlier when discussing electric motors we said that if the speed is doubled then the torque is halved and vice versa. In applying this to a gear system we can say that, assuming no power is lost,

Output torque × rpm = Input torque × rpm

which, since the gear ratio is

$$\frac{\text{rpm at input}}{\text{rpm at output}}$$

can be rearranged to give

Torque at input = Gear ratio × Torque at output

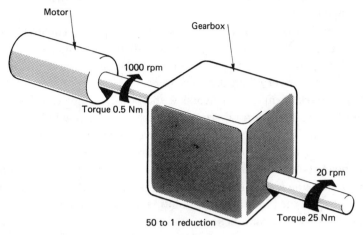

Fig 5.40   Speed and torque conversion

For example, figure 5.40 shows a gear system with a ratio of 50 to 1. If the input shaft has a torque of 0.5 N m and a speed of 1000 rpm then the output shaft will have a speed of 20 rpm and a torque of $50 \times 0.5 = 25$ N m.

In practice, because of friction in the gearbox, some of the available power is used up just turning the gears round. The output torque will therefore be less than that calculated by an amount proportional to the power loss in the gearbox.

Different Types of Gear Drive

Through the ages many different types of gear drive have evolved. Figure 5.41 illustrates some of the more common forms used in robotics.

Spur gears are so called because they look similar to the toothed wheels once used in spurs for horse riding. They come in two forms: *straight cut*, where the teeth are parallel to the shaft (this is the common form), and *helical cut*, where the teeth are cut at an angle. Helical gears produce a smoother drive

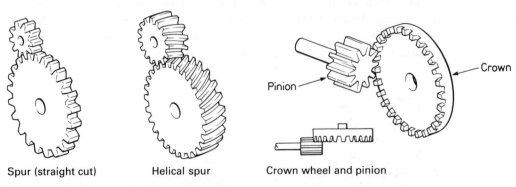

Spur (straight cut)   Helical spur   Crown wheel and pinion

Fig 5.41   Different types of gear drive

and with less backlash than straight cut gears but they are much more expensive to make.

Crown wheels are so called because they resemble crowns. Crown wheels mesh with a small straight-cut spur gear. The toothed edge of the crown wheel has to be quite thin to avoid jamming in the pinion and this makes them suitable only for very light drives or toys.

Bevel gears are made from a disk with a bevelled edge, hence the name. The teeth of bevel gears are tapered and mesh over their whole length, making them suitable for use in heavy-duty drives. Except for some uses in toys, anything crown wheels can do, bevel gears can do better. Straight-cut bevel gears have the teeth pointing towards the shaft but they can also be cut at a slant in the same way as in helical spur gears. The teeth can also be cut so that, when meshed, the pinion shaft is pointing above or below the other shaft; the bevel gears used in car axles are often like this.

Skew gears look rather odd. They are similar to spur gears except that one wheel has been skewed with respect to the other wheel. Normally the shafts are at right angles but the teeth can be cut so that any other angle is possible.

Worm and worm-wheel are always abbreviated to worm and wheel. Worms are probably so called because they look similar to pointed woodworking tools for boring holes which in turn look and act like garden worms. The wheel looks very similar to a straight cut spur gear except that the teeth are at a slight angle as if it could be helical cut, but they are also dished so the worm sits in the teeth. Normally the worm has only one tooth which is wrapped round and round and looks identical to a machine screw thread. It is also possible to have a two start worm which has two teeth wrapped round side by side. Similarly three or more start worms are possible.

Axis Conversion   In the systems just described, note that the gears are able to change the axis of rotation as well as to perform speed and torque conversions. This facility is useful as it gives designers more freedom to choose a convenient position for the actuator.

An extension of this is the **rack and pinion** system whereby rotary motion can be converted to linear motion and vice versa. In this system (figure 5.42) a small gearwheel (the pinion) turns against a straight-toothed bar (the rack). If the pinion is the driving element then the rack will be driven linearly; if the rack is the driving element – for example connected to a hydraulic or pneumatic actuator – then the pinion will be made to rotate.

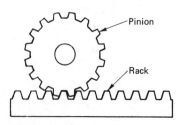

Fig 5.42   Rack and pinion transmission

Harmonic Drives Harmonic drives are the latest development in robot transmission systems. With these, extremely large ratios can be obtained using only two gearwheels and hence the backlash can be kept to a very low level. To see how they work, try rolling a coin around the inside of a lid using your finger in the centre of the coin. You will find that you have to move the coin in several circuits of the inside of the lid before it revolves once.

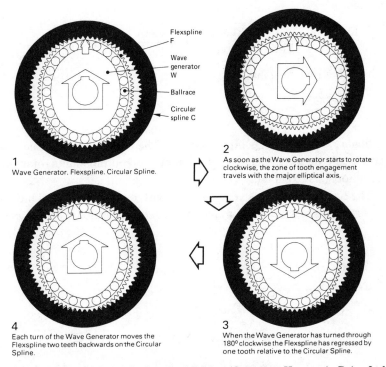

1
Wave Generator. Flexspline. Circular Spline.

2
As soon as the Wave Generator starts to rotate clockwise, the zone of tooth engagement travels with the major elliptical axis.

4
Each turn of the Wave Generator moves the Flexspline two teeth backwards on the Circular Spline.

3
When the Wave Generator has turned through 180° clockwise the Flexspline has regressed by one tooth relative to the Circular Spline.

Fig 5.43   Principle of the harmonic drive (Courtesy: Harmonic Drive Ltd., Horsham)

The harmonic drive, shown diagrammatically in figure 5.43, consists of three basic components: a wave generator, a flexspline, and a circular spline. The flexspline F is a flexible toothed steel ring which is forced into the shape of an ellipse (greatly exaggerated in the diagram) by the elliptically shaped wave generator W. The wave generator can slide round on the inner surface of the flexspline, changing the shape of the flexspline as it turns. Ball bearings (in the form of a ballrace) reduce the friction between the contacting surfaces of the flexspline and wave generator.

The wave generator and flexspline together are fitted inside the circular spline C, which is a solid steel ring with teeth on its inner surface. The teeth on F only mesh with those on C at two areas, around the bulges of the ellipse. Although the sizes of the teeth on both F and C are the same, there are about 1% more teeth on F than the total number on C.

In operation, rotation of W causes successive teeth at the bulges of F to engage with those on C. The difference in the total number of teeth between the two components will cause F to move backwards by two teeth each time W turns one complete revolution, as shown in the sequence of diagrams (figure 5.43).

In this system, because we are looking at relative motion, all three components may serve as either input or output elements. The effective ratio of the drive depends on how it is used, but, for example with the wave generator as input, the flexspline as output and the circular spline fixed, the effective ratio becomes:

$$\frac{\text{Flexspline teeth} - \text{Circular spline teeth}}{\text{Flexspline teeth}}$$

which in a real case might be

$$\frac{200 - 202}{200} = \frac{-1}{100}$$

giving a reduction in speed of 100 to 1. The negative sign in the result of the above calculation indicates that the input and output shafts rotate in opposite directions, as expected.

The harmonic drive is very efficient with low backlash and high reliability. Figure 5.44 shows a photograph of a practical harmonic drive system.

Fig 5.44   Harmonic drive (Courtesy: Harmonic Drive Ltd., Horsham)

Belts and Chains

Belt Drives

Figure 5.45 illustrates a simple **belt drive** system. Now how do we calculate the transmission ratio and hence the torque increase of a belt drive? There are no teeth to count here. To help us, suppose one of the pulleys turns so that

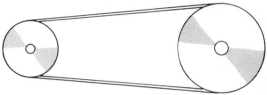

Fig 5.45   Belt drive

some given point on the belt moves 1 cm. If the belt does not stretch then all points on the belt move 1 cm. So, 1 cm movement at the circumference of one pulley results in 1 cm movement at the circumference of the other pulley. From this it follows that the transmission ratio is in fact the ratio of the circumferences of the pulleys. However, since the circumference of a circle is in proportion to its diameter, we can say that the transmission ratio is simply the ratio of the diameters of the pulleys.

We cannot however just measure the diameter anywhere on the pulley. It has to be a diameter equivalent to the pitch circle diameter on a gearwheel. It turns out that this effective diameter is very near to where the centre of the belt is when it is wrapped round the pulley. This is illustrated in figure 5.46.

Ordinary belts are useful when general speed reduction and hence torque amplification is required in a drive system but there is nothing apart from friction to stop them slipping on the pulley, and it is difficult to determine the precise reduction ratio. This problem is overcome by the use of a toothed belt.

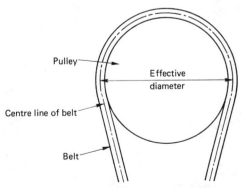

Fig 5.46   Effective pulley diameter

Toothed Belts A toothed belt is shown in figure 5.47 and is used when precise reductions are required. Toothed belts are also called timing belts since, because they do not slip, they are often employed where the rotation of a pulley controls the timed opening and closing of valves or switches.

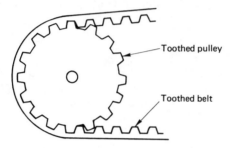

Fig 5.47   Toothed belts

Calculating the transmission ratio of a timing belt is easy; simply count the teeth on the two pulleys and calculate the ratio as if they were gearwheels in mesh. So, for a reduction drive the ratio is

$$\frac{\text{Number of teeth on large pulley}}{\text{Number of teeth on small pulley}}$$

Beaded Cable Drives One of the problems with belts is that they cannot go round sharp corners. For light drives this can be overcome by using a beaded cable drive, shown in figure 5.48. Beads are bonded to a cable at regular intervals and these fit into special recesses in the pulleys. As the cable can be bent sideways, the drive can be taken round corners.

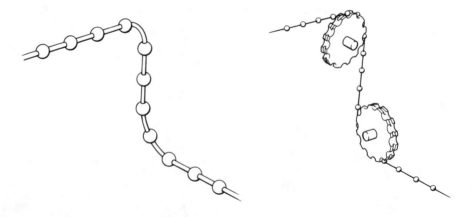

Fig 5.48   Beaded cable drive

Chain Drives

Everyone must be familiar with **chain drives** since they are used on nearly all bicycles. The teeth on a chain wheel are called sprockets. Chain drives are heavy and noisy, but they are capable of transmitting very large forces.

To calculate the transmission ratio of a chain reduction drive we use exactly the same procedure as for toothed belts. The ratio is simply

$$\frac{\text{Number of sprockets on large chain wheel}}{\text{Number of sprockets on small chain wheel}}$$

Backlash in Belt and Chain Drives Just as in gear drives, belt and chain drives also have backlash.

Plain belts rely on the elastic tension of the belt material to grip the pulleys and because of this there is backlash due to elastic stretch along the length of the belt.

Toothed belts rely on their teeth to grip the pulleys and usually are reinforced to prevent elastic stretch; because of this, backlash is virtually eliminated where short belts are used. The same is true for beaded cable drives.

With chain drives however, it is virtually impossible to prevent some backlash. Chains are heavy and because of this they sag under gravity between chain wheels. This gives rise to backlash when the load changes because the load alters the tension in the chain and therefore the amount of sag.

6 End Effectors, Sensors and Robot Vision

End Effectors: Introduction

The versatility of a robot depends largely on the device fitted to the end of the robot's arm – this device is known as the **end effector**. Often, end effectors may not look very impressive when compared to the human hand. The human hand is, after all, very versatile and perhaps you think that some attempt should be made to design an end effector with the same degree of flexibility. Robots, however, have one great advantage that we humans don't have – if their hand is not suitable for the job, then a different one can be fitted in its place. There is a vast range of end effectors for robots, most of which are tailor-made according to the requirements of the customer. Here we shall be examining some common types of end effector along with the general principles of their operation.

Types of end effector divide naturally into two groups:

1 Grippers These are devices which can be used for holding or gripping an object. They include what you might call mechanical hands and also anything else like hooks, magnets and suction devices which can be used for holding or gripping.

2 Tools These are devices which robots use to perform operations on an object. Examples could be drills, paint sprays, grinders, welding torches and many others.

Figure 6.1 shows a selection of end effectors. Study it and decide which you think are grippers and which are tools.

Robot Motion and End Effectors The design of an end effector and whether it is a gripper or a tool will depend on the way in which a robot is controlled.

Consider a gripper – say a mechanical hand – which picks up an object from a table and places it in a box. The starting position (the table) and the final position (the box) are very important. The exact path that the robot takes between the table and the box is not important, provided of course that it does not collide with anything on the way. With this type of end effector, the robot can be controlled by a method known as *point-to-point control* (see Chapter 2). The design of a gripper should take advantage of the possibility of using point to point control. It should be designed so that it requires the minimum amount of manoeuvring in order to grip the workpiece.

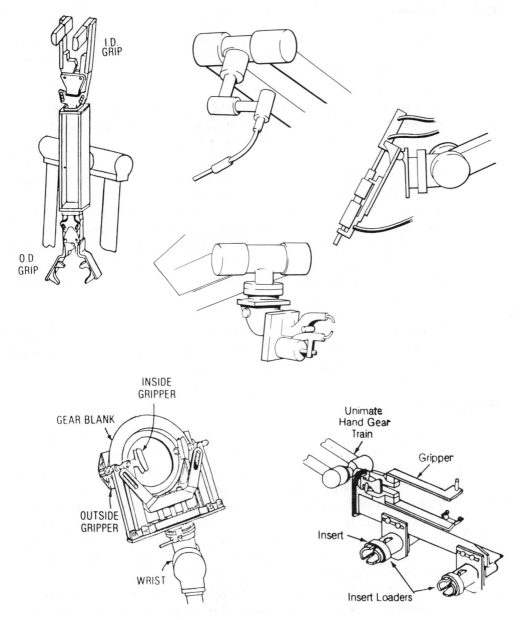

Fig 6.1   End effectors: tools and grippers

Now think about the movement of a tool. A tool could, for example, be a paint spray gun. Not only the path but also the speed of the end effector has to be carefully and continuously controlled at every moment. (This is known as *continuous path control*.) If the spray gun moves too quickly, then the coat of paint will be to thin. On the other hand, if it moves too slowly, the coat of paint will be too thick, causing "runs" (and in large-volume production, the extra cost of using too much paint could be considerable.)

Types of Gripper

It is worthwhile here to examine the various categories of work which a robot may be involved in. Here is a list of four categories. Each one makes different requirements of the gripper.

1 *No gripping*   The workpiece is held in a jig (a purpose-built holder) and the robot performs an activity on it. Jobs in this category include paint spraying, spot welding, flame cutting and drilling.

2 *Coarse gripping*   The robot holds the workpiece but the gripping does not have to be precise. Examples in this category include handling and dipping castings, unloading furnaces, stacking boxes or sacks, etc.

3 *Precise gripping*   The robot holds a workpiece which requires accurate positioning. Examples of this are loading and unloading machine tools.

4 *Assembly*   The robot is required to assemble parts. This calls for very accurate positioning and also some form of sensory feedback to enable the robot to monitor and correct its movements. Only about one per cent of robots at present come into this category.

What we want to do now is to look at the different principles on which grippers operate (mechanical, suction, magnetic and so on) and get an idea of the sort of applications for which each is suitable.

Mechanical Grippers

Loosely speaking, we might refer to a **mechanical gripper** as a robot hand. Pick up some object with your hand. Notice how you secure it by wrapping your fingers around it. Robot hands are different. Usually they have only two or three fingers and these fingers do not have many joints like your own. Figure 6.2 shows a robot hand with two fingers. The point is that a mechanical hand of this type has to rely on friction in order to secure the object it is holding.

Friction between the gripper and the object depends on two factors. Firstly, it depends on the types of surface in contact – for example, metal on metal, rubber on metal, smooth surfaces, rough surfaces.

Secondly, friction depends on the force which is pressing the surfaces together. In order to obtain the required amount of friction, some thought has to be given to the surface of the gripper.

Gripper Pads   Often, pads made of polyurethane (a type of plastic) are fitted to the gripper. This provides greater friction. Polyurethane is also compliant – that means it "gives" when compressed – so it is less likely to damage the workpiece through excess force being applied. Bear in mind, however, that plastic is not suitable for handling very hot material.

The shape of the workpiece should also be taken into account. For gripping curved surfaces it is often possible to use curved gripper pads which match the

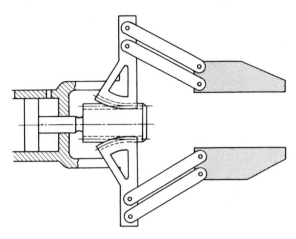

Fig 6.2   Robot hand with two fingers

Fig 6.3   Curved gripper pads may make contact at only two points on a curved surface

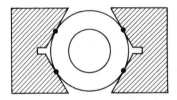

Fig 6.4   The use of V-shaped gripper pads ensures contact at four points on a curved surface

surface. A compliant material such as polyurethane will then make contact with all parts of the surface when the gripper is closed. But, if the gripper pads are made of a hard material such as steel (and this may be necessary for gripping hot objects), then a curved surface can cause problems. This is because it is difficult to match two curved surfaces exactly. The result could then be that contact is only made at two points as shown in figure 6.3. The solution to this problem is to use V-shaped gripper pads. These will always make contact at four points as shown in figure 6.4. They also have the added advantage that they can be used with a wide range of objects of different curvature. Since steel gripper pads are not compliant like plastic pads, it is sometimes necessary to make the gripper itself compliant. This can be done by incorporating springs into the mechanical linkages, or by operating the gripper with compressed air. These are simple methods of preventing a workpiece from being damaged by excessive force.

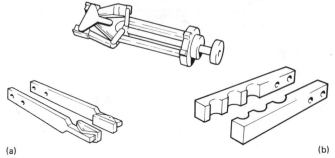

(a)   (b)

Fig 6.5   A versatile standard hand
      (a) Fingers with pivoting gripper pads
      (b) Finger for gripping three different-sized objects

Figure 6.5 shows a versatile type of standard hand to which different fingers can be fitted. Most of these would be made to order to suit the customer's requirement. Shown in (a) and (b) are two very different examples of fingers that can be used. The fingers shown in figure 6.5a have pivoting gripper pads. With these, a rectangular-shaped object can be securely gripped because the pads pivot round to lie flat along the surface. Figure 6.5b shows a pair of fingers designed to grip round objects of three different sizes. The robot has to be programmed to position this gripper so that the most suitable part of the finger is used.

Special Grippers   Grippers used for handling small compact objects are all similar in appearance, apart from the design of the gripper pads. Some more unusual looking grippers are shown in figure 6.6. Figure 6.6a shows a gripper designed for lifting light cardboard boxes. It consists of two fingers connected to each end of a long backplate. The gripper can be adjusted for smaller cartons by repositioning the fingers and actuators on the backplate. A gripper designed to overcome another type of problem, that of removing a small package from a shelf, is shown in figure 6.6b. This gripper has one movable finger and a fixed thin platform that is slid under the package. Another special type of gripper, for a quite different application, is shown in figure 6.6c. This gripper is fitted with rubber cones which enable it to be used with glass tubes of different internal diameters.

Dual Grippers   We all know that "two hands are better than one" and this old saying applies equally well to robots. Dual grippers, of the types shown in figures 6.7 and 6.8, can greatly improve productivity in a number of production processes. In the example shown in figure 6.7, the two grippers are mounted at opposite ends of a bar. The bar is rotated by 180 degrees to bring either gripper

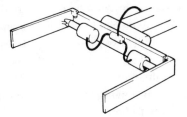

(a) Gripper for cardboard boxes

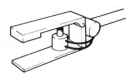

(b) Gripper for small packages

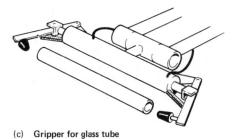

(c) Gripper for glass tube

Fig 6.6   Other types of gripper

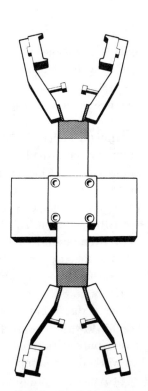

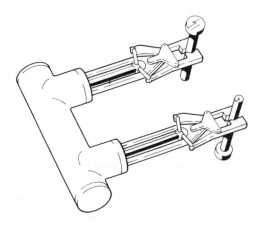

Fig 6.8   Dual gripper for load/unload operation

Fig 6.7   Dual gripper: rotating the bar 180 degrees brings second gripper into use

into use. A typical application for the dual gripper shown in figure 6.8 is in the loading and unloading of a machine. While the machine is processing one part, the robot can be busy picking up another, raw, part. When the process is completed, the finished part can be unloaded and the raw part loaded with no time lost. This arrangement can reduce load/unload time by more than 50 per cent by avoiding the problem of the robot having to be idle, waiting with an empty gripper until the machine is ready to be unloaded.

Other situations where dual grippers can be used to advantage are:

a) With machines that have two workstations. One robot can load two parts in a single operation. There also exist four-part grippers so that load/unload time can be reduced as for the dual gripper working with a single workstation machine.

b) Operations in which part sizes change due to the machining process. It often happens that the raw part is larger or very different in shape from the finished part and may therefore require a different-shaped gripper.

c) Where the cycle time of the robot is too slow to keep up with the production rate of other machines. A robot being used to, say, transfer parts from a conveyor may not be able to keep up with the rate at which parts are arriving. A dual gripper solves this problem by enabling two parts to be transferred simultaneously.

Suction Grippers

Figure 6.9 shows a picture of a robot lifting some packages with a **suction gripper**. Think about the problems of designing a mechanical gripper to do the same job. It seems that the designer of this system thought that a suction gripper was the best solution. There are two types of suction gripper in use:

1 *Devices operated by a vacuum.* A cross-section through one of these types of gripper is shown in figure 6.10. The vacuum may be provided either by a vacuum pump, or, more conveniently, by compressed air using a venturi. The principle of producing a vacuum by a venturi is shown in figure 6.11. As compressed air passes through the venturi (a tube with a narrowing outlet), it drags with it the surrounding layer of air, so creating suction. This is particularly useful since many factories will already have a compressed air supply available. In some designs, the venturi is built into the gripper itself.

2 *Devices with a flexible suction cup* which presses onto the workpiece. In this case, compressed air is blown into the suction cup to release the workpiece. The real advantage of this type of gripper is that it is fail-safe. In the event of a power failure, the workpiece will not fall down. However, as you will know if you have ever used a suction clamp, they only work reliably on clean smooth surfaces. By contrast, suction devices worked by a pump do not have to make an air-tight seal with the workpiece, provided the pump is powerful enough to maintain a sufficient vacuum.

Fig 6.9　Lifting packages with a vacuum gripper

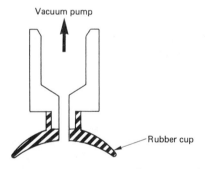

Fig 6.10　Pump-operated vacuum gripper

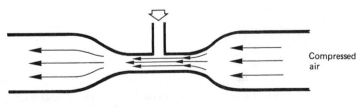

Fig 6.11　Principle of a venturi

Let us now draw up a list of the advantages and disadvantages of this type of gripper. Before reading on, you might like to see what points you can come up with yourself.

Here's our list of *advantages*:
● It is only necessary to have access to one side of the object being lifted.
● There is no danger of crushing fragile objects.
● The exact size and shape of the object is not important.
● The gripper does not have to be precisely positioned on the object.

And now the *disadvantages*:
● The object must have at least one smooth surface to make contact with the suction pad.
● The robot system must include a form of pump for air.
● The level of noise may cause annoyance in certain circumstances.

From this list you should be able to draw some conclusions about the suitability of suction grippers.

Lifting Capacity of Vacuum Operated Grippers So far we have said nothing about the weight that can be lifted by a vacuum operated gripper. With a mechanical gripper, the lifting capacity will of course be limited mainly by the robot. With a vacuum gripper, the lifting capacity will normally be limited by the size of the suction cup, and it is useful to be able to make an estimate of this limit. Table 6.1 gives some approximate figures for the lifting capacities of suction cups of a range of diameters. The table quotes a 25 per cent vacuum, quite a realistic figure for a system in normal use. Notice that doubling the diameter of the suction cup more than doubles the lifting capacity. In fact, the lifting capacity increases in proportion to the square of the diameter (that is, in proportion to the area): check from the table that a 2 cm cup has four times the lifting capacity of a 1 cm cup.

Table 6.1
Approximate lifting capacity of vacuum grippers operated at 25% vacuum

Diameter of suction cup (cm)	Approximate lifting capacity at 25% vacuum (kg)
1	0.2
2	0.8
5	5
10	20

If you would like to make your own calculations for suction cups of other diameters you can use the following formula, in which d is the diameter of the cup in centimetres:

$$\text{Lifting capacity in kg} = \frac{0.785 \times \text{Percentage vacuum} \times d^2}{100}$$

Use the formula to check the values given in Table 6.1 (for a 25% vacuum).

Operating Speed of Vacuum Grippers   Operating speed is almost always a consideration in industry, and shortening an operation by just one second can make a big difference if the operation is to be carried out thousands of times a day. When a suction cup makes contact with a workpiece, a certain time must be allowed before a sufficient vacuum is produced and it is this which will introduce a delay into the cycle time of the robot. There are two ways of minimizing this delay. The first way is to use a suction cup of larger diameter so that sufficient lifting force is produced before the maximum vacuum has been given time to develop. The second way of reducing the delay is to mount the suction cups on the ends of long springs, so that contact is made with the workpiece and a vacuum begins to form even while the robot is moving into position.

Grippers Operated by Compressed Air   Another type of gripper which works by compressed air incorporates an inflatable bag or tube. Two versions are available. In one, designed for holding awkward-shaped hollow glassware, an inflatable bag is inserted into the mouth of the glassware. In the other version, an inflatable tube is fitted around the neck of the glassware as shown in figure 6.12.

These types of gripper are comparatively slow both to pick up and set down the object, owing to the time required to inflate and deflate the bag or tube.

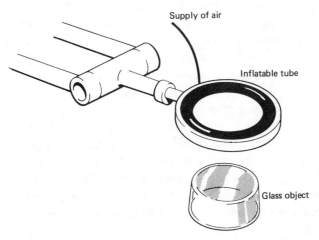

Fig 6.12   Gripper operated by compressed air

Magnetic Grippers

In some situations **magnetic grippers** are used for lifting metal objects. Like vacuum grippers, they have the advantage that precise positioning is not necessary, and that they can be used with objects of different sizes. A further advantage is that they act instantaneously when contact is made. However, not all metals can be attracted by a magnet – see if you can pick up a coin using a magnet. Those metals which can be magnetized are known as ferromagnetic and include nickel, cobalt and iron (steel contains upwards of 99 per cent iron). Quite a few commmon metals are not affected by a magnet and these include copper, aluminium, lead and zinc.

For maximum effect, the surface of the magnet has to make complete contact with the surface of the metal to be gripped. Any air-gaps will reduce the strength of the magnetic force. Flat sheets of metal are therefore most suitable for magnetic grippers, but it is also possible to pick up objects with irregularly-shaped surfaces if the magnet is sufficiently strong. For some applications, a magnet is used whose shape matches that of the surface of the object to be lifted.

Temperature is also a factor which has to be considered when using magnetic grippers. Permanent magnets tend to become demagnetized when heated and so there is the danger that prolonged contact with a hot workpiece will weaken them to the point where they can no longer be used. The effect of heat will of course depend on the time the magnet spends in contact with the hot part. Most magnetic materials are relatively unaffected by temperatures up to around 100 degrees centigrade, but for temperatures higher than this, magnets made of special materials have to be used and these are naturally more expensive.

Either permanent magnets or electromagnets can be used in grippers. **Electromagnets** are operated by a DC electric current and lose almost but not quite all their magnetism when the current is switched off. Therefore, to ensure that the load is released quickly and at exactly the right moment, a small reverse current is used to offset any residual magnetism remaining after the main operating current has been switched off. **Permanent magnets** are also sometimes used in situations where there is an explosive atmosphere, and sparks from electrical equipment would cause a hazard. The workpiece is released from the permanent magnet by pushing it away with an ejector pin fitted to the centre of the gripper.

An electromagnetic gripper suitable for lifting sheets of metal is shown in figure 6.13. Care has to be taken to see that the surface of the metal to be lifted is clean. Swarf (small pieces of metal from drilling and cutting) and dirt on the surface of the metal will reduce the holding power of the magnets. The size and thickness of the metal sheet to be lifted has to be considered as well as its weight. A thin sheet of metal may sag in the middle, forcing the surface away from the magnets.

An advanced design of magnetic gripper (made by Shinko Electric) is shown in figure 6.14. This is sometimes referred to as a *form adaptable gripper*. When the electromagnet is off, the bags of iron powder adapt to the shape of the workpiece. Switching on the electromagnet causes the iron powder to clump together into a solid mass. This design has the advantage of being uncomplicated while at the same time being adaptable to many different shapes and sizes of workpiece.

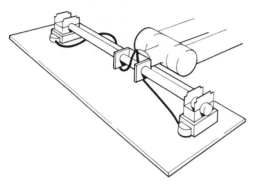

Fig 6.13   Electromagnetic gripper for sheet metal

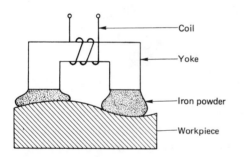

Fig 6.14   Form-adaptable electromagnetic gripper

Fig 6.15   A ladle for molten metal

Hooks and Scoops

These are of course the simplest types of end effector that can be classed as "grippers". A simple **scoop** (or ladle) such as the one shown in figure 6.15 is commonly used to scoop up molten metal and transfer it to the mould.

For certain applications a simple **hook** may be all that is needed to lift a part. Precise positioning of a part being lifted with a hook is not really possible, but this may not be important if the part is being dipped, for example.

Special Types of Gripper

The conventional types of gripper that we have so far looked at cannot always be adapted to every type of manufacturing process. Some processes present special gripping problems which have to be solved by new innovations. As an illustration of this, we examine the problem of using a robot in the clothing industry to lift pieces of cloth.

Cloth presents a particular difficulty because layers tend to cling together and different types of cloth have different textures and thicknesses. Vacuum grippers are not suitable because the air flow will penetrate the cloth, causing two or more layers to bind together. Pinching the cloth with a mechanical gripper has been used in some factories, but the method is not completely satisfactory; setting up the gripper so that only one layer of cloth is taken at a time is a difficult operation, and delicate fabrics can sometimes be damaged. Adhesive fingers are another possibility, particularly for lifting light, delicate fabrics.

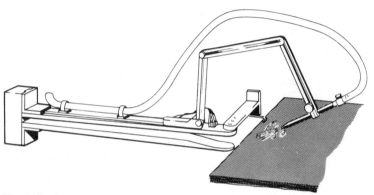

Fig 6.16   A special gripper for cloth

Figure 6.16 shows quite a sophisticated solution to the problems of lifting cloth. Air blown across the surface of the cloth causes the top layer to lift on to the gripper jaws while at the same time the vibrations set up by the air prevent layers from sticking together. Sensors detect the position of the cloth to control the air jet and jaws.

Tools

Now we will look at some examples of commonly used tools. Unlike we humans, a robot does not need to use its hand to hold the tool – this would be inefficient. Any tool that is required can be fitted directly on to the end of the robot's arm. A robot can even be programmed to select and change tools without the intervention of a human operator.

Welding Tools

Welding, which in this context means joining two pieces of metal by melting them at the joint, is a fairly common activity in industry and figure 6.17 shows

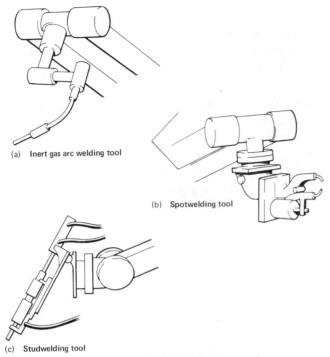

(a) Inert gas arc welding tool

(b) Spotwelding tool

(c) Studwelding tool

Fig 6.17　Welding tools

three different examples of welding tools. Figure 6.17a shows an *inert gas arc welding* torch. This tool, which requires sophisticated control, is used to make long continuous seam welds. The weld is produced by passing a high electric current between the electrode of the welding tool and the workpiece. Oxygen in the atmosphere, if allowed to come into contact with the molten metal, would cause oxidation and prevent a proper joint from being formed. In inert gas welding, oxidation is prevented by a continuous stream of argon or helium supplied to the tip of the tool. As with all types of seam welding, additional metal (called a filler) has to be fed into the joint as the weld proceeds. The most common method of adding metal is to make the electrode of the tool itself the filler, and continuously replace it from a coil of wire. This method is known as *MIG (Metal Inert Gas)* welding. An alternative method now being used with robots is to make the tip of the tool out of tungsten, which will not melt. A separate filler is then fed into the joint. This method of welding is called *TIG (Tungsten Inert Gas)* welding.

Figure 6.17b shows a *spotwelding* gun. Spotwelding (as opposed to continuous welding) is faster and therefore cheaper to do. In robot applications it has the added advantages that control and programming of the robot are also simplified.

Figure 6.17c shows a *stud welding* tool, used for fastening sheet metal together by welding studs into pre-drilled holes. Studs are fed into the tool from an overhead hopper.

Paintspraying, like welding, is another common use of industrial robots. A spray gun tool is shown in figure 6.18, and figure 6.19 shows a similar tool being used to spray part of a car body.

Figure 6.20 shows a *deburring tool* being used during one stage of the manufacture of a steering component for a car. The head of the tool has to be replaced periodically and the robot is programmed to present the tool to the operator for replacement after every 300 operations.

For some applications, rotating tools are driven by compressed air rather than by an electric motor. This is the case for the pneumatic *nut runner* shown in figure 6.21, used for tightening nuts in assembly operations. The operating pressure of the air can be controlled to prevent overtightening of the nut.

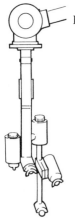

Fig 6.18   Spray gun

Fig 6.19   Spraying a car body
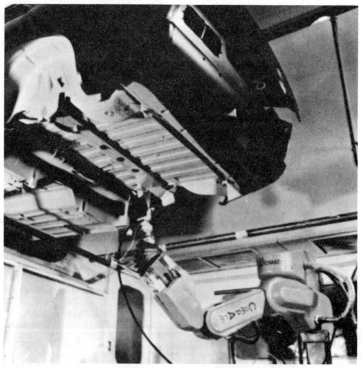

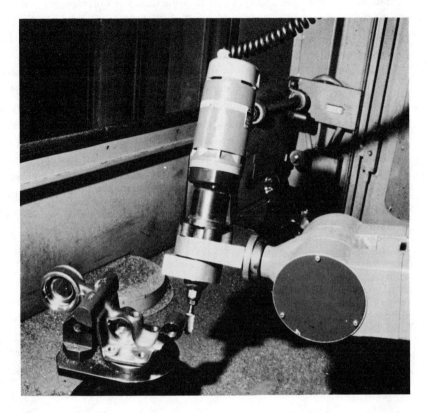

Fig 6.20   A deburring tool being used on a steering component of a car

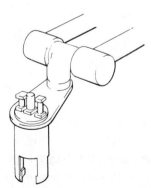

Fig 6.21   A pneumatic nut runner

Programmed End Effector Changing

As we mentioned above, it is possible to program the robot to change end effectors during the work cycle. Technically this is not difficult and figure 6.22 shows one example of a system for doing this. The end effectors needed for the work are retained in a row of cradles. To remove an end effector the robot lowers it into the cradle and disengages it by withdrawing the wrist. Fitting the new end effector is a reverse of the same procedure.

The option of using a programmed end effector change has to be carefully evaluated since it may not necessarily prove to be the most cost effective solution. Firstly, there is the high capital cost of the tooling. Secondly, the work cycle (the time taken to perform all the operations on the workpiece) will be considerably lengthened due to the time required to change tools. The relative importance of these factors depends on the number of items to be produced. As the size of the production run increases, capital cost becomes less important whereas short cycle time becomes more important. For large production runs, the alternative of using two or more robots to do the different jobs may therefore be a more cost effective solution.

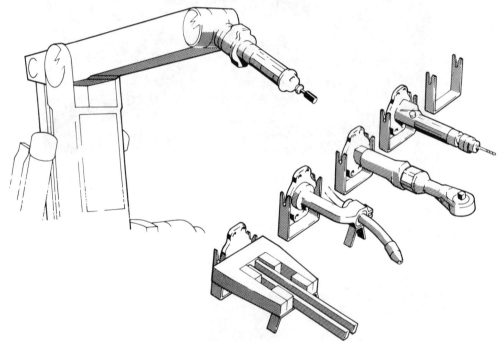

Fig 6.22 Programmed end effector changing

Another alternative to selecting different end effectors is to mount several of them on a turret, as shown in figure 6.23. This solution is particularly suitable where small light end effectors have to be frequently changed such as in the application of inserting differently shaped electronic components into printed circuit boards. Here, a saving of up to 30 per cent cycle time can be achieved

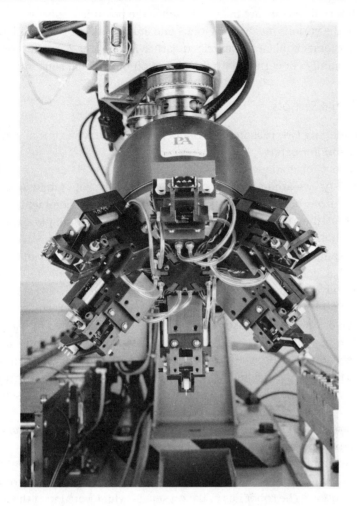

Fig 6.23   End effectors mounted on a turret (Courtesy: PA Technology)

over the alternative method of tool changing. Care must however be taken to design the end effectors so that the turret assembly does not obstruct parts of the workpiece.

Sensors: Introduction

Having dealt with end effectors, we now need to consider *the various means by which information (data) about the current situation of the robot is collected for use by the controlling program.* A large variety of devices are available for this purpose and these are all referred to generally as **sensors**.

In robotics, sensors are divided into two categories: *external sensors*, which are fitted outside the robot, and *internal sensors*, which are fitted inside the robot. Internal sensors are needed to sense the positions, speeds and accelerations of the various mechanical joints and linkages of the robot and form part of the servomechanism as described earlier in Chapter 2. In this chapter we shall be mainly concerned with the operation of external sensors.

The Need for External Sensors

We can identify two reasons for robots needing to have external sensors:
1 Sensors for safety.
2 Sensors for guidance.

By "safety" we are including both the safety of the robot, that is protecting the robot from damaging itself, and the safety of the equipment, parts and people that the robot is working with. Here are two simple examples to illustrate both these cases.

First example: suppose a robot is moving into a new position and it encounters an obstruction – it might be another machine, for example. If the robot does not have a sensor which will enable it to detect the obstruction, either before or after contact is made, then some damage could result.

A second example of sensors for safety is nicely illustrated by the problem of a robot picking up an egg. If the robot is fitted with a mechanical gripper, then a sensor must be used to measure the force on the egg. Gripping too tightly will break the egg and not gripping tightly enough will allow the egg to fall. You will probably be able to think of many other examples of sensors for safety.

Now what about sensors for guidance? This category is very broad but here are two examples for you to consider.

First example: parts on a conveyor arrive in front of a robot which is programmed to spray-paint them. What happens if a part is missing or is in the wrong position? The robot has to have a sensor which can detect the presence of the part – otherwise it would quite cheerfully spray the empty space. In this case no damage would be done, but it is not an ideal way to run a factory.

Second example: sensors for guidance need to be quite sophisticated in welding. To carry out the operation successfully, the robot has to move the welding torch along the seam line of the weld, and it has to move it at the right speed and keep it at the right distance from the surface.

Some General Points about Sensors

There is a whole range of sensors available and they come in different shapes and sizes according to the principle on which they work. There are, for example, many types of sensor which can be used to convert heat to an electrical signal. Some of these are large and insensitive, others are small and delicate, and there is a whole range in between. So, how will we choose which type of sensor is most suitable? Essentially, when choosing a sensor, we need to answer some or all of the following questions:

- Is the sensor small enough to fit where it is needed?
- Is it accurate enough?
- Will it work over a suitable range? (You wouldn't weigh a fly on bathroom scales.)
- Will it disturb the quantity it is trying to measure? For example, if an enormous heat sensor were plunged into a tiny quantity of hot water, it would have the effect of cooling the water down.
- Might it wear out too quickly in the proposed application? Is it suitable for the environment? It may be made of a material which would melt at the temperatures it would be exposed to.
- Will it cost too much?

In addition to the points mentioned above there are also some technical terms such as linearity, sensitivity and frequency response which need to be considered.

Linearity Many types of sensor produce some continuously changing output signal in response to a continuously changing input. For example, a heat sensor may produce a voltage when exposed to heat. When this is the case, we will usually need to know exactly how the output varies with input, and the information is best displayed on a graph. Figure 6.24 shows the graphs for two possible types of heat sensor. The straight line seen in figure 6.24a shows a *linear response* whereas the curve seen in figure 6.24b shows a *non-linear response*.

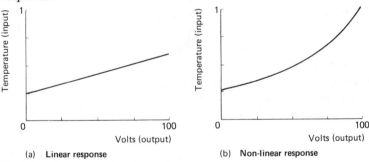

(a) Linear response   (b) Non-linear response

Fig 6.24 Output of a heat transducer

In most cases, a sensor with a linear response is preferred because there is a simple relationship between input and output. Taking a heat sensor as an example: if a rise in temperature of one degree produces an increase in output of two volts, then a rise of ten degrees will produce an increase of twenty volts, and so on.

This simple relationship makes it easy to calibrate the sensor. Knowing the voltage produced at just two temperatures, say 0°C and 100°C, makes it possible to calculate the response at any other temperature.

Sensors with a non-linear response also have a role to play. A response such as the one shown in figure 6.24b makes it possible to cover a wide range of temperatures with the output varying over only a comparatively small range. The difficulty of course is in calibration, but usually it is possible to fit a mathematical equation to the curve which relates output (say voltage) to input (say temperature). Using a computer it is then a simple matter to calculate the value of the input for any output produced.

Sensitivity Sensitivity, as the name implies, tells you how sensitive a sensor is to the quantity it is designed to measure. Sensitivity is always given as a number which indicates the "change in output per unit change in input".

An example will make this clear. A certain heat sensor may have a sensitivity quoted as being "one volt per degree", meaning that a *change* of one degree in input would produce a *change* of one volt in output. Another heat sensor may have a sensitivity of "two volts per degree" in which case it would be *twice* as sensitive as the former. Of course, in all this we need to know also about the linearity of the sensor. If it is linear then the sensitivity will be the same over the whole range of measurement. A sensor with a response like that shown in figure 6.24*b* would be *more* sensitive at higher temperatures than at lower temperatures (at higher temperatures, a small change in temperature produces a large change in voltage).

Frequency Response The frequency response of a sensor tells us how quickly it can respond to a change in input. As an example of an instrument with a very poor frequency response we will take a mercury-in-glass thermometer. This is not in fact useful in robotics because it does not produce electrical signals, but will illustrate the point we are making. The input is temperature and the "output" is the position of the mercury thread. Assume that the temperature (input) is changing smoothly and continuously with time as shown in figure 6.25*a*. The frequency is the number of cycles in one second and is given in units of hertz (Hz). [1 hertz means 1 cycle per second, 1 kilohertz means 1000 cycles per second.]

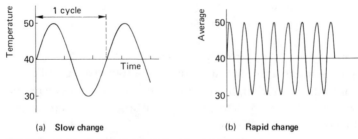

(a) Slow change (b) Rapid change

Fig 6.25 A continuously changing temperature

At low frequencies, that is when the temperature is changing slowly, the thermometer would faithfully follow the changes in temperature. However, if the temperature were changing comparatively rapidly (figure 6.25*b*) then we wouldn't expect to see much movement of the thermometer thread. The thermometer is sluggish and would only show the average temperature. Whether or not this is satisfactory depends on the application we have in mind and how quickly we expect the temperature to change.

There are various ways of expressing the frequency response of a sensor. Sometimes the output power or voltage may be quoted for a particular input frequency, for example "one millivolt at 500 hertz". Often the frequency response will be different at different frequencies and a graph may be pre-

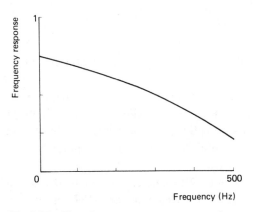

Fig 6.26   How frequency response can change with frequency

sented showing how the frequency response varies with frequency (see figure 6.26). The frequency response may also be given in decibels (dB) which is a unit for *comparing* the power output at one frequency with that which would be obtained at a reference frequency.

Bearing all this in mind, you will see why it is useful to have a number of different types of sensor available even though they appear to do exactly the same job.

Types of Sensor

By and large sensor systems involve some device which is able to convert a physical effect into an electrical signal. Robots, after all, are controlled by computers and computers can only respond to electrical signals. Where the physical effect contains some energy, such as heat or light or a mechanical vibration, then the device which converts this into an electrical signal is called a **transducer**. Figure 6.27 shows a range of physical effects for which trans-ducers are required.

We will now look at some commonly used types of sensor and see what they can do.

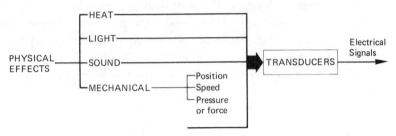

Fig 6.27   Transducers convert physical effects into electrical signals

Optical Sensors

Using beams of light is quite a useful way of detecting the presence of objects. The key element in all of these types of optical sensing device is an **optical transducer**, a device which can convert light into an electrical signal. A few types of optical transducer are available. They differ mainly in the colour of light to which they are most sensitive (some are only sensitive to infra-red) and in how quickly they can respond (their frequency response).

Light-dependent Resistors (LDR) The chemical called cadmium sulphide has the useful property that its electrical resistance decreases when light falls on it. This effect is put to use by depositing a long thin track of the chemical onto an insulating base and enclosing it in a metal case with a transparent window. Figure 6.28a shows one of these devices, known as a light-dependent resistor, or just LDR. Compared with other types of optical transducer, LDRs respond very slowly, in hundredths rather than thousandths of a second.

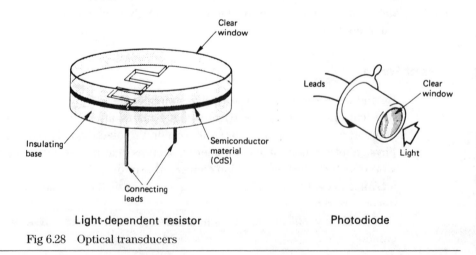

Light-dependent resistor   Photodiode

Fig 6.28   Optical transducers

Photodiodes and Phototransistors Silicon, the material from which transistors and integrated circuits are made, undergoes a change in electrical resistance when it is exposed to light. Photodiodes and phototransistors are nothing more than ordinary diodes and transistors encased in a transparent material, instead of the usual metal or plastic, in order to allow light to reach them. When incorporated into an electric circuit, photodiodes and phototransistors can be used to produce electrical signals which depend on the amount of light falling on them. Figure 6.28*b* shows a typical example.

Fig 6.29   An optical point sensor

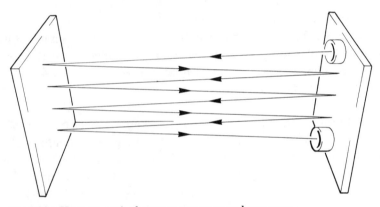

Fig 6.30   How an optical sensor can cover a large area

The least-complicated arrangement of optical sensor consists of a single light source and a single light-sensitive detector arranged as shown in figure 6.29. This is referred to as a *point sensor*. The detector senses when the beam of light is broken and the information can be made available to a computer or other electronic controller.

Figure 6.30 shows an alternative arrangement using two mirrors. By "lacing" the beam backwards and forwards, the sensor is made to cover a larger area. Breaking the beam at any point will trigger the detector.

A slightly more complicated arrangement is a *linear sensor*. This consists of light source placed opposite a line of light sensitive detectors, as shown in figure 6.31. Each detector acts independently. Notice that this operates in a different way from the arrangement shown in figure 6.30, because it can be used to distinguish between objects of different height. If a large number of detectors are used, it begins to approach something of a rudimentary vision system, discussed below.

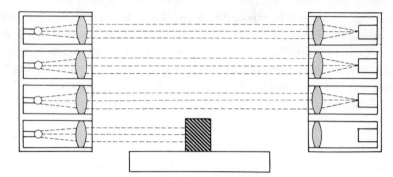

Fig 6.31　An optical linear sensor

Heat Sensors

There are many operations carried out in manufacturing where it is necessary to measure temperatures. This may be done for reasons of safety, to make sure nothing is overheating, or it may be done because the temperature of some material, a plastic for instance, has to be controlled at a certain value. There are a number of devices, called **heat sensors**, which can detect heat and produce an electrical signal.

The Bimetallic Strip This is an old and simple device consisting of two strips of different types of metal, welded together, as shown in figure 6.32a. When heated, one of the metals expands more than the other and this causes the strip to buckle (figure 6.32b). If an electrical contact is fixed in the right place, then the buckled strip can be used to close an electrical circuit. The temperature at which this happens can be altered by adjusting the gap between the strip and the point of electrical contact.

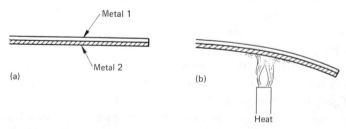

Fig 6.32　The bimetallic strip: (a) before heating; (b) after heating

Electrical Resistance Thermometers When a metal, any metal, is heated, its electrical resistance increases by a small amount. This effect forms the basis of electrical resistance thermometers. In practice, the metal used is platinum in the form of a fine element deposited onto a heat-resisting base.

Platinum, although expensive, has the ideal properties of having a high melting point (1773°C) and not reacting with most chemicals. The platinum element forms part of an electronic circuit which produces a change in voltage when the resistance of the platinum changes due to heat. The typical range for these thermometers is −50°C to +500°C.

Thermistors Whereas the resistance of metals *increases* with rising temperature, the resistance of certain materials called semiconductors (of which silicon is one) *decreases* with rising temperature. Heat sensors made of semiconductor material are known as **thermistors**. Thermistors are made for use over a similar range of temperatures to platinum resistance thermometers.

The change of resistance in a thermistor can be quite dramatic. A typical thermistor may have a resistance of around one hundred thousand ohms at room temperature, but only ten ohms when placed in boiling water. This fast change in resistance is made use of when very small changes in temperature need to be detected.

Thermocouples For the measurement of very high temperatures, up to 1000°C, a sensor known as a thermocouple is used. A thermocouple works on the principle that, if a circuit is made using two dissimilar types of metal as shown in figure 6.33, then a voltage is produced which depends on the difference in temperature between the junctions. For accurate work, the "cold" junction is kept at a fixed and known temperature, in iced water, rather than left at room temperature. Practical thermocouples are made in various shapes and sizes, typically in the form of a long probe.

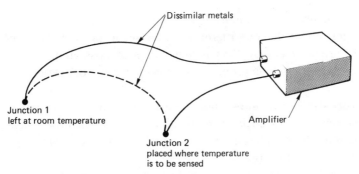

Fig 6.33   Principle of a thermocouple

Tactile Sensors

In people, tactile sense is provided by the skin. Through the skin, it is not only possible to sense when contact with another object has been made but also to sense how much pressure is being applied and the shape and size of an object. Although it is useful to have all of this information, it is usually possible to make do with much more limited forms of **tactile sensing** in robotic applications. We will look at some examples of the types of tactile sensor in use.

Point-contact Binary Sensors These devices consist of a sensitive switch which detects when contact is made at a single point. They are sometimes called binary contact sensors – "binary" because they have only two conditions, on or off. Depending on their intended use, binary contact sensors can be coarse, like an ordinary push button switch, or extremely sensitive and able to be triggered by a movement as little as one thousandth of a millimetre.

Point-contact Analog Sensors Sometimes it is necessary to measure the force with which a robot is gripping an object, as in the case of the egg mentioned earlier. An analog point sensor produces a voltage or current which varies according to how much force is being applied at the point where the sensor makes contact. There are many different designs, based on various principles. The point-contact analog sensor shown in figure 6.34 is a photomechanical type. As the probe is pressed down, the screen attached to it

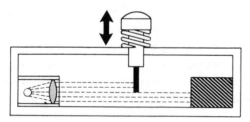

Fig 6.34   A point-contact analog sensor

progressively prevents more light from reaching the detector. The electrical output from the detector therefore varies according to the force being applied to the probe. Of course, the whole device is encapsulated, so from the outside it just appears to be a probe with some electrical connections.

Piezoresistive Sensors There is a range of materials (some man-made, some natural) which change their electrical resistance when pressed or squeezed. These materials are called piezoresistive (the word "piezo" is from the Greek word for press).

A simple analog contact sensor can be made by sandwiching a piece of piezoresistive material between two metal electrodes as shown in figure 6.35. When a force is applied, the piezoresistive material is compressed, its resistance changes, and therefore the electric current passing through it also changes.

Matrix Sensors The limitation of a single analog sensor is that it can only measure force at a single point – where the probe is situated. By taking a large

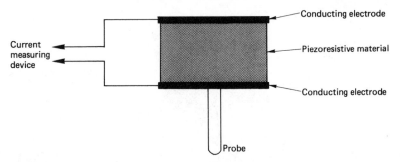

Fig 6.35   A piezoelectric analog contact sensor

number of binary or analog point sensors and arranging them in rows and columns, like a chess board, it is possible to end up with a composite sensor which can not only detect the presence of an object, but also its shape and orientation. Such an arrangement is called a matrix sensor, and the technique of analyzing the data from a matrix sensor is called **form recognition**.

One way of building a matrix sensor is by making use of a piezoelectric material. Piezoelectric materials (don't confuse with piezo*resistive*) have the useful property of producing a small voltage when they are pressed or squeezed. An example of a fairly recently developed piezoelectric material is a plastic called PVF$_2$, which stands for polyvinylidene fluoride.

Figure 6.36 shows how a number of individual piezoelectric sensor elements can be built up to produce a matrix sensor. The matrix sensor itself can be thought of as a form of artificial skin. Figure 6.37 shows the "image" produced by bringing this artificial skin into contact with a metal casting. So far, artificial skin of this type is still being researched but when the technology is perfected it could perhaps be used to provide robots with a sense of touch rather like our own.

A Pneumatic Sensor   Figure 6.38 shows a useful pneumatic tactile sensor that does not operate electrically at all. It is used as a safety device on robots driven by pneumatic linear drives. The sensor consists of a tightly coiled spring. When contact is made with an obstruction, the spring bends and allows the compressed air (which drives the robot) to escape to the atmosphere.

Acoustic Sensors

A familiar example of an **acoustic sensor** is the microphone. A microphone is a device for converting sound waves into electrical signals – but that is just the beginning. The problem involved with an acoustic sensor lies in interpreting the sounds that it senses, and this requires a computer.

At the simplest level, it may be required for a robot to respond to a human shout or the noise of an explosion. For this it is only necessary to have a sensor

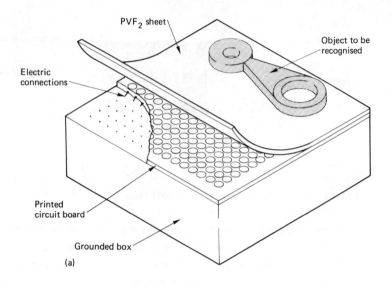

PVF$_2$ sheet

Object to be
recognised

Electric
connections

Printed
circuit board

Grounded box

(a)

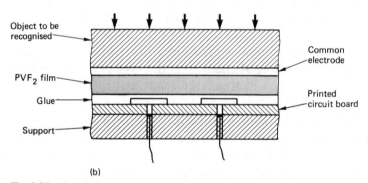

Object to be
recognised

Common
electrode

PVF$_2$ film

Glue

Printed
circuit board

Support

(b)

Fig 6.36   A matrix sensor

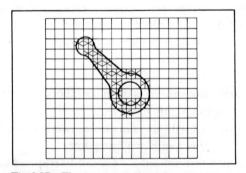

Fig 6.37   The image produced by an object in contact with a matrix sensor

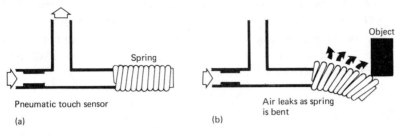

Spring

Pneumatic touch sensor

(a)

Object

Air leaks as spring
is bent

(b)

Fig 6.38   A pneumatic tactile sensor

system which can respond to some preset level of sound. A more sophisticated sound-sensing system would be able to recognize words and take the appropriate action. For this purpose the computer has stored in its memory a number of words which it can compare with words spoken to the robot. This process is known as **speech recognition** and you should not confuse it with the more complicated process of "speech understanding". In a speech recognition system, the robot can only respond to individual words such as "stop", "start", "up", "down" and so on. Speech understanding, in which the robot could make sense of a complete spoken sentence, is far more complicated and is still a subject of research.

Gas Sensors

Figure 6.39 shows a robot with a **gas sensor** attached to the end of its arm – this robot can smell! An interesting application for robots with a sense of smell has been developed by British Leyland to test cars for leaks. Previously, all car manufacturers tested for leaks by spraying the car with water and then

Fig 6.39   A gas sensor

carrying out a manual inpection of the interior to see if water had seeped in. The British Leyland system represents a breakthrough in car production technology. A mixture of air and helium is pumped under pressure into the interior of the car. A robot stationed outside the car then sniffs along all of the rubber seals to detect any leaks.

Proximity Sensors

A **proximity sensor** is a device that can sense the presence of an object, just by being close to it. Sensors of this type have been made by utilizing the magnetic effect induced by the presence of metals, the effect on electrical capacitance induced by the presence of most other materials, or by detecting reflected light or reflected ultrasonic sound (sound of such a high pitch that it is inaudible to the human ear). [We are including ultrasonic sensors here rather than under Acoustic Sensors.]

Figure 6.40 shows a selection of proximity sensors which work on the principle of reflected infra-red light. A sensor itself consists of a light source and next to it a detector, all contained in a single package. A reflective object placed anywhere in the sensitive area will cause light from the source to be returned to the detector.

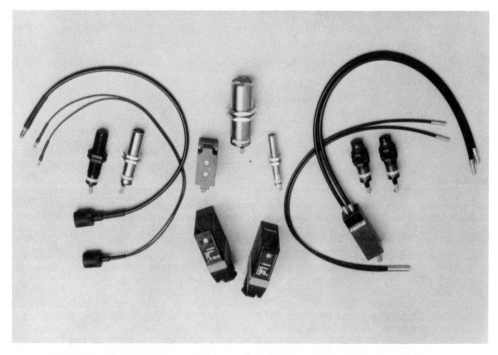

Fig 6.40   Photoelectric proximity sensors (Courtesy: Huntleigh Technology, Cardiff)

Robot Vision

Equipping robots with sensors, even sophisticated matrix sensors, still does not solve all of the problems which may occur. After all, if you walked into a factory and found people working with their eyes closed, you'd be a bit surprised. Nevertheless, at the moment, only a tiny percentage of industrial robots are equipped with vision – and even this is of a rudimentary type. So what are the problems with **computer vision systems**; what jobs can robots do with them and what jobs can they do without them? It would be nice if robots could be equipped to see in the same way that we can see. The technology to make this possible (at least in part) is only just becoming available and development of vision systems is an area of intensive research.

The main parts of a vision system consist of a camera connected to a computer, and a control system (to control the movement of the robot). A basic configuration is shown in figure 6.41. The image produced by the camera is analyzed by the computer. The monitor is for our benefit, not the robot's! Notice that the image seen on the monitor appears to be made up of many separate **points** (figure 6.42).

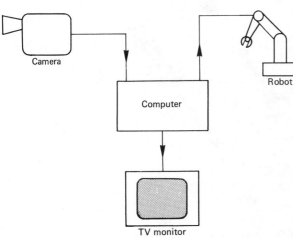

Fig 6.41 Basic arrangement of a vision system

Fig 6.42 The image is made up of separate points
(Courtesy: *Robotics Age*)

Actually, if you looked closely enough, you would see that all pictures are made up of points. A normal TV picture contains about 24 thousand points, and an ordinary 35 mm film, about 4 million points (too small to see without a microscope). Even the image formed by the human eye is made up of points – about 16 million of them. so many in fact, that we are never aware of them.

Obviously there is an advantage in having a large number of points. The more points there are, the more detail we can see. We refer to this as having high **resolution**. But does an electronic vision system need so many points? Well, a large number of points means more memory and more processing time for the computer. With the technology available at the moment, we have to say that the fewer points we can make do with the better, because this means less memory and faster processing time.

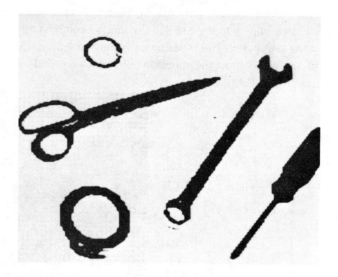

Fig 6.43   How the computer sees different objects (Courtesy: *Robotics Age*)

Figure 6.43 shows how the computer "sees" several different objects. In order for the computer to learn each shape, the shape is shown to the camera. In a typical system the computer may have the capacity to learn, say, ten different shapes. This does not necessarily mean that the vision system will then be able to recognize ten different objects. Some objects (probably most that you can think of) can lie in one of several stable positions. Each position will be seen as a different shape by the computer and therefore have to be learned as such. The reason for limiting the number of shapes is again to do with the amount of memory needed by the computer to store each shape and the time taken to process the information. More shapes means more memory and more memory means that the information takes longer to process (we're talking here about times around several seconds which for mass production may become an unacceptable delay).

Given the limitations of technology in vision systems you should be prepared to accept that we have not yet reached the stage (nor are we close to the stage) when a robot can "look" at any scene and know what it is looking at. Robot vision systems can only recognize one of a few shapes that they have learned. Any other shape or even a learned shape in an unlearned orientation will be rejected. Although this sounds like a very limited capability, it does allow a robot to be used for many jobs which could not be done "blind". Here we should mention that some situations are not suitable for vision systems. Oil, smoke or dust in the atmosphere will obscure the camera lens. Excessive vibration may also be a problem. Obviously, adequate lighting has to be provided, but this would not normally be a problem unless the workpiece was liable to be affected by light as in the case of photographic material.

Required Properties of Vision Systems

We have already said what we mean by the term *resolution* and that higher resolution enables the computer to see more detail. As resolution is increased we can achieve higher levels of computer vision. We can list these levels as:

1 *Detection*: determining whether an object is present or not. This is not truly classed as vision because it can be achieved with the optical sensors described above.
2 *Orientation*: determining the orientation of an object. This does not require precise information on the features of the object.
3 *Recognition*: classifying an object to the point of being able to say whether it is a nut or a bolt for example.
4 *Identification*: being able to describe the object precisely, given the information available.

With each of these levels of vision, we can identify a range of jobs which the robot can carry out.

Orientation Generally speaking, determining the orientation of a workpiece is a more important requirement than recognizing or identifying a workpiece. This is especially true in assembly operations. It is often not a problem to organize the production process so that only the required parts are fed to the robot. For example, screws may arrive on a conveyor, but the orientation of the screws will be random, even though all of the screws are the same. The robot is required to move its gripper towards a screw and pick it up in the correct orientation to perform the next operation (say, inserting the screw into something). Here, the gripper would need some form of tactile sense to know when contact with the screw had been made.

For reasons that we shall explain later, this type of vision system operates in an open loop manner. This means that the camera takes only one picture of the workpiece (the screw in this example) and the computer then passes instructions to the control system to move the gripper to where the screw is to be found. While the gripper is moving, the workpiece must therefore either stay in position or move only at some predetermined speed, otherwise the gripper will not know where to find it.

Recognition A robot is obviously more useful to us if we do not have to carefully organize the production process to enable it to cope. In the last example we said that the screws arriving on the conveyor were all of the correct type. Only their orientation had to be determined. But of course, sorting the screws (or whatever they happen to be) in the first place is an additional operation. A person standing at the conveyor could quite easily pick out the correct type of screw from several different types present. This is not so simple for a robot.

Identification If a vision system has a high enough resolution then it can give precise information about an object. It is not difficult to think of situations in which a vision system with this capability would be useful. In assembly operations for example, the robot may be required to select one of several similar-looking parts, and insert it in the correct place. The use of robots for assembly is one of the exciting growth areas. It is also the point where we can see robots as really doing the sorts of jobs that people can do.

Touching and Overlapping Parts If you see your pen sticking out from underneath a book, you have no problem at all in recognizing the pen. In fact, probably if you could only see as little as half an inch of it, you would still be able to recognize it – and if you had several different pens, you would be able to say which one of them it was. For a computer vision system though, recognizing an object which is partly covered (the technical term is **occluded**) represents a major achievement. Vision systems have been developed which can successfully recognize partly occluded objects, but these are not generally in commercial use. These systems work by extracting features from objects such as holes or corners, and analyzing the information. In the factory, the problem of **touching or overlapping parts** can be dealt with in one of two other ways:

1   The first way is to organize the production process so that parts are separated before arriving at the camera position. If one or more parts are touching or overlapping, the vision system will reject them, which will then result in the parts being recycled. Although not an entirely satisfactory solution to the problem it may be necessary until "cleverer" vision systems become widely available.

2   The second way of dealing with the problem is for the robot to nudge the touching or overlapping parts to separate them, whenever the vision system sees something it doesn't recognize. This solution is not really very satisfactory at all because of the time involved in the operation.

Bin-picking

There are many things which are not manufactured in just one single stage, but a few stages. A metal tool, for example, might first be cast, then filed, then polished, and finally packed. The usual procedure is for the parts to be put into a container (a "bin") after the completion of each stage. In the traditional arrangement a person will then come along and pick parts out from the bin to perform the next operation on them. If this job, known in robotics as **bin-picking**, is to be done by a robot, there are several difficulties to be overcome. Not only are many of the parts overlapping, they are also not lying flat and are not all at the same distance from the camera. If you looked into a bin containing a heap of different parts, you would have little trouble picking one of them out. But think for a moment about all that information which your brain has to sort out. To solve this problem properly, we need either cleverer computers or cleverer computer programmers (probably both!) but in the meantime we have two approaches to the problem of bin-picking.

One approach is to use a mechanical method to transfer the parts from the bin onto a conveyor. Once there, the parts lie flat and the usual type of vision system can be used to recognize them. You probably feel that this approach is not so much solving the problem as getting around the problem!

A second approach has been built and demonstrated and is already in use. A tailor-made computer program is written to enable the position of a part in the bin to be determined from the picture seen by the camera. The robot arm is then directed to a position above the part, and moves down in a straight line to seize it, aided by tactile sensors in the gripper. At this point, the part may be in any orientation, but once it has been successfully picked up it can then be re-gripped at a later stage. The disadvantage of this system is of course that it requires custom-written programs for each type of part it is to be used with.

Recognition Time

When you look at something familiar, you recognize it instantly, but a vision system may take anything from a quarter of a second to about five seconds to process the information. The **recognition time** for the computer turns out to be an important factor. In a moment we will discuss the limitations that this imposes, but first of all we shall just go over the reasons for there being a delay in the first place.

The shape which the camera sees is analyzed, point by point, by the computer to determine whether it compares with a known shape (stored as data) in its memory. This process takes time, and the time that it takes will increase with the number of known shapes which the computer has stored (it has to make a comparison with each one) and with the number of points that each shape is made up from (that is, the resolution). Different techniques have and are being developed for reducing the recognition time but the sorts of times we have come to expect from computers (measured in thousandths of seconds rather than tenths of seconds) are still a long way off.

Why are we interested in reducing the recognition time? One obvious answer is that if the time taken for the operation is fast, then the production rate can be increased – obviously an advantage. But, there is more to it than that. The incentive for reducing recognition time is so that the vision system can be used for closed-loop control. Suppose, for example, the problem is for the gripper to fit a part into a hole. In a closed-loop vision control system, the camera would continuously be looking at the part and the hole, and the computer would be evaluating the distance between them and using the information to correct the position of the gripper. This is, of course, exactly the way that you would do it yourself. To carry out this operation smoothly, the vision system would need to look at the scene at least several times per second. If the recognition time were say one second, it could take several minutes for a robot to complete the operation using this system. The alternative therefore is for the vision system to take one look and then move the gripper without any further checking. This is all very well provided that:

(*a*) Nothing moves in an unpredictable way in the meantime.

(*b*) The drive system of the robot is sufficiently accurate.

Field of Vision

The area that a vision system can look at, at any one time, is known as the **field of vision**. The greater the field of vision, the more things can be seen at any one time. But there is a disadvantage in having a large field of vision, because if the computer has more things to look at, then not only does the recognition time increase, but also the resolution of each of the objects in the picture becomes less. The approach used to solve this particular difficulty is for the computer to set up a window. A **window** is an area, a part of the screen, that the vision system wants to home-in on. If the field of view contains, say, ten objects, the vision system can be used to analyze only one or two of the objects at any particular time.

Practical Vision Systems

The Camera

Having discussed the general requirements of a vision system, we shall now turn our attention to the more practical details, beginning with the camera.

The **camera** is of course the sensor of the vision system. The job of the camera is to convert the image into a series of electrical signals which will be analyzed by the computer. Vision systems mainly use one of two types of camera, the vidicon tube or the CCD (charge coupled device).

The **vidicon tube** is the familiar and commonly used TV camera. It basically consists of a large glass vacuum tube and in principle works like a television in reverse. The electrical signal which comes out of this type of camera is in the form of a varying voltage (that is, an analog signal). Since computers can only deal with digital information (see Chapter 4), the analog signal from a vidicon camera must first be digitized.

The **CCD camera** is a more recent invention. Unlike the vidicon, it has no vacuum tube and is referred to as a *solid state* camera. The basis of the CCD camera is an array of light-sensitive elements. Each of the elements can be individually "read" by the computer. If an element is illuminated by light from the image, then the computer detects this. The output from a CCD camera is therefore digital.

The resolution of a CCD camera can never be greater than the number of light-sensitive elements that it contains. This, together with its higher cost, puts the CCD camera at a slight disadvantage. It does, however, have the important advantages that it is robust (because it is solid state) and that its output is digital in nature. The output of a vidicon camera is analog and must must first be converted to a digital signal before being passed to the computer. A drift in the level of output voltage can lead to errors creeping into the resulting digital signal. However the vidicon tube has the advantage that the resolution is determined by the electronic circuitry and not by the physical construction of the camera.

Storing the Image

In order that the computer can analyze what the camera sees, it is first necessary to reduce the picture to what amounts to a list of numbers. This process is called **digitization**. Look at figure 6.44 which shows the digitized image as it would appear on a TV monitor. The original image as seen by the camera is shown in figure 6.45.

Each of the small squares in the image in figure 6.44 is called a **pixel** (a word made up from "picture cell"). In the example we are looking at, every position in the image can either be occupied by a pixel or not. There is nothing in-between to indicate shades of grey on the original object. An image of this sort is called a **binary image**. All pixels below a certain brightness are represented in the computer by a 1. Pixels above a certain brightness are represented by storing a 0. In this way, the whole of the image can be represented inside the computer's memory by a list of 1s and 0s.

Now we can make a calculation about the amount of memory needed to store a binary image. Take as an example an image which has a resolution of 256×256 pixels (i.e. a total number of 65 536).

Since each pixel is represented by either a 0 or a 1 the computer will need one bit to store each pixel. A total of 65 536 bits will therefore be required. Now divide this number by eight to change it to bytes (remember 8 bits equals one byte) and divide the number of bytes by 1024 (that is, 2^{10}) to change it to kilobytes (kB). The result is 8 kB – not very much, considering that most home

Fig 6.44　The digitized image as it would appear on a tv monitor (Courtesy: *Robotics Age*)

Fig 6.45　The image seen by the camera before it is produced (Courtesy: *Robotics Age*)

microcomputers have memories of 64 kB. Suppose we were to increase the resolution to 512×521 pixels. Do a similar calculation to the one above and show that this would require a memory of 32 kB. Notice how quickly the amount of memory required increases with the resolution.

Remember, so far we have been talking about binary images. Binary images do not contain any information about colour or degrees of brightness. This information is deliberately discarded to save memory. To store information which includes details about the brightness of the object, we shall require more memory both to store and to process the image. Now we will look at such a method of storing information about the brightness of each pixel.

Grey Scale Information about the brightness of an image is stored by giving each pixel a number. The higher the number, the blacker the pixel. A common system is to have 256 levels of brightness (grey levels) for each pixel. The brightest pixel would be 0 and the blackest pixel 255. A scale of brightness such as this is called a grey scale. The number 256 may seem an odd choice, but all should become clear when you remember that, in binary notation, 256 can be represented by 8 binary digits.

Now, let us do a similar calculation to the one we did earlier for the binary image. We will take an image with a resolution of 256×256 pixels. Remember, each pixel now requires eight bits of computer memory to store the information about its brightness. The binary image with this resolution required 8 kB, so the grey scale image will use eight times as much, that is 64 kB. Remember, 64 kB is the entire addressable memory capacity of a typical small microcomputer. Remember also that this is the amount of memory required just to store the image from the camera. Additional memory is required to store previously learned images and to process the information. It should not surprise you to learn, therefore, that most vision systems in use today do not operate with 256 grey levels

High Resolution and Low Resolution With current technology, high resolution means more memory and this in turn means increased cost and increased processing time. It is therefore important to examine the application to see if high resolution is really needed.

Normally, we would expect a robot vision system to have a resolution of around 256×256 pixels. Low resolution is usually considered to be around 64×64 pixels and very low resolution (VLR) less than 50×50 pixels. Recognition of binary images with a resolution of only 25×25 pixels has been demonstrated (see figure 6.46). Whether or not this is appropriate depends very much on where the system is to be used. It may be, for example, that several quite different parts pass along a conveyor and a robot is required to recognize a particular one. An inexpensive VLR vision system may be all that is needed here.

Economies can also be made on the memory requirements of grey scale vision systems. One system uses 64 grey levels instead of 256.

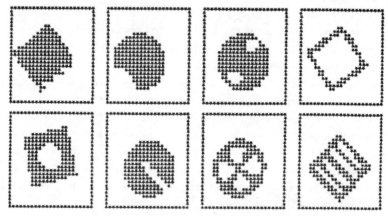

Fig 6.46   Very low resolution images of the test objects shown (Courtesy: IFS
(Publications) Ltd)

*How much memory could be saved by reducing the number of grey levels
from 256 to just 64?* (You need to store a number in the range 0 to 63 inclusive,
so start by writing 63 in binary.) The answer is that you would save only one
quarter of the memory. (That is you would still need three-quarters of the
memory.) This is not much of a saving when you consider that the number of
grey levels has been reduced from 256 to just 64.

[*Note* The number 63 can be written with 6 bits as 111111. The number 256 is
11111111 and therefore requires 8 bits. Therefore, 64 grey levels require 6/8ths
of the memory, that is 3/4.]

Analyzing the Image

Now we know how the computer can store an image; the next point to look at is how the computer can analyze an image. In other words, how does the computer know what it is looking at? So far, all we have said is that the image is stored in the computer's memory as a list of numbers.

In order to analyze the image, the computer has to be able to isolate from the background the object (or objects) it is looking at. There are two main ways of doing this. The first is called *boundary tracking* and the second is called *connectivity analysis*. As you read on, don't forget that, although we shall use words like "image", the computer itself does not *see* anything. The pictures we see on the monitor help us to understand what is happening, but the computer only stores and manipulates lists of numbers.

Boundary Tracking The purpose of boundary tracking is to end up with a description of the outline of the object. This includes any holes or shapes within the object (see figure 6.47).

Fig 6.47   An image produced by boundary tracking (Courtesy: *Robotics Age*)

The computer is able to identify pixels which are on the boundary of an object by looking for jumps in the brightness (that is, grey level) within groups of pixels. This process is not always one hundred per cent successful for every pixel, but in most cases an outline with very few gaps can be achieved. It helps, of course, if the object contrasts well with its background. In a factory, it should be possible to arrange for black objects to be placed on a light-coloured conveyor belt for example.

Connectivity Analysis Connectivity analysis is the main method of isolating an object from the background. In this method, the image from the camera is examined line by line. Pixels are examined to see whether they are the same brightness (that is, grey level) as neighbouring pixels. If they are, then the computer treats them as being connected. In this way, regions of the image are built up which consist of clusters of pixels of the same brightness. These clusters of connected pixels are referred to as "blobs". Study the picture in figure 6.48 which shows the image on the monitor which results from connectivity analysis. A single image will consist of several blobs. Everything that is known about a blob is stored in the computer as a list of data which is called a "blob descriptor".

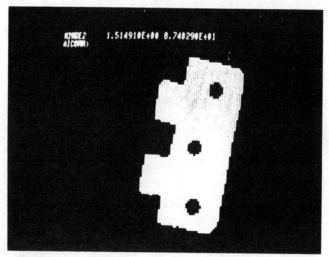

Fig 6.48   An image produced by connectivity analysis (Courtesy: *Robotics Age*)

Interpreting the Image

After boundary tracking or connectivity analysis, the object will have been isolated from its background. At this stage we can say that the object has been "detected". Suitable computer software could now be used to move the gripper of the robot into a position where it could grasp the object. In many cases, though, the vision system is at least required to recognize the object under the camera. For this, further processing will be necessary.

Template Matching   Template matching is a commonly used method in vision systems for recognizing an object. The computer has stored in its memory the shapes of one or more objects that it knows. These known shapes are called templates. Templates first have to be learned by the computer, usually by "showing" the known object to the vision system camera with the computer in its learn mode. When the computer sees an unknown object, it tries to match it to one of the templates. Figure 6.49 shows the idea here, but do not lose sight of the fact that the computer is only really working with lists of numbers.

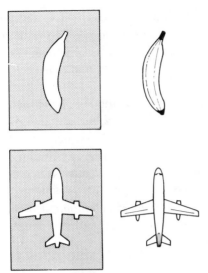

Fig 6.49   Template matching: the computer tries to match an unknown object to a template stored in memory

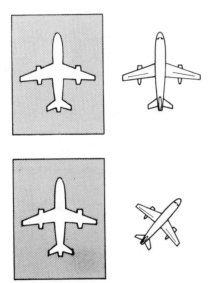

Fig 6.50   The orientation of the stored template will usually be different from that of the object being analyzed

Before the computer can begin to match the template to the image, some preliminary operations have to be performed. The orientation of the template will not usually be the same as that of the image being analysed (see figure 6.50). Either the image or the template will therefore have to be rotated. At each stage in the rotation, the computer must test for a match and continue the process either until a match is found, or until all of the possibilities have been exhausted. Normally, the size of the image will also have to be adjusted to match the size of template.

Another point to consider is that an object can rest in several different positions. Each position presents a different view to the camera and so it requires a different template. So, even for one object, the computer may have to try several templates. All this takes up memory and time.

Discrimination Discrimination is another method of object recognition and does not involve the use of templates. Instead, the computer holds in its memory a list of features which are unique to the object it is attempting to recognize. Examples of these features might be the area, position of the centre of gravity, position of holes or corners, etc. Some features (that is, character-istic numbers) which are calculated mathematically remain the same what-ever the orientation of the object. These are called *moment invariants*. The use of moment invariants avoids the need for rotating and scaling the image as in the case of template matching.

7 Robotics in Industry

Work Cells

In the traditional factory, machines have alway been arranged with, for example, all the lathes in one section and all the milling machines in another. This **functional layout**, shown in figure 7.1, was used because tasks were split up into single operations, each being performed on a separate machine. We can also identify the human equivalent of the functional layout. In car factories, for example, lines of people add their component to each car as it goes by on the conveyor. This way of working is nowadays considered to yield less than

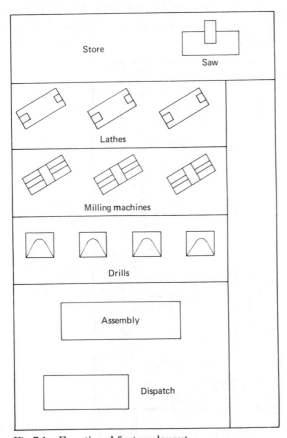

Fig 7.1   Functional factory layout

optimum productivity but has in many cases resisted change for technical and economic reasons and because of social pressures.

Today, with the availability of computer-controlled machine tools, the functional layout of machines has made way for a machine layout that maximizes throughput and productivity. This new layout is called **group technology** and involves the configuration of machines into **work cells** whose constituent members are designed and arranged for the processing of a limited group of products. Within this work cell the material goes in one end, is processed, and comes out the other end as a finished product.

The overall layout of a modern factory is now one in which work cells have become *islands of automation* linked by an automated material transport system. Material is moved from the automated warehouse then passes through a single cell or a series of cells until the tasks are completed. The transport system then collects the value-added material and takes it to the warehouse where it is stored until dispatch, or takes it to another cell in a different part of the factory.

Logically, it would seem to make sense to have a one-way route through the work cells but often, for technical reasons, this is not feasible. For instance, within cars, the engines, gearboxes, lights and facias are often the same. These would be made in separate cells and then taken back to a central store until they are required. Figure 7.2 shows one possible arrangement of the integrated but separate manufacturing cells.

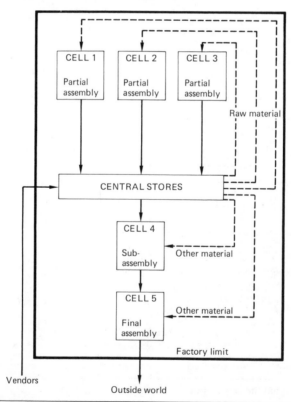

Fig 7.2 Integrated (but separate) manufacturing cells

The Robot Work Cell

Since a robot is a flexible and programmable device, it seems ideally suited to the work cell concept. We can consider two possible arrangements in which a robot may be incorporated into a work cell. In the first, it is the central feature of the cell and is fed by auxiliary equipment or by people. An example of this would be a welding or painting cell. In the second, the robot is servicing a number of machines so that, although it is physically the central feature of the cell, it is in fact subject to the demands and limitations of these machines. Significant changes to this type of robot cell would incur a relatively large amount of capital expenditure, since it would require other machines and possibly also expensive modifications to tools and equipment.

Setting Up a Work Cell – a Case Study

It will be useful if we consider some of the problems that can occur and the decisions that have to be made during the setting up of a work cell. For our example we will take a work cell that involves the processing of two die-cast items produced together. The casting is placed into a press that separates and deflashes them prior to their subsequent machining.

Before we start to physically set up the manufacturing cell we must know what we want to achieve technically and what economic criteria have to be applied. The technical processes are:

Remove the items from the die-casting machine.

Separate the individual items from each other and deflash them.

Machine one face of the component flat.

Drill and tap two holes.

Inspect the items.

Place the finished items into a magazine ready for dispatch.

Having determined the technical needs of the product, the next stage is to quantify the economic criteria. These are:

What is the maximum acceptable manufacturing cost?

What are economic batch sizes?

How quickly must the item be made in order to satisfy predicted or known demand?

Task Analysis

The time occupied by the item within the cell is known as the *throughput time*; the time spent in adding value to the item is known as the *cycle time*. In functional machine layouts there is a considerable difference between these two values; however, in work cells the difference is minor.

The cycle time is governed by the slowest operation within the cell. This does not necessarily mean the slowest machine. If for example a machine had a cycle time of 20 seconds, a product cycle time of 10 seconds could be achieved merely by installing a second machine to run in parallel with the first.

Let us now consider the operation times for each activity within the die-casting cell:

Casting	60 seconds
Separation	2 seconds
Machining face	15 seconds
Drilling and tapping	20 seconds
Inspection	10 seconds

The robot servicing this cell has to perform all of the transfer operations within the cycle time of the die-casting machine. If it does not, then the die-casting machine will have to wait until the robot is free before the unloading can continue. This will result in underutilization of the machine and possibly some process problems may also arise because it is not functioning continuously.

We must also not forget that the other processes must be accommodated within the sixty second process time of the die-casting machine. We can work out the available time for robot transfer by taking the difference between the cycle time of the die-casting machine and the sum of the cycle times of the other processes. Using the times given above, the available time for robot transfers is therefore

$$60 - (2 + 15 + 20) = 23 \text{ seconds}$$

The inspection operation will be conducted using a vision system at the dispatch magazine. This means that the components only have to be placed in the inspection machine and that after processing they will be palletized by a device controlled entirely by that machine. The information on quality will be fed back to the other units of the cell, as and when adjustments are needed.

Figure 7.3 shows the desired physical arrangement of the cell and we must now select the robot that can service this arrangement. The robot's work envelope must be capable of enclosing all of the elements within the cell. The robot must also have the speed and repeatability such that the work is completed within the time allowance and that items are picked up, transferred and placed with the desired precision. Let us assume that, for various reasons, the robot shown in figure 7.4 was selected as being suitable. The quoted velocities of the robot are:

Slew	120 degrees per second
Horizontal extension of arm	1.2 metres per second
Vertical lift of arm	0.5 metres per second

The arc of approximately 270 degrees (shown in figure 7.3) has to be covered *twice* in the available robot transfer time. This is because the robot has to reverse in order to return to its starting position. Since the various pick-and-place stations cannot usually be arranged to lie on a single arc, the robot must extend and contract its arm. It must also move vertically so that objects can be lifted or lowered. In terms of tasks, it must go to five separate places in the cell: the die-casting machine, the press, the mill, the drill and the inspection/

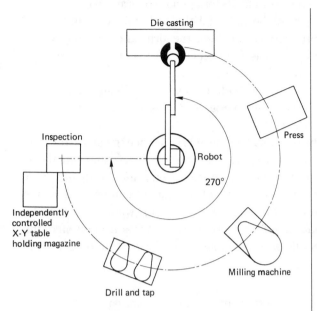

Fig 7.3 The desired physical arrangement of the cell

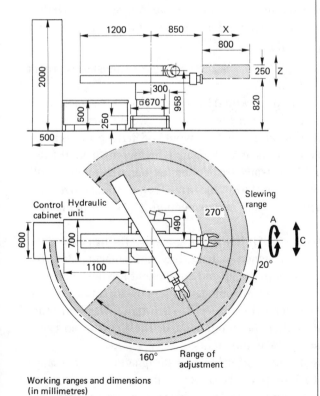

Working ranges and dimensions
(in millimetres)

Fig 7.4 The robot selected for the cell

Table 7.1 The Robot Cycle

1. Extend arm
2. Lower to grasp casting
3. Close gripper
4. Lift arm and casting from platen
5. Contract arm out of die-casting machine
6. Rotate arm to press
7. Extend arm into press
8. Lower arm so that casting enters trimming tool
9. Open gripper
10. Lift arm
11. Contract arm out of press
12. Wait for trim cycle to finish
13. Extend arm into press
14. Lower arm onto the two items
15. Activate gripper
16. Lift arm and components out of die
17. Contract arm out of press
18. Rotate to milling machine
19. Extend arm into milling machine work space
20. Lower arm and components into jig
21. Release gripper
22. Lift arm
23. Contract arm
24. Wait for milling cycle to finish
25. Extend arm
26. Lower arm to pick up processed parts
27. Lift arm
28. Contract arm
29. Rotate to drilling and tapping machine
30. Extend arm
31. Lower arm to place components into jig
32. Release gripper
33. Lift arm
34. Contract arm
35. Wait for drilling and tapping operation to finish
36. Extend arm
37. Lower arm to pick up processed parts
38. Activate gripper
39. Lift arm
40. Contract arm
41. Rotate to inspection station
42. Extend arm
43. Lower arm and components into jigs on inspection machine
44. Release part
45. Lift arm
46. Retract arm
47. Rotate arm back to start position

153

magazine station. The robot cycle includes four pickup operations: those at the die-casting machine, the press, the mill and the drill; and four placement operations, one each at the press, the mill, the drill and the inspection/magazine station. The robot cycle (assuming it is ready to enter the die-casting platen with its gripper open) is shown in Table 7.1.

In total there are 47 actions to the cycle with very few, if any, that can be performed simultaneously, because of the problems of collision with the different machines within the cell.

It is fairly evident that the robot will not be able to service the cell in the time available. If we consider some of the motions you will understand why this is so. The velocities quoted for the robot are maximum and since we do not know the accelerations that the robot is capable of, we cannot compute the actual arm velocities that would be realized. However, even if we assume that the stated velocities are valid for all of the motions, then the return motion of the arm will require 2.25 seconds and, assuming that all in/out motions are 0.8 metres, we have

$$(16 \times 0.8)/1.2 = 10.7 \text{ seconds}$$

We also have sixteen up/down motions of 0.25 metres that equal

$$(16 \times 0.25)/0.5 = 8.0 \text{ seconds}$$

and eight gripper operations of say a quarter of a second each, giving a time of 2 seconds. Finally we have the four inter-machine angular motions, which if they are equal come to 67.5 degrees each. Therefore the *minimum* traverse time is

$$(4 \times 67.5)/120 = 2.25 \text{ seconds}$$

The total time by the above computations is 25.2 seconds or almost ten percent over that allowed.

So what can we do? One approach would be to have a double-armed robot with an angle of 135 degrees between the arms; this would mean that the output of two cycles of the die-casting machine would be in the process at the same time. In practice this would mean picking up components from the die-casting machine *and* the mill and transferring them to the press and the drill; after these operations are complete, the double-armed robot would move them from the press *and* the drill to the mill and inspection. The cycle then starts from the beginning again.

In every manufacturing cell it is of prime importance that the jigs into which the components are placed are designed such that any minor placement errors are automatically corrected. If both the jig and component are designed with this in mind, then there should be few problems. Other considerations are for the jigs and machines to be cleaned every cycle such that swarf and other debris do not contaminate either the component or the jigs and so cause setting errors that could scrap the components.

This example of a single manufacturing cell was designed for processing a single type of product. In Chapter 8, where we deal with computerised manufacture, we shall go on to look into the viability and reasons for an integrated system able to process a wide range of different products.

Identifying the Robot, Options and Problems

Having got some appreciation of the problems involved in setting up a work cell, we now turn our attention to the practical problem of how to go about selecting a suitable robot for a given task. We can deal with this problem in one of three ways. The first is to contact a number of robot companies and get them to quote for a solution using their robots. The second option is to use consultants who will conduct a feasibility study based upon what has to be achieved. The third option is to do research into what robots are available and determine which robot is best. Each of these options has its own limitations and benefits.

The robot companies will only quote for robots that they market. Consequently, although the robots will be technically capable, they may be an overkill in sophistication and cost. Furthermore, because of the many companies marketing robots and the slow adoption rate of robots by industry, we can expect that these companies will soon begin to charge for formal quotations. Just as we shop around before making a purchase, so industry too is shopping around, requesting quotations from many different robot companies for each and every project being evaluated. This means that six robot companies may be competing for the same project which typically will not result in an order for at least a year.

If a consultant is employed then the cost of the consultant's fees must be taken into account. One should also be aware that many consultants are employed by approved consultancies operated the robot companies and may therefore be biased.

If a company decides to conduct the investigation and recommendation themselves, then outwardly this would appear to be the least expensive option. However, the problem with using people within the company to conduct the investigation is twofold. Firstly, they are close to the product and its problems and therefore might not see the obvious solution or difficulties. Secondly, they might not be aware of what is happening within the robotics world and consequently may overlook new robots and processes that could be of benefit.

Whichever option is used, the procedure is essentially the same and comes down to getting the closest match between a robot's claimed performance and the parameters that have been laid down as necessary to perform the task robotically. Obviously, if we can categorise the task, for example, paint spraying, arc welding, assembly, etc., then the choice of available robots is more clearly defined.

From a set of technically suitable robots the next stage is to check the robot's claimed performance against its actual performance. This can be done either by arranging to have demonstrations, or by asking for the names of companies using that robot in similar activities. The aim of this is to have a number of quotations for robots and a feel for how reliable the specifications are.

Matching the Robot and the Task

Despite the wide range of robots to choose from, it is not always possible, or even desirable, to install a robot to perform a task that was previously performed by some other means. It is usually necessary to adapt the task, to some extent, to match the capabilities of the robot. The best way to achieve this is to think of each task in "machine terms". Thinking in machine terms means thinking how a robot would best "like" to do a given task. By doing this it is usually possible to suggest ways of changing the task to make it more suitable for robotization. If we are honest, then we must admit that everything we design or do is based upon how we would do it ourselves. Robots are not structurally, mentally or physiologically like people, so why not design tasks and products to suit the robot? Every task and activity should be considered on the basis of what robots can do and what the task is in machine terms. By analyzing a product and its relevant processes we might find that it contains a number of redundant features, or that a process can be performed robotically in another way that will give better quality at lower cost.

Figure 7.5 shows how a simple design change to a component can help cure one of the problems of automatic production. The component in question has a stud at one end and a hole at the other. The initial design (figure 7.5a) made the diameter of the hole slightly larger than that of the stud. When the components were stacked in an automatic feeder ready for insertion into the final assembly, it was found that the components slotted into each other and became stuck.

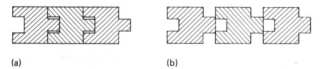

(a)   (b)

Fig 7.5   (a) The stud diameter is less than the hole diameter; the components stack together and jam
(b) The stud diameter is greater than the hole diameter, so the stacking can no longer occur

Figure 7.5b shows how the problem was overcome quite simply by making the stud of larger diameter than the hole. You can see that in this case there would be no stacking problem. Of course, similar alterations had to be made to other parts of the final assembly so that the new design would be compatible.

Figure 7.6 illustrates how the inclusion of a new, albeit functionally redundant, feature can aid the performance of a task. The figure shows a device on which four electrical terminals are mounted. Although the terminals are required to be electrically isolated from each other in operation, for manufacturing purposes it was decided to make them as a single unit and then to break the connections once the device was assembled. The reason for this is that as individual items they are light-weight, springy and difficult to handle, but when

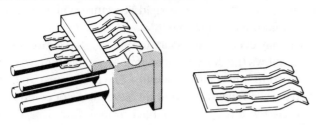

Fig 7.6   Introduction of new feature simplifies production

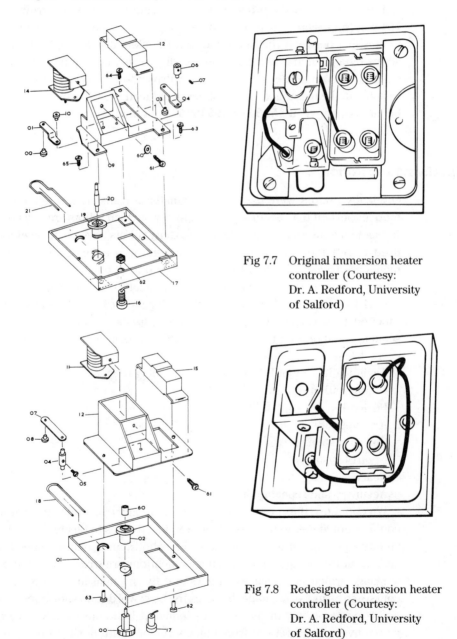

Fig 7.7   Original immersion heater
controller (Courtesy:
Dr. A. Redford, University
of Salford)

Fig 7.8   Redesigned immersion heater
controller (Courtesy:
Dr. A. Redford, University
of Salford)

joined together as shown they form a rigid structure which is more easily manipulated by the automatic equipment.

In some cases, it may even be necessary to redesign the entire product. For instance, figure 7.7 shows the drawing of an immersion heater controller prior to it being redesigned for automatic assembly. The redesigned unit, shown in figure 7.8, contains seven fewer parts and the percentage of components that can be automatically fed has almost doubled from 33% to 61%. The original design incorporated three self-tapping screws (63,64,65), one of which was a different size from the other two and, in addition, the grub screw (07) was virtually impossible to feed automatically because of the difficulty of distinguishing between the plain end and the slotted end. Replacing the grub screw by a headed screw and making all screws of a common size allows a single feeder and one automatic screwdriver to be used. The redesign has resulted in the manufacturing cost being reduced by 30%, which will yield cost benefits of between £50 000 and £100 000 per annum.

Specifying the Robot

Originally, robots were used only for material transfer, where payload was more important than accuracy. Whilst heavy payload robots are still necessary for spot welding and forging, lighter-capacity robots have been developed and used for activities such as material coating and arc welding. The latest developments are robots designed for assembly and inspection tasks which require extreme accuracy plus the ability to communicate and react both with sensory and vision systems. This increased intelligence of robots allows them to function in situations where, for instance, items are presented in random sequence and orientation and the robot has to identify them and perform the correct task.

Technically a robot is categorized according to its

Configuration
Payload
Arm velocity
Power system
Control system
Reach
Accuracy and repeatability

We could use these parameters to measure any task and state that a robot could or could not do that task. Our next job, then, is to be able to understand and interpret this information from the robot manufacturer's specifications and literature. One problem is that specifications are written in "robotese" – a language which is not easily understood by the man in the street. It is, of course, an artificial language that uses the buzz words and shorthand technical words common within the robotics industry. Examples of such words are: work envelope, degrees of freedom, continuous path or CP, point to point or

PTP, servoed and non-servoed axes, memory, inputs and outputs, repeatability, drive through, lead through, coordinate entry. In addition, confusion is caused by not knowing the conditions under which the stated specifications are true.

Configurations Robots are designed to service a given type of work envelope and to perform certain tasks. However, a suitably shaped work envelope does not necessarily mean that the robot will perform a given task. To explore this difficulty let us consider a robot used for an assembly task. If we analyze an assembly process then we are likely to come to the conclusion that all of the components of the product should be placed in position by straight-line motions. The reason is that an assembly task can be considered as a sequential process of adding components to each other until the product is complete. Therefore the most logical approach to assembly is to start with a base and then to fit parts onto this base and onto each other until the top is reached. In this way the process is completed without having to disturb the base. We can consider an electric motor as a practical example of this philosophy. It contains a lot of components all mounted along a common centre axis, which is itself the joining member between the top and bottom cases.

If it is logical to use a straight-line motion robot to perform assembly tasks then we might ask the question "why is the Unimation PUMA robot (see figure 7.9) used in many assembly tasks?" This robot has a virtually spherical work envelope and no straight-line elements in its construction. The actual reasons

Fig 7.9 The Unimation PUMA robot engaged in the assembly of a cylinder head (Courtesy: Unimation (Europe) Ltd.)

are manifold and illustrate some of the problems of simply applying logic to the selection of robots for specific tasks.

The PUMA (Programmable Universal Machine for Assembly) was the first robot to be designed specifically to replace people on product assembly lines. Since it had to fit into existing situations the specification was for a design that could mimic human actions – hence the arm and elbow configuration. The robot was designed for General Motors and consequently did not have to be marketed as a concept before it was accepted by industry. It has a long track record of use within industry, performing a variety of tasks, so a lot of its design faults have been highlighted and ironed out. The PUMA control system and high-level teaching language VAL is very comprehensive and sophisticated – a necessary feature for any robot used for assembly tasks because of the need to monitor, control and react to many different activities which occur simultaneously within the assembly work cell. Finally the price is very competitive. Many of its cartesian or gantry rivals are more expensive.

Robot Geometry   The basic configurations of robot arms were dealt with in Chapter 5. The illustrations are shown again here in figure 7.10.

Looking at the robots in figure 7.10 you will see that there are two types of joint – those that allow rotation and those that allow motion in a straight line. Joints which allow rotation are sometimes referred to in manufacturer's specifications as *revolute joints* and those which allow movement in a straight line as *prismatic joints*.

We can describe the size of each robot's work envelope by the motions of the joints and the length and arrangement of its links. In the case of circular envelopes, the mechanical problems of providing power and control to each axis mean that the robots can often not move through a full 360 degrees. If we attempted to allow each axis unlimited rotation, then we would end up with twisted and possibly sheared power cables. Clearly, prismatic joints do not have this complication. However, the cartesian configuration which contains only prismatic joints does have the disadvantage that the work envelope is adjacent to the robot structure, whereas robots employing revolute axes have their structure inside the work envelope. Therefore we can say that in some cases cartesian robots may require a bigger floor area than robots of other configurations having similar size work envelopes.

Degrees of Freedom and Axes of Motion   The subject of degrees of freedom and axes of motion has been dealt with in Chapter 5. Recall that more axes of motion increase the manoeuvrability at the expense of making the robot more complicated to program.

For certain tasks, such as conveyor tracking in which we use the robot to perform a task on a moving object, we can mount the robot on a trolley, giving the system an extra servoed axis of motion. This lengthens the work envelope in the horizontal direction and is generally synchronized to the speed of the conveyor. As the conveyor speeds up or slows down, both the trolley motion

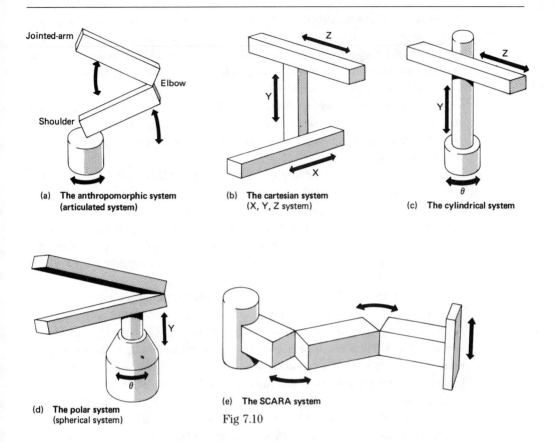

(a) The anthropomorphic system
(articulated system)

(b) The cartesian system
(X, Y, Z system)

(c) The cylindrical system

(d) The polar system
(spherical system)

(e) The SCARA system

Fig 7.10

and the process are adjusted by the robot's control system.

Many robots and especially process robots such as those used for arc welding allow us to link their motions to other devices containing the work to be processed. Often these devices, called positioners, allow work to be loaded and unloaded outside of the robot's work envelope. Figure 7.11 shows a positioner which rotates to simultaneously offer the unprocessed work to the robot and the processed work to the unloader/loader. The positioner, while it is within the robot's work envelope, is entirely servo-controlled and activated by the robot program. The rotation of the positioner to remove and offer the work is authorized by the loader/unloader and operated by the robot.

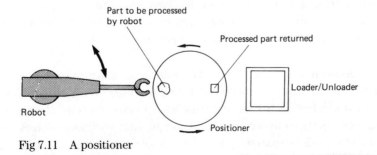

Fig 7.11   A positioner

Accuracy and Repeatability   These two terms cause the most confusion both within and without the robotics industry and in many data sheets and specifications they are mistakenly used interchangeably. The source of the confusion is that both terms are stated in the same units, as "plus or minus so many millimetres or fractions of a millimetre".

The term *accuracy*, when correctly used, relates to how closely the robot can be programmed to move to a particular position. On the other hand, *repeatability* tells you about the ability of the robot to return, time after time, to the programmed position.

An everyday example of accuracy and repeatability will make the idea clearer. Let us say that you have a thermometer that *always* reads 2 degrees centigrade when it should read zero. Such a thermometer is *not* accurate but it *is* repeatable (even though it is always wrong!). Now think about this question:

· If you were given the choice of having some device (it could be a thermometer if you like) that had *either* good accuracy *or* good repeatability which would you choose?

For most purposes it would be sensible to choose good repeatability. After all, using the thermometer as an example, you can make allowance for the 2 degrees error provided that you can be sure that it is always wrong by the same amount. The same logic applies to robots. Inaccuracies due to axis misalignment, feedback sensors, payload, mechanical wear and so on, can all be compensated for if the robot has high repeatability for each axis.

A typical example of a figure quoted for repeatability in a manufacturer's specification sheet might be 0.5 mm. This refers to the ability of the robot to return to the same position to within 0.5 mm. There are however two points to be careful about here:

The first is that the figure of repeatability often refers to the repeatability of each axis; the point of real interest is the repeatability in the position of the *end effector* and this is the result of the motion of several axes. So the repeatability of the end effector position may not be as good as the repeatability stated for each axis.

The second point to be careful about is that repeatability depends upon speed. The repeatability will improve if the arm is moved more slowly. Repeatability is worsened if the robot is moving a heavy load since this will affect the inertia of the arm.

For very good repeatability (less than 0.05 mm) we must use either hardware stops (see Chapter 2), very slow cycle times, or hard automation. The performance repeatability of robots using software stops is in the range 0.05 mm to 2.50 mm, with a typical value for these "true robots" of about 0.10 mm.

Drive Systems   In Chapter 5 we dealt with drive systems available for robots. Simplistically we could say that hydraulic power is used for heavy-duty robots and electric drives are used for precise motion. However, recent advances in micro-hydraulics have meant that hydraulic drives are being applied to produce extremely precise robots such as the IBM RS1 and Microbot MR models. Therefore, unless the robot is to be installed in some explosive environment, the type of drive system should not necessarily exclude its use for a given task. In many cases the purchaser may even have no choice in the matter since robots designed for certain activities almost always have the same power system. If there is a choice of drive system then it is usually made on subjective grounds, such as "hydraulic systems always leak" or "we might as well standardize on electric systems", or even "well let's try out the new microhydraulic drives".

Control Systems   Nowadays, we can safely say that all robots are supplied with a user-friendly programming system, so let us look at what there is to choose between the different systems available.

There are three basic types of *pattern control*. These are point-to-point (PTP), continuous path (CP), and a hybrid that combines the speed of point-to-point with the smooth motion of continuous path. All are based on the storing of coordinate information as discrete points. These points are recorded at a rate in the range of 2.5 to 20 samples per second (that is, between 0.4 to 0.05 seconds between samples). Under playback conditions, the robot will duplicate the taught pattern with only minute errors. The magnitude of the errors will depend upon the sampling rate.

As explained in Chapter 2, the method of programming known as point-to-point differs from continuous path in two ways. The first difference is that in point-to-point we only program those coordinates we are interested in. For example in an assembly or spot welding task we program only the points of action and not all of the intermediate transfer points. We might in addition program a few intermediate points to ensure that the robot takes the path that we want between the points of action, rather than some totally random path. The second difference is that the path taken between points is determined by the controlling computer and therefore cannot easily be predicted by the operator. The hybrid method is similar to the continuous path process except that the sampling rate is much slower – between 0.8 and 6.4 seconds between samples. The result is that under playback the robot's path only approximates to the path which was taught.

Programming of large or complex patterns can be very time-consuming. However, we can reduce the programming time and the risk of error through the use of interpolation routines (see figure 7.12). Interpolation of straight lines from their extreme points, or interpolation of curves through their two end points and one midpoint, are available as standard routines on a number of robots. This facility allows accurate programming to be achieved with minimal use of memory.

Methods of Programming   There are four methods by which teaching (that is, programming) is done. Various terms are in use to describe these methods (lead through, walk through, drive through, off-line) but, with the exception of off-line, not all manufacturers use these terms to mean the same thing.

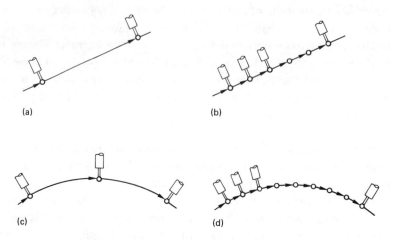

(a)

(b)

(c)

(d)

Fig 7.12   Interpolation routines:
(a) Teaching at 2 points suffices
(b) Teaching at every 25 to 30 mm (1 to 1.2 inches) is necessary
(c) Teaching at 3 points suffices
(d) In continuous path control, the position of the end effector is sampled 50 to 100 times per second

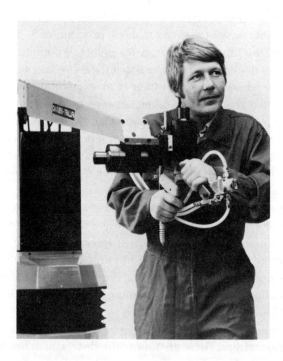

Fig 7.13   Teaching a robot by moving its end effector over the desired path
(Courtesy: The DeVilbiss Company)

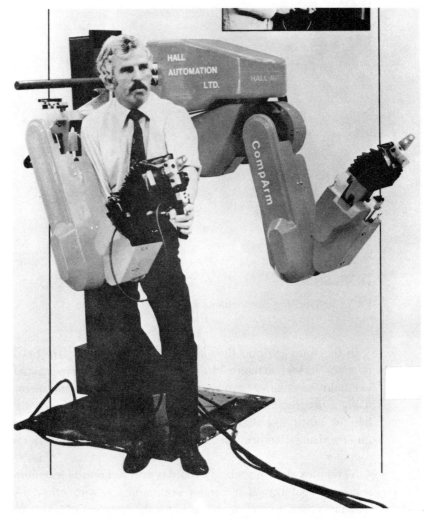

Fig 7.14   Teaching a robot using a teach arm (Courtesy: Hall Automation Ltd.)

The majority of robot programming is done by grasping the robot by its effector or teaching handle and physically moving its arm over the desired path. Figure 7.13 shows this being done with a paint spraying robot. As the robot is being moved, the computer samples the position from between two and twenty times per second, recording the coordinates in its memory.

A similar method of programming makes use of a teach arm, like the one shown in figure 7.14. The teach arm is necessary since the robot itself would be difficult for a man to manoeuvre owing to the heavy springs fitted to the joints to prevent the structure from sagging when the power is switched off.

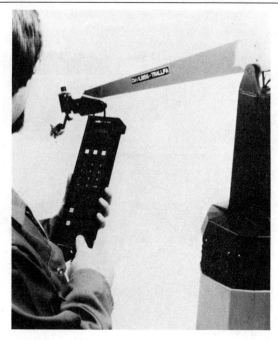

Fig 7.15   Teaching a robot using a teach pendant (Courtesy: The DeVilbiss
            Company)

In the third method the programmer moves the arm by using a "teach pendant" as seen in figure 7.15, to drive the axes either individually or together.

Finally, an engineer can sit down and write a program to control the robot, using a programming language. This method, called *off-line programming*, has the advantage that the robot can be made an integral part of a computerized manufacturing process, in which machines and other robots all work together.

A complex system such as a robot is only as good as its communication and sensory capability. If it cannot communicate with other people or other machines then it can only be used for the simplest of tasks. We humans can instantly recognize an item and can distinguish one item in a batch of jumbled parts. We observe our immediate environment and know what is happening from the smallest bits of information. If a robot is to be used for more than the simplest tasks then it must therefore be able to duplicate the human capacity for recognition, communication and analysis.

We have dealt with sensors and computer interfaces between robots and other equipment in Chapter 6. To some extent we can guage the suitability of a robot for a task by the number of input/output ports and the sophistication of its software. In a complex system we are dealing with a dynamic situation involving a lot of different machines and robots, all of which are performing different tasks at the same time. To ensure order within these systems the machines and robots must communicate with each other. Since the robot is usually the focal point of these systems it must have the capability to communicate with all of the other elements within the system and to make the appropriate jump, abort, inspection and warning routines.

Arm Velocity   Many specifications state arm velocities as a certain number of metres per second and wrist motions in degrees per second. If we consider a cartesian or gantry robot then we can assume that the claimed linear velocity has some relevance. However, for other configurations where the motions are portions of arcs, the stated linear velocity may be misleading since it depends on the radius of the arc being traversed. Another point to bear in mind is that a cartesian robot with a lower velocity may not necessarily be slower; it moves in a straight line between two points covering less distance than a robot that moves through an arc.

Apart from depending on configuration, velocity also depends on the direction of motion, the starting position, and the payload being moved. We know that an arm moving downards has gravity assisting its motion, whereas motion in the opposite direction does not. Every action accelerates from a starting velocity but the arm has to travel a certain distance before maximum velocity can be achieved. If the action is short then the arm may not reach maximum velocity and consequently the stated velocities cannot always be used to predict cycle times. Finally acceleration is dependent on the mass being moved, so a robot with a large payload will accelerate more slowly than one with a small payload. Therefore, the velocity used in cycle time predictions must take into account the payload being transferred.

Payload   The payload listed in a specification sheet refers to the weight that can be carried at the extreme end of the robot's arm. It must not be forgotten that the total payload also includes grippers and any other equipment as well as the component being moved. One important payload-related factor that is omitted from many specification sheets is that of the allowable torque that can be applied to the robot's arm. Even small weight at a large offset from the end of the arm could be difficult to handle because the torque (turning force) will vary considerably as the arm moves from one attitude to another. This applies especially to the wrist motions which are structurally weaker than the main drive systems and are used to obtain finer motions. Any unbalanced forces in the gripper are therefore liable to lead to an exaggerated lack of repeatability in performance. Consequently, tests should be conducted to determine how the payload affects and is affected by arm velocity, arm extension and final accuracy.

Price   Earlier we saw how the price of the robot was but a small percentage of the total system cost. Price is a useful comparator of similar robots, but it should not be used as the final or sole criterion. For a given problem we can have two solutions: either a complex robot with a simple gripper, or a simple robot with a complex gripper. Both options will perform the desired task, but the final decision will be based on more than just the cost of the robot.

For example, even though a simple robot has the payload and reach to perform a task it might not have the desired repeatability. In this case it is possible that a complex gripper could be designed to incorporate sensors that would allow its position to be corrected. However, the robot being a standard off-the-shelf device will have had most of its design faults highlighted by usage and consequently it will have high reliability. On the other hand if a specially designed complex gripper is used, its performance will be unknown.

A discussion of some typical manufacturers specification sheets is given in Appendix III.

Installation and Commissioning

Having dealt with the selection of a suitable robot we now go on to discuss the steps to be taken by a company during the installation and commissioning of the robot.

Training and Preparation After finalization of the installation schedule and contracts to the various vendors have been issued, work must begin to arrange operator and maintenance training at the vendor's premises. At the same time the purchasers premises must be prepared by clearing the installation sites for the new equipment and ensuring that all necessary services are laid on. In any project there will be a number of activities occurring simultaneously, so care must be taken to ensure that all activities are coordinated and monitored. Techniques such as Critical Path Analysis and PERT (Project Evaluation and Review Technique) are employed for coordination and monitoring of the total project. These techniques can be manual or computerized and they are used to plot the progress of activities against their scheduled progress. Using them, it is possible to determine the effect upon total cost and completion date of the project date to acceleration or delay of various activities.

Project Management If a major project is being dealt with, it makes sense to have a project team whose members represent each of the vendors who are directly involved. A Project Manager who will have the power and authority to manage the project should be appointed to lead the team. The project team will then meet at regular intervals to discuss progress and to determine how problems will be resolved. Any grey areas of responsibility will be resolved by the manager and, if necessary, penalties will be imposed or new contracts will be made.

Commissioning The commissioning stage of the project begins when all of the equipment is on site. This is the time when everything seems to go wrong. It is the time of debugging each of the pieces of equipment individually and then gradually linking them together so as to form an integrated system. At this stage the operators can also begin to be involved. Supervisor and maintenance personnel can begin to use the "real" equipment so that they understand what is happening and can assist with the trouble-shooting.

Once the robots are installed they must be tested and programmed. Although they should not be run at full speed until the full safety system is installed, they can nevertheless be operated, programmed and tested by authorized persons who are protected by a primitive safety system. Until the fine tuning and debugging is complete, the installation of a total safety system is potentially more hazardous than for a simple primitive system. This is because the problems and pressures associated with commissioning can be exaggerated by continually having to access the equipment and control systems, which means reactivating the robot after it has automatically closed down and/or overriding the integrated safety network.

Safety To the casual observer a robot seems to operate in an unpredictable manner. There are periods during which the robot is stationary when it is either performing a scheduled pause or waiting for an input signal before it continues. Whilst we know what is happening – or at worst we know what is probably happening – the uninformed observer does not know whether the robot is shut down, faulty, or awaiting an instruction. Consequently, sudden changes in arm configuration as the robot continues its program can spring surprise. An additional hazard is that, unlike a machine, a robot performs movements which may extend far outside the position of its fixed base.

Another aspect of safety is prevention of damage to the robot itself through collisions with other equipment. In order to prevent damage to the robot we have to ensure that each action is monitored before movement and checked after completion. In this way we can be sure that, for example, the robot will not try to enter the dies on a moulding machine either before they are open or just as they are closing. Similarly, if we use tactile or proximity sensors – and program the robot correctly – then the possibility of collisions with other robots or structures within the work zone will be minimized.

At the moment there are no hard and fast rules concerning the safety aspects of robots. We must therefore work on the principles of "What if . . .?" and protect both robot and company personnel from damaging each other.

The safety risks to people fall into three categories; those of direct injury from the robot, those of indirect injury from the robot, and those possible during programming.

Direct Injury The risk of direct injury from a robot occurs if a person enters the work envelope and becomes trapped by the robot arm against some other structure. To minimize this risk we should ensure that the robots and their immediate work area are caged, like the one shown in figure 7.16, with access permitted only through approved gates. Entry through the gates causes the robot to be powered down through the action to pressure mats, infra-red detection beams or switches on the locking mechanism of the gates.

Indirect Injury Indirect injury occurs when, for instance, poor gripper design allows a component to fly from the gripper and enter the general

Fig 7.16   A protective cage placed around the robot minimises the risk of injury to
personnel (Courtesy: Eaton Ltd., Hounslow)

working area of the factory. Another example would be where the robot is
moving a vat of hot or dangerous liquid and strikes an obstacle which results in
the liquid being sprayed or splashed outside the protected area. In both these
cases, provided that we recognize the potential problem, we can arrange for
the safety cage to be high enough and strong enough to minimize the risk of
injury outside the protected area.

Programming Dangers   The third category of risk is during the actual
programming of the robot. It is at this time that a person is in very close
proximity to the moving robot. Fortunately, programming is performed at low
speed and low power and the risk to the programmer is usually limited to
personal embarrassment rather than extensive physical injury. Obviously with
off-line programming the risks are minimal since the programming is performed without the robot being operated.

System Start-up   When all of the debugging has been completed and the
equipment has been tested both individually and as an integrated whole, then it
is time for it to be handed over to the production personnel. The designer's
responsibility does not end here, since from this point on the system will be
expected to perform at its specified level of quality and output. During the
commissioning stage any problems or deviations would be dealt with sympa-
thetically, but this will no longer be the case during production. Consequently

the designers must ensure that they are kept informed of what happens as both the operators and the system go through their learning curves that will eventually lead to the optimal system performance.

Reliability and Maintenance

Installation and commissioning of the robot is not the end of the story. We should always remember that a robot is simply a machine, albeit a sophisticated one, and as such requires maintenance to keep it in good working order. We shall now look at some of the terms and formulas used in dealing with the reliability and maintenance of robots and manufacturing systems.

Mean Time to Failure (MTTF) [denoted by θ, the Greek letter theta] is defined as the average of the lifetimes of devices before failure occurs. In effect, it tells you how long an average device will continue to work before something goes wrong.

Of course, not all devices will fail after the same length of time, even if they appear to be identical. For a single item, the chance of it surviving (that is, not failing) after a certain length of time is illustrated by the curve shown in figure 7.17*. Such curves can be plotted after gathering statistics taken from a large number of tests. The MTTF, marked as θ on the horizontal axis, is calculated mathematically from the data, and in fact turns out to be the length of time for which there is a 36.8 per cent chance of survival.

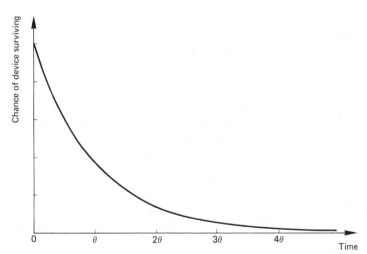

Fig 7.17   The chance of a single device surviving after a given time

---

* If you have done any advanced mathematics, you will recognise the graph in figure 7.17 as being the exponential function. The actual equation is
$$f(t) = \exp(-t/\theta)$$
where t is the number of hours and θ is the MTTF.

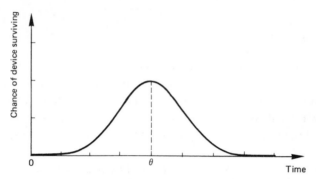

Fig 7.18   The chance of a complex device surviving after a given time

The curve shown in figure 7.17 does not usually apply to complex devices made of many separate components (such as a robot, a machine or a car). For these types of device, the curve is as shown in figure 7.18*. Again, the MTTF is marked on the horizontal axis as θ (but this time it turns out from the mathematics to be the length of time for which there is a 50 per cent chance of survival). What this curve is saying is that if you tested a large number of robots then most of them would fail after a time equal to the MTTF, as shown by the position of the peak of the curve. A smaller number would fail quite early on and a similarly smaller number would last longer than the MTTF.

Reliability is defined as the probability that a system will perform satisfactorily for at least a given period of time, when used under known and stated conditions.

Unlike MTTF which is given in units of time (usually hours), reliability is simply a number with no units. As an example, if we said that the reliability of a certain system was 0.99 over a 200 hour time frame (that means an operating period of 200 hours) we would mean that the chance of it performing satisfactorily over that period would be 0.99 (or 99% if you prefer). Looked at another way, you could say that 99 out of 100 of these systems would be expected to last the 200 hour period.

Reliability is connected with the curves shown in figures 7.17 and 7.18. As you might expect, a device that has already survived for several MTTFs must fail sooner or later and is therefore going to be less reliable in the future. Using mathematics together with the information shown by the curves in figures 7.17

---

* The curve shown in figure 7.18 is a well known curve in statistics and is called a Normal or Gaussian distribution. The equation for the curve is

$$f(t) = \frac{1}{\sigma\sqrt{2\pi}} \exp[-(t-\theta)^2/2r^2]$$

where θ is the MTTF and σ is the standard deviation.

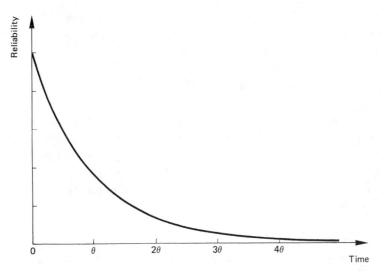

Fig 7.19   The decrease in reliability of a single device with time

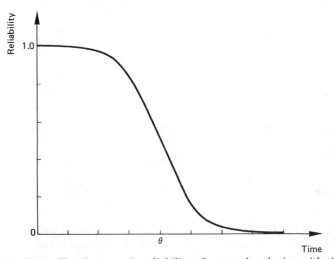

Fig 7.20   The decrease in reliability of a complex device with time

and 7.18 it is possible to produce curves of reliability plotted against time. For a single device, reliability decreases with time as shown by the curve in figure 7.19 (this happens to be the same general shape as the curve in figure 7.17). For a more complicated device, consisting of many components, the curve is as shown in figure 7.20.

Once you know the reliability of a device, you can calculate the reliability of a process (a system) in which a number of devices operate. The formula for reliability of a system in which the failure of any element means the failure of the entire system (a so-called *serial system*) is found by multiplying the reliabilities of each element within the system:

$$R_{system} = R_a \times R_b \times R_c \times \dots \times R_n$$

As an example, let us say that a particular robot has a reliability of 0.98 (a figure we will be using again in a moment). The reliability of three such robots working on an assembly line would be

$$R = 0.98 \times 0.98 \times 0.98$$

(a neater way to write this would be $R = 0.98^3$)

$$R = 0.941$$

So, as you might have expected, the reliability of three robots working serially (where one depends upon the other) is *less* than the reliability of one robot working alone. If you have a calculator handy you might like to work out the reliability of say four or five robots working serially.

For a parallel system, one in which the system functions until *all* elements within it have failed, the formula is

$$R_{system} = 1 - (q_a \times q_b \times q_c \times \dots \times q_n)$$

where $q = 1 - R$ and is called the *unreliability* of each element.

Figure 7.21 illustrates the reliability of a flexible assembly system which contains one automated warehouse and three workstations each with two robots. The figures are for an eighty hour work shift.

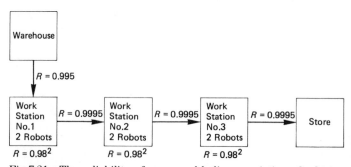

Fig 7.21   The reliability of an assembly line consisting of robot work stations

The calculation assumes that each robot has a reliability of 0.98, hence the 0.98^2 for 2 robots. The failure of material transportation from the warehouse has been given as one in two hundred operations. This means that 199 operations out of every 200 are successful, so

$$R = \frac{199}{200} = 0.995$$

which is the figure given in the diagram. This does not, of course, automatically assume that there will be a mechanical failure, since a problem in material transportation could be caused by a stockout of material, meaning that there is no material to move. Failure of material transportation between work stations has been given as one in two thousand operations (1999 out of 2000 are successful) giving a reliability figure of

$$R = \frac{1999}{2000} = 0.9995$$

Since we are dealing here with a serial system, we calculate the overall reliability by multiplying the reliabilities of each element of the system. Therefore the overall reliability of the system is

$$R = 0.995 \times 0.98^2 \times 0.9995 \times 0.98^2 \times 0.9995 \times 0.98^2 \times 0.9995$$

$$= 0.88$$

Mean Time To Repair (MTTR) is the expected time taken to effect a repair on the system including identification, preparation, correction time and checkout time.

Availability is the fraction of the time that the system is in an operable condition:

$$\text{Availability} = \frac{\text{Total time} - (\text{Number of breakdowns} \times \text{MTTR})}{\text{Total time}}$$

Here, total time is the time frame under consideration, for instance one shift of so many hours, or one year. Availability is often given as a percentage of the total time.

As an example we will calculate the percentage availability of a robot over a 2000 hour year, if it has six breakdowns and an MTTR of one hour:

$$\text{Availability} = \frac{2000 - (6 \times 1)}{2000} \times 100$$

$$= 99.7\%$$

Mixed Robot-Man Systems

If we use a robot or some other form of automation, then we know that within the confines of that equipment's reliability we can predict the output per shift and also anticipate the quality level of that production. Once we introduce people as elements within that manufacturing system we introduce uncertainty into the productivity equation. Since we are dealing with reliability and quality, we must consider the negative aspects of humans as they affect a manufacturing system. It is acknowledged that people have many positive attributes, such as intelligence and flexibility, but these should not be held up as reasons for the continued use of people as productive elements within industry.

Over an eight hour working shift the output rate of people will vary as they get tired, or as it approaches a break time. For many reasons the manual process is not continuous, even if operators change over at frequent intervals so that washroom and coffee breaks can be taken. The quality level is also variable because the instructions given to each person allow for variation in what is actually performed. For instance, if one task involves adhesive application, then a manual process often allows the person to be inconsistent over the amount of adhesive dispensed and the way it is applied.

In the same way that machines break down, people are ill or absent; however, machines are usually more responsive to treatment. Furthermore, if a person is ill or absent, then the company still pays wages even though that person is not contributing to the company's revenue.

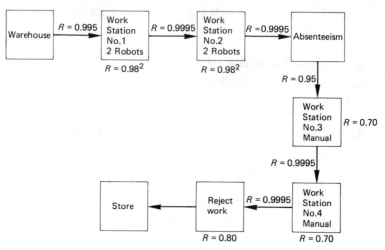

Fig 7.22   The reliability of assembly line consisting of manual and robot work stations

Figure 7.22 shows the reliability figures for an assembly line that incorporates both manual and robot work stations. Values shown reflect the reject level of the process and the attendance patterns of the operators. Like the calculation for figure 7.21, we assume that each robot has a reliability of 0.98, that the failure of material transportation from the warehouse is one in two hundred operations, and that the failure of material transportation between work stations is one in two thousand operations. Manual work stations have been given a reliability of 0.70.

As before, we calculate the overall reliability by multiplying the reliabilities of each element of the system. Therefore the overall reliability of the system in figure 7.22 is

$$R = 0.995 \times 0.98^2 \times 0.9995 \times 0.98^2 \times 0.9995 \times 0.95 \times 0.70$$
$$\times 0.9995 \times 0.70 \times 0.9995 \times 0.80$$
$$= 0.34$$

Maintenance

Maintenance is the activity that restores the system to its optimal operating condition. The type of maintenance activity performed depends upon the age of the system and the type of failure anticipated. There are two types of maintenance. The first is that of *"fire fighting"*, in which failures are dealt with as they occur. The second is *preventive maintenance* which involves a regular schedule of servicing procedures that minimize the risk of failure between services. For example, our cars have preventive maintenance schedules every 6000 miles or so, whilst punctures and broken windscreens are dealt with as and when they occur.

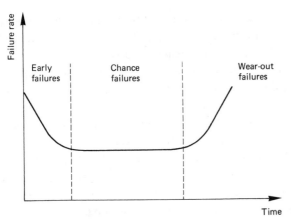

Fig 7.23   Age-specific failure rate with time

In terms of failure, a system's life is in three stages, which when plotted as age-specific failure rate against time assumes the "bath tub" curve as shown in figure 7.23, which has been shown to be an expression of the instantaneous failure rate of a system during its life cycle. In this context, life cycle means the time between the completion of a system or the manufacture of a component and its being either scrapped, or overhauled in such a way as to restore it to as-new condition. It does not however refer to the life cycle of the design of the system, which refers to the market value given to a product or system over time. Within this curve there are three stages of failure:

1   *Early Failure*, which is associated with the running-in period and is due to substandard parts or excessive stress due to initial maladjustment. It can also be due to poor design or the failure of a manufacturer to use adequate quality control.

2   *Chance Failures* are so called because they arise from a chance combination of circumstances in design and manufacture. Since these failures occur randomly, they will be randomly distributed in time. Over a long period of time, the failure rate will be constant and the effects of these failures, as well as the probability of their occurrence in specific periods of time, can be readily predicted. It is not possible in any rational way to predict the time at which any such event will occur or the time between any particular pair of successive events. Preventing such failures by planned maintenance is therefore not possible; breakdown and repair after an occurrence is the only method.

3   *Wear-out Failures* are caused by systems and components that survive chance failures long enough to encounter the increased failure rate. The

relationship with age can be predicted and the whole system can be returned to time zero by overhauling the equipment. Thus there is scope for preventive maintenance.

Quality

Finally, having dealt with the reliability of the manufacturing system, we will end this chapter by noting that the **quality** of manufacturing materials also has a bearing on the reliability of the system as a whole.

The reliability of a product depends upon the quality level of the components used within it. A manufacturing system assumes that the materials being fed to it are within the quality limits specified for the tasks. If this is not so, the product will be less reliable or the process could be stopped because of jammed parts or components that have failed during manufacture.

A production line often contains several workstations with a number of intermediate inspection stations. The output of acceptable quality parts should not be assumed to be identical to the number of items processed at the first station, since with each operation and introduction of "new" components the risk of rejection or failure increases.

8 Computerised Design and Manufacture

The first link in the chain in which data can be input for the computerised manufacturing process is CAD, Computer Aided Design. CAD is a technique for designing products with the aid of a computer and, more importantly, the means by which we are able to enter product-related information into the computer system. From this information we can build our products, order materials, schedule work, invoice customers and generally enable the entire system to operate.

Design

Before launching into the subject of CAD let us pause to examine what we mean by the term "design".

A **design** is a plan or a scheme for the implementation of a project but the word also includes the drawings, notes and mathematical equations which define the product. The design may be for the internal furnishings of a house (interior design), the house itself (architectural design), an aeroplane (aeronautical design), clothing (fashion design), a school timetable (curriculum design) . . . and there are many others that could be added to the list.

The design is used by designers both to transmit their ideas to other persons involved in the project and to formalize and develop their thoughts for their own benefit.

The second term which we must understand is **design process**. By this we mean the steps that have to be undertaken to produce the design.

One path is for the process to start as an idea, perhaps a flash of inspiration in the mind of one innovator. The seed of the design has been sown, but it still has a long way to go before the final product emerges. The first tangible sign of the design may be some preliminary sketches and calculations on a notepad (or typically, the back of an envelope!). More detailed sketches follow, many are discarded, most are re-drawn and amended until eventually the designer is satisfied that the idea has some validity.

Another possibility is that a requirement is identified for a particular product and a specification is written. This specification is the first stage of the design and may state the purpose for which the product is required, the dimensions in which it must be fitted and other details to guide the designer. The designer still has to go through the process of drawing, discarding and redrawing until a satisfactory design emerges.

For a simple product, the design phase may be very short, the final drawings being available very soon after the process has begun. For more complex projects, however, the design process may take several months or even years and involve teams of hundreds of designers each working on one part of the total project. What started as a simple idea or specification may easily expand into a complicated series of sub-projects.

The final stage of the process is the production of the finished design – consisting of drawings, documents, etc. – which can be used for the implementation of the project.

In order to see how the final design is arrived at, it is important to understand the thinking behind the design process. The responsibility of a designer is to design a product that will best carry out its designated task. To do this, the designer must consider all the factors relevant to the design. A number of conflicting requirements is not unusual and decisions must be made which will optimize the design in the face of these conflicts. In fact a large element of the creative aspect of design is the seeking of ingenious compromises in these situations. "Trade-off" is a term used in this context as the designer establishes priorities and incorporates them into the design.

Design Considerations

Let us look at some of the factors that need to be considered by the designer.

- *Dimensions*   What is to be the size of the object? What tolerances will be allowed in its measurements?
- *Materials*   Of what material is it to be made?
- *Components and assemblies*   Is it to consist of one item or an assembly of smaller items? If it is to be an assembly, then each individual component must be individually designed or specified as must the way in which they fit together.
- *Environment*   Where will the product go? A decision must be taken as to whether the object needs to be particularly rugged or to operate in a hot or cold, humid or arid climate, or to blend with a particular background. All these and many other environmental considerations need to be taken into account.
- *Production details*   Can it be made? There is no point in designing an object that cannot be produced, or would be prohibitively expensive to produce. Assuming that it can be made, the method to be used for its manufacture must be determined.
- *Reliability*   How will we determine whether the finished object is suitable for the purpose for which it was designed? A programme of testing has to be devised to ensure that the item will work within the limits specified.

- *Finance*   What will it cost to produce the article? In every product there are budget constraints and the product must be designed to fit in with these restrictions. There may be more than one way to design a certain product and the most cost-effective method will usually be sought.
- *Maintainability*   Can the product be easily serviced? Parts that will frequently need changing should be made accessible. Very often, simple rearrangement of components can lead to hours of servicing time being saved.
- *Alternatives*   Can parts of the design be changed? Some specified components may not be available and it may be necessary to suggest replacements.
- *Time*   How much time is available for the design? It may be necessary to leave out certain features from the product in order to finish the design within a certain time limit.
- *Space*   How much room is there? If the overall dimensions are limited, the designer may again have to decide which features to include and which to leave out, which are "essential" and which are merely "desirable".

Similar decisions will have to be made in the face of considerations such as appearance, usability, ease of manufacture and a long list of other factors that vary according to each particular situation.

Producing Designs

The majority of a designer's time is usually spent working on the drawing board. Ideas may evolve elsewhere and may in fact take very little time to conceive but the formal expression of ideas requires the drawing board and a great deal of time. However, this is not wasted time because by setting out the ideas in a visual form the designer is able to view the product and then continually to adjust this view until satisfied.

Each drawing is supported by documentation relating to parts lists, component suppliers and assembly instructions, and carries a unique code number which identifies it among the scores of other drawings used on the project. The total of all these documents provides the complete information for the manufacture of the product in its final form and is usually referred to as the **product design file.**

Testing the Design

In an engineering context the end result of the design process described so far is usually a set of plans or drawings describing the product to be made.

It would be foolhardy to commence volume production of such a product on the basis of this information alone. No matter how good the design there will always be the possibility that the final product will contain design faults. To overcome this problem, an engineering **prototype** is usually manufactured.

This will be subjected to a series of tests to determine its performance and any faults that were not apparent at earlier stages of the design process.

Prototype testing often leads to further design amendments – some major, some minor. These amendments have then to be incorporated into the prototype and the cycle continues until a satisfactory product is finally developed.

Implications of Traditional Design Methods

The design process we have described is **iterative**, that is the design is subject to repeating cycle of change and improvement before it is finalised. As a result of this, a great deal of effort is put into generating drawings and documents which are never used. Elements of these drawings and documents may be incorporated in the'final design but this often involves complete re-draughting. For the sake of a component or two, a complete new drawing or even a set of drawings may need to be produced. There are a number of disadvantages to this traditional approach:

Cost Every drawing produced during the design process is drawn to the formal industry standards required. After all, at the time the drawing is being prepared, it is not known whether this is the final design or whether changes may still need to be made. This means that all draughting is of high standard and is therefore costly. The more re-draughting that is necessary, the greater the cost of the project.

Time Continual re-draughting increases the delay between the origination of the initial design and the appearance of the final product. This delay can be critical in an aggressive marketplace where competitors are anxiously trying to launch a similar product. The first to succeed is likely to take the lion's share of the market.

Morale When design staff have to spend a large proportion of their time on formal and repetitive tasks they are liable to become frustrated. This will lead to a decrease in efficiency.

Variations Even when the design is complete and the set of final drawings and documentation has been produced, there may still be a need for re-draughting because different drawings of the same object may have to be produced according to the requirements of the manufacturing process.

How can the disadvantages be overcome? There is obviously pressure, both commercial and professional, to make the design process more efficient. Commercially, a reduction in time and cost will lead to a faster turnround time and higher profits. Furthermore, the removal of repetitive and tedious elements of the design process will make for a more satisfactory working environment. These advantages can be achieved by the use of a computer, both as a design aid and as a draughting aid.

The Computer in Draughting and Design

The use of the computer to help in **draughting** stems from its *ability to handle and manipulate graphical information.* Working with the image on a VDU screen instead of on paper, the designer is able to easily modify drawings, and can instruct the computer to insert, erase or move points, lines and shapes until satisfied with the result.

Repetitious tasks such as drawing the same shape several times can be accomplished by entering the shape once only and then directing where it is to appear on the screen. Each occurrence of the shape can be in a different orientation and even of a different size. A *library* of often-used shapes and symbols can be stored and called up when required. This is extremely useful, for example, when drawing electronic circuit diagrams. Once the design has been fixed, the information can be stored on disc or tape for subsequent re-use.

A modular system of design can be developed by combining elements stored in the library. Combinations of elements can themselves become modules so that higher levels of design can be achieved by the combination of more complex modules. These are known as **macros**. This process removes the tedium associated with the conventional approach which requires each element to be individually redrawn every time it is used.

As a **design aid**, the benefits arise from the *ability of the computer to rapidly carry out complex calculations.* Earlier we made the point that design is an iterative process, with the designer trying out ideas and and modifying the original design. CAD also allows the designer to carry out "what if" experiments on the design. If a certain amendment is not viable then another can be tried. Using this power, a number of elements of the design process can be made more efficient. For example, if the computer is provided with data on the characteristics of different materials, then it can provide the designer with information as to how the product will behave if manufactured out of these materials. In addition, information relating to cost can be provided and the designer can choose the most cost-effective way to manufacture the product.

Animation

Many products are designed with moving parts. Conventional design techniques do not allow the designer to see how these parts actually move until the first prototype has been built.

With advanced CAD systems, it is possible to draw the individual components and then to combine their images on the screen and move them so as to examine their dynamic behaviour. Any problems that show up can be solved by amending the design. The benefit of this application of CAD is to obviate the need for prototype building and to greatly shorten the design time, by efficiently providing optimum solutions to problems. The process of having the computer carry out these "what if" and animation tasks is known as **simulation** or **modelling** and later we shall see how the computer is able to carry out these functions.

Computer Graphics

The ability of the computer to manipulate drawings – called computer graphics – is the basis of its use in CAD. Handling graphical data on a computer can be split into three main areas:

Data Input
Data Output
Software

Data Input

The keyboard on its own is not an ideal tool for entering graphical information. What is required is the equivalent of a pencil with which the user can "draw" the information into the computer. Three types of device are commonly used:

Light pen
Cursor control devices
Graphics tablets

Light Pen This device (see figure 8.1) may be used by the operator to "write" directly onto the screen. To accomplish this effect, the light pen senses the electron beam which scans the screen and uses this to trigger a signal to the computer. From the timing of the signal, the software is able to calculate the position of the pen. As the light pen moves it can be tracked by the software which then causes the appropriate actions to take place such as drawing lines on the screen where the pen has been placed.

Another use for the light pen is as a pointer. In this mode there are areas of the screen on which certain commands appear, such as "change colour of display" or "erase". To implement these commands the light pen can be used to point to the various options displayed on the screen. When the software detects the light pen at one of these positions the relevant action is initiated.

Cursor Control Devices Lines and curves can be drawn on the screen by directing the movement of the cursor (a flashing cross or other marker symbol which appears on the screen). The most convenient method for doing this is by means of either a joystick or a tracker ball (figure 8.2). Movement of the joystick or ball in any direction sends appropriate signals to the computer to move the cursor.

Other controls such as keyboard or keys attached to the joystick are usually used together with light pens and cursor control devices in order to produce various effects such as colour, brightness, shading, rotation, enlargement, etc.

Graphics Tablet (Digitizer Pad) A graphics tablet consists of a flat board in which a fine rectangular grid of electrical wires is embedded. A special stylus connected to the computer is moved across the tablet and, by sensing signals in the wire grid, the computer tracks the position of the stylus and

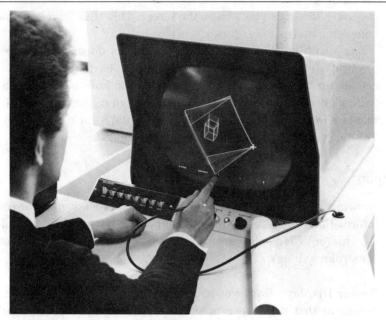

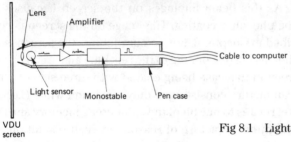

Lens Amplifier

Cable to computer

Light sensor Monostable Pen case

VDU
screen

Fig 8.1 Light pen

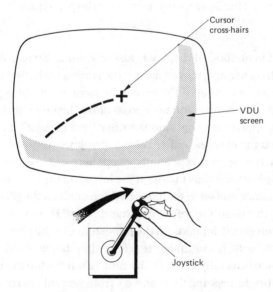

Cursor
cross-hairs

VDU
screen

Joystick

Fig 8.2 Joystick

generates the traced pattern on the screen. This allows accurate pictures and complex patterns to be drawn.

Since with most graphics tablets the stylus does not have to come into physical contact with the tablet itself, it is possible to place a sheet of paper or acetate on top of the tablet. This sheet could have a drawing on it and, by tracing over this drawing, we have a method of digitizing an existing design – that is, a method of storing the design in digital form in the computer system. This is a very valuable feature of graphics tablets.

Data Output

Drawings can be displayed on the VDU or, if a permanent record of graphical information is required, hard copy output can be produced on a plotter. Two systems for VDU display are used, known as Raster Display and Vector Display (or stroke writing).

Raster Display   Raster display makes use of conventional television technology in that the screen is scanned continously and very rapidly by an electron beam. As this beam impinges on the screen it causes light to be emitted from the phosphor coating. The image on the screen is composed of pixels as described in Chapter 6. For colour pictures the screen is scanned by three electron beams corresponding to the red, blue and green elements of the picture; the screen in this case being coated with three sets of phosphors.

In a raster scan picture consisting of only black and white (i.e. ON and OFF) pixels, each pixel relates to one bit of the computer's memory and the screen is said to be **bit mapped**. A picture of reasonably high resolution, say 1024×1024 black and white pixels, would require around one million bits of memory (equal to 128 kilobytes). This large use of memory is the principal disadvantage of raster scan.

Vector Display   This method of display is also known as Stroke Writing. In this system the electron beam is moved across the screen under the control of the computer. Since no scanning of the screen is carried out, the software is required only to store the information needed to move the beam from point to point. The lines that appear are continuous rather than consisting of pixels.

Stroke writing systems may use either refresh displays or storage displays. In **refresh displays**, the beam is repeatedly swept across its designated path to re-excite the phosphors and thus maintain the image on the screen. **Storage displays** use a secondary emission technique which enables the picture to be maintained without the need for refreshing the display. How frequently the display needs to be refreshed depends on the persistence of the phosphor (that is, the length of time that it continues to glow after being excited by the electrons). *Persistence* is usually given as the time taken for the image to fade to 10% of its original brightness and this can vary from several microseconds to several seconds. A screen with a long persistence phosphor may need to be refreshed at 10 to 30 frames per second. A screen with a short persistence phosphor may need to be refreshed as often as 60 frames per second.

There are advantages and disadvantages in both the refresh and storage mechanisms. To change an element of an image on a storage display, the whole picture has to be erased and then redrawn. The delay involved in re-drawing the screen rules out its use for producing animated graphics. On a refresh display, each time the image is refreshed the information can be updated, thus allowing an animated display to be created if required. However, the main advantage of the storage display is that a flicker-free picture is always obtained. On a refresh system, once the screen becomes crowded with detail more time is spent during the refresh phase and the consequent delay results in the image appearing to flicker.

Raster scan is the system in most common use today. There are several reasons for this:

1 The technology is the same as that used in domestic television sets and is therefore highly developed and relatively cheap.

2 Although the system requires a large amount of computer memory, this consideration is becoming less important as the cost of storage is falling rapidly.

3 Coloured graphics can be produced easily.

4 The system permits the use of a light pen.

5 Fairly high picture resolution is obtainable.

6 A fair degree of animation is available.

Hard Copy Devices

Pen Plotters   These are devices in which a pen is made to draw onto a sheet of paper directly under the control of the computer. They may be either drum plotters or flat bed plotters.

Drum Plotters (see figure 8.3)   With this type of device the paper is wrapped round a rotating drum. The pen is attached to a gantry and can move side to side as the drum rotates. These devices are being superseded by flat bed plotters.

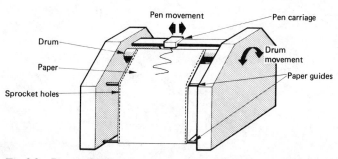

Fig 8.3   Drum plotter

Flat Bed Plotters (see figure 8.4)   In these devices the paper is held on a flat base, often by means of a vacuum, and the pen can be moved in any direction. These devices are manufactured in a variety of configurations. One variation is to have a multi-pen plotter by "parking" spare pens of different colours on the side of the machine. Under software control any one of these parked pens can be selected and attached to the penholder. This enables multi-coloured drawings to be produced. An alternative is for the parked pens to be of different thicknesses, thus providing a different type of flexibility in drawing prod-

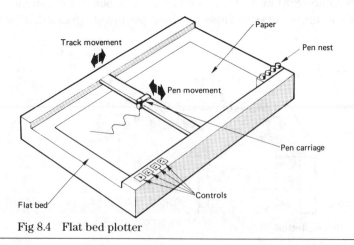

Fig 8.4   Flat bed plotter

uction. Further alternatives include using a photosensitive drawing material and replacing the pen with a light source. This system allows the production of the artwork which may be required for electronic or other processes.

Electrostatic Plotters The time taken to produce a drawing using a pen plotter is relatively slow and hundreds of times longer than the time taken to display the same picture on a VDU screen. Plotting devices capable of faster speeds have therefore been developed. An example is the electrostatic plotter. This system is similar to the drum plotter except that, instead of a pen moving across the paper, a row of styluses is used. These are set very close together and, using an electrostatic process, can attract ink droplets or powder on to specific points on the paper to build up the required image. In common with other types of plotter this device can also produce text output, in which case it becomes a fairly fast printer (typically 1200 lines per minute).

Other Techniques Other methods of producing hard copy also exist – these include drawing on heat-sensitive paper, using dot-addressable dot-matrix printers (see figure 8.5), and computer output to microfilm (COM) units. Other schemes are available to directly photograph the output from VDU screens to produce hard copy.

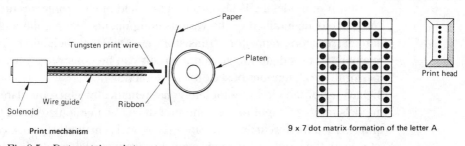

Print mechanism

9 x 7 dot matrix formation of the letter A

Fig 8.5   Dot matrix printer

CAD Software

Modelling – Software

The word "model" is an important one to understand in the context of computer graphics and CAD. In normal English usage there are many meanings to the word but, for our purposes, a model can be defined as:

a graphical and/or mathematical representation which enables us to investigate the structure and/or behaviour of an object.

There are many ways of building such models but here we are concerned with **computer-modelling**. In this scheme of things, we attempt to create a computer program that will behave as the system being modelled and allow us to investigate its behaviour. Obviously this short description hides an enormous amount of detailed mathematical programming and data manipulation but, for our present purposes, it is sufficient. (A more detailed treatment can be found in the references at the end of this chapter).

An important aspect of computer models is that they can be readily manipulated. By this we mean that by altering one of the variables or parameters, we can see how the model, and hence the system being modelled, will react. In CAD terms this is what enables the designers to carry out their "what if" experiments mentioned earlier. Modelling-software is concerned with expressing the data describing a system in the most efficient digital form and then operating on this data to calculate the behaviour of the object under differing conditions.

Among the tools available to designers using modelling techniques is the *finite element method* (FEM) – see figure 8.6. Using this method, a structure or solid component can be defined as a mesh of discrete elements joined together at corner points where the material is assumed to have constant properties. Each element of the thousands that totally describe a component can have its performance defined under certain circumstances by a set of equations. By solving to determine the behaviour of each element, the behaviour of the whole component can be predicted.

This method is used to calculate factors that affect solid objects such as stress, heat transfer, vibration, creep, pressure and electric or magnetic loading. It is the method used to produce the image of a bridge bending under heavy loads.

A form of modelling is also used in the field of electronic circuit design. A *database* is maintained of the various components that can be included in a circuit (resistors, capacitors, transistors, etc.) and their behaviour. This data is maintained in a digital form and a circuit can be constructed by a program performing calculations based on the interaction of this data and modelling the behaviour of the circuit completely mathematically. Once the data for these models has been input to the computer, it can be manipulated and the appropriate calculations carried out. Since the model is in digital form, it can also be stored on tape or disc and made available again at a later date. In addition, the

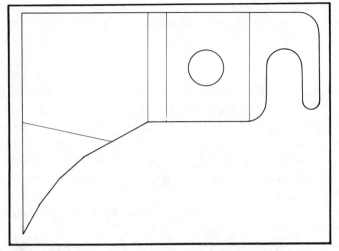

(a) *Definition of structure*

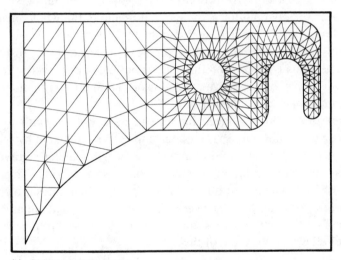

(b) *Division into finite elements*

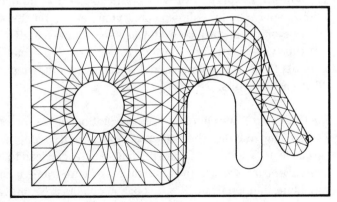

(c) *Effect of stress on elements*

Fig 8.6   Finite element analysis

data relating to the model can also be sent via computer communication networks to distant machines for further analysis or display.

Display Software

The computer model is stored as binary data and manipulated by mathematical programs. In theory, this could be achieved without the need to display anything to the CAD user but in practice, of course, the design procedure is interactive. This means that in giving an instruction for an action to take place the designer wants to see the effects – probably on a VDU screen. In order to achieve this, **display software** is used to obtain a number of different effects:

Orientation   The object can be displayed from any angle, and plan, elevation and isometric views can be obtained.

Shading   Parts of the display can be shaded or cross-hatched, as required.

Zooming and Scaling   A portion of the total picture can be selected and displayed in an enlarged form. Similarly, if required, the whole image can be enlarged or reduced in one direction only.

Clipping and Windowing   The picture can be made to fit inside certain bounds, portions lying beyond the bounds not being displayed.

Colouring   Parts of the image can be displayed in different colours to highlight certain areas or to aid clarity.

Text Insertion   The displayed model can be annotated with explanatory legends or with dimensions. The dimensions can be adjusted by scaling.

Curve Fitting   For the purpose of mathematical modelling, a curve is represented as single points linked together by short straight lines. This representation, although convenient for computer analysis, is not desirable when the image is to be displayed. To overcome this, various mathematical "spline functions" exist which generate smooth curves that pass through every point – figure 8.7 shows an example of this.

Three-dimensional Display   Software is available for modelling solid objects which displays a three-dimensional view, either on the screen for interactive work or on a hard copy device (see figure 8.8). The problem addressed by this type of software is known as *depth cueing* – that is, creating the illusion of depth on a two-dimensional surface. The following techniques are available to achieve this:

Wire-frame Drawings   By choosing the orientation of the object and by drawing a wire-frame drawing, the object can appear to have depth. However, this scheme can lead to ambiguities and too much detail can lead to confusion.

Hidden Line Removal   Most of the ambiguities of wire frame images disappear when the lines hidden from view by opaque objects are removed. This is an important technique, extensively used but requiring a considerable amount of computation. See figure 8.9.

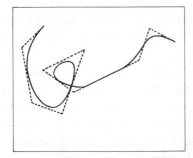

Fig 8.7   Curve fitting

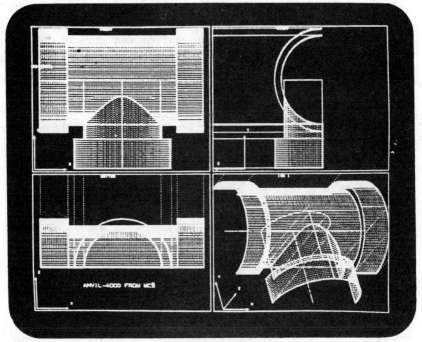

Fig 8.8   Three-dimensional data entry

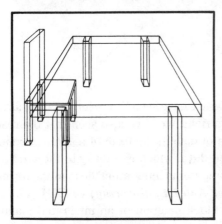

Fig 8.9   Hidden line removal

Perspective Projection   Wire-frame ambiguities can be reduced by the use of perspective. Here the illusion of depth is created by making nearer objects larger than more distant objects. However, perspective implies image distortion and this may not be acceptable.

Intensity Cues   An inexpensive method suitable for displaying simple objects is to draw the parts of the object nearer the observer in a more intense shade than those further away. This is not suitable for more complex shapes.

Surface Smoothing   An extension of the technique of curve fitting (see above) is to apply the curve fitting functions in three dimensions so as to present the impression of a smooth surface.

Shading   The greatest realism is achieved by shading the image (after removing hidden lines and carrying out smoothing operations). This is a complex process taking into account the surface properties of the object and the properties of the simulated source of illumination. If the shading includes gradations of colour and shadows, then the resultant effect can be very realistic indeed. See figure 8.10.

Dynamic Effect   By displaying the image in a series of different positions and in different orientations, the effect of motion can be achieved. This provides an impressive visual display.

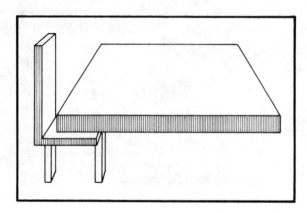

Fig 8.10   Shading

Other Uses for the Computer Model

Towards Integration   So far we have seen how useful CAD is as a draughting and design tool in its own right. We have also seen that the result of the whole process is a collection of data in the form of a computer model. This model is the **product-related data**, which is the key to the total process of integration. This use of the computer in integrating the manufacturing process is known as **CAE** (*Computer Aided Engineering*) or **CIM** (*Computerised Integrated Manufacture*). A block diagram of an integrated manufacturing system is shown in figure 8.11.

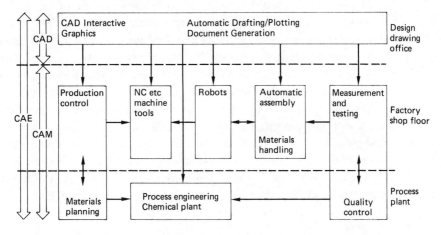

Fig 8.11   Schematic of an integrated manufacturing system

An example of the use of product data is where an item being designed is to be manufactured using NC (*numerically controlled*) machinery. Previously NC machines were *free-standing*, that is the information needed to drive them was derived manually from the product information and punched on to paper tape. The tape was then fed into the machine to control its actions. Later developments of this technique have led to CNC (*Computerised Numerical Control*) with the input data usually on magnetic disk instead of paper tape. However, the data for the disk is still generally provided from the product information by an intermediate manual stage. The way forward, using integration, is for the data for the machinery to be generated as a direct byproduct of the design phase. In this way a great deal of pre-production time and effort can be saved and costly mistakes can also be avoided.

Similar uses of the product information are to provide information for the generation of robot programs, for the design of jigs, dies and tools, and for the design of moulds for components made by casting. The same information can be used to generate parts lists, ordering and production schedules, and for manpower planning

File Handling   In addition to the software which deals with manipulating the model and presenting it to the viewer, there is also a requirement for software to handle the data created and to organize it into files.

As the computer graphics facility is built up, a library of such files will be created for use by the designers. Some of the files will contain elemental designs, others will hold complete pictures. For example, in an architect's system there will be files containing window shapes, door shapes and other standard symbols. There will be others containing finished designs of houses and even housing estates which will be made up of components from the elemental files.

There are two major routes for the transmission of these files to the manufacturing and commercial sectors. One way is for the data to be stored on disc and the disc physically moved to the computer dealing with the manufacture or accounting procedures. The other way is for the various computers to be joined by communications links, which may include telephone lines, so that data can be freely exchanged between them.

The basic database of information is stored centrally and the various functions – design, manufacturing, commerce – link in to the database extracting and updating the information. This is the direction in which modern industry is aiming and which promises to provide enormous improvements in design and production efficiency. A diagrammatic representation of the hardware and software required for this integration is shown in figure 8.12.

Computers in Automated Manufacturing

Let us now examine the areas where computers are being used in manufacturing industry. There are six main areas:

1 Data Logging
2 Production Control
3 Scheduling
4 Production Costs
5 Product Quality
6 Machine Control

1 Data Logging Data logging is the gathering of information on what is happening during the process. It also includes the analysis of product-related information for the detection of process faults and drift in quality standards.

Take as an example the case of a factory assembling electronic circuit boards. Each circuit board has to be tested to ensure that it functions correctly. Also, production levels must match demand patterns. If too few are made, because of slow throughput or high reject levels, then orders cannot be fulfilled. If too many are produced, then they may have to be stocked until they can be sold and this can be costly in terms of storage and capital outlay.

The data gathered from the assembly operation and all of the other activities between assembly and final inspection is of great value to management, and for determining the difference between the total output of circuit boards and the quantity of saleable circuit boards made per unit time. Management information includes:

Parts usage per unit time.

Energy usage per unit time.

Maximum capacity of process in circuit boards per unit time.

Uptime of various machines per unit time

Reasons for machine stoppages during that time frame.

Actual capacity of good circuit boards per unit time.

Reject rate at various points in the production process.

Reasons for reject circuit boards for that time frame.

Of course this information can be collected manually, but this has two disadvantages:

1　The data collection is prone to error.

2　Analysis of the data is very time consuming.

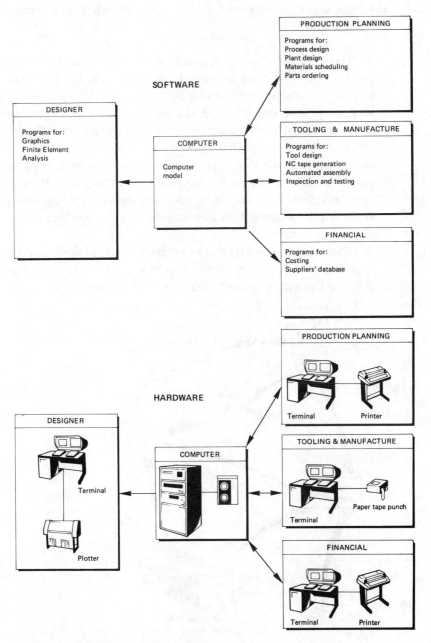

Fig 8.12　Integrated manufacturing

2   Production Control   Computers are used extensively for controlling production processes in most modern facilities in the manufacturing industry. The computer database holds all the relevant information about the orders being processed. By using this database, the production machines, auxiliary equipment and material warehouse can be programmed to manufacture orders on demand.

For example, let us look at the use of computers to monitor and control production in a modern steel works. This is shown from a computer's viewpoint in Figure 8.13.

1   The steel is melted in furnaces and impurities are removed. The computer has specified the amount of steel billet that has to be placed in the furnace and also the types and quantities of additive that have to be mixed with the melt so that the product meets the customer's specifications.
2   Samples are taken from the molten steel and are immediately sent to an automated laboratory. Here they are cooled and placed by a robot in an automatic machine that shapes and polishes the surface of the samples ready for close examination. This ensures that they have the correct structure and chemical analysis to meet the customer's requirements. If the results of the analysis indicate variance from the specification then corrective action is taken.
3   When the melt is certified to be correct it is poured into a continuous casting machine. The particular machine has been identified by the computer as having the correct mould and as being free.

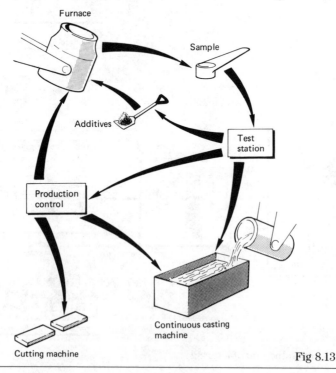

Fig 8.13

4   The steel leaves this machine as a continuous billet or slab of metal and is moved automatically to a cutting machine. This machine has again been selected and set by the computer so that the sliced material is the correct length to satisfy the needs of the order and the cast material is used in the most efficient way to minimise waste.

3   Scheduling   Scheduling is concerned with making the best possible use of the machines available. If we take again the example of the steel works, suppose that we have:

(*a*)   Three furnaces in which the steel melting and chemical additions can be performed

(*b*)   Two continuous casting machines for transforming the steel into slabs

(*c*)   A teeming bay in which the steel can be poured into moulds to make ingots.

A batch of orders will differ in the following details:
   Quantity
   Grade of material, through chemical additions.
   Shape of material (slab or ingot).
   Sizes of individual pieces of material.

If the relevant information from the orders is computerised then the work-load for the various machines can be organized (scheduled) in a logical manner. The criteria would be maximum usage of machines and minimum wastage in the form of offcuts that need to be reworked. Computerised scheduling determines the common groups within a set of orders and logically plans their manufacture to optimize throughput of work, cost of production, and mean time to complete an order.

The computer balances all the different parameters using a process called *linear programming*. The costs, mixes, availabilities of materials, deadlines, etc., are all rationalised to yield the maximum benefit. Whilst linear programming can be performed manually, it is time consuming if more than a few variables are involved. Computerization means that many more variables can be used and the optimum answer is displayed in minutes rather than hours.

The computer is an ideal medium for scheduling the work through a manufacturing plant. It can cope with constantly changing situations – manual systems cannot. The computer enables alternative schedules to be developed quickly, so that management can assess the long-term implications. In addition, real-time updates are available to take account of new events such as:
   New customer order.
   Panic or urgent orders that take priority.
   Stocks of raw materials available.
   Machine breakdown (so reducing the scheduling options).
   Machine availability because of work being processed.

4 Production Costs

Balancing the Flow Computers can bring about savings on the shop floor in three ways:

By achieving a balanced flow of parts.

By better use of raw materials, reducing scrap.

By speeding up a process to reduce labour costs.

Production costs can be kept low by ensuring that throughput is balanced. If, for example, we schedule 1000 cars per week, it is important that there are 1000 sets of parts, such as bodies, rear axles and engines, scheduled and available at the right place at the right time on that production line. If we find that 1020 rear axles have been ordered, then we have incurred unnecessary costs in manufacture, storage and transportation for those 20 items.

Scrap Reduction The value of the material scrapped during the machining operations is lost. Even if the material is reclaimed, the scrap value is low compared with that of the original raw material. The computer can help in several ways to reduce costs due to material wastage. If we look first at sheet metal work, then we can use the computer to lay out the components in a pattern that gives minimum wastage from a standard sheet. If we consider other shapes of material we find that we can use a microcomputer-controlled forge to produce components to a fine tolerance, doing away with a large amount of machining. This "near net shape machining" gives savings in both material and energy.

Labour Costs Labour costs are part of the setting up, operation, maintenance and supervision of a machine or process. It is possible to use computers to speed up the process or to monitor and control the process more precisely such that the in-process time is minimized, with a consequent saving in labour cost. For example, in the pottery industry the time taken for cups and saucers to be fired is very dependent upon the control of the furnace. Microcomputer control of the furnace profile, with critical temperature gradients guaranteed and maintained allows for a consistency of process that reduces the necessary throughput time. The shorter the time in the furnace the more items per shift that can be processed. In addition, precise temperature control means energy control, with its cost advantages.

5 Product Quality

Computers can be used in several ways to improve quality standards. We mention two types here: consistent quality and exact measurement.

Consistent Quality The quality of an automatic or semi-automatic machine depends on the precision with which that machine repeats the activities of the process. Without computers the machines are operator-controlled through manually-set stops or are automatically controlled through the use of cams. In these situations, variances can be caused by vibrations that move the stops, by wear that changes the profile of the cams, by wear of the cutting or measuring tools, or by dirt that changes the effective position of the datum surface. The use of computers allows non-contact measurement techniques to be adopted enabling the normal wear and tear of machinery to be accommodated.

Exact Measurement   This type of quality is usually applied to mixes such as food or plastics. In each case the exact measurement of the ingredients determines the quality of the product. Computers used for weighing out ingredients ensure that the set limits are not exceeded. Automatic recording of batch weights gives statistical information about product ingredients, material usage (for stock control purposes), and product total weight (to comply with weights and measures standards).

6   Machine Control   Computer-controlled machines likely to be met in today's manufacturing industry are lathes, machining centres, punching machines, laser and plasma cutters, and, of course, robots.

Take for example a CNC drilling machine which has been designed to put holes in printed circuit boards (PCBs). The batch size for each set of PCBs will not exceed 50 and, after each batch has been processed, the machine has to be re-programmed with data for the next batch. This data will be in the form of X and Y coordinates for the movement of the table beneath the drill head and the instructions controlling the up and down motions of the drill head itself. The drill will be continuously running and will include an integral computerised monitor to check for drill breakage.

Perhaps the most topical computerised machine tool is the industrial robot. Robots use computers for two purposes:

1   Operation and control of their axes of motion: for instance, transferring a desired vertical motion of the robot's gripper into control signals for each of the independent revolute joints.

2   Overall control of a number of robots within a large manufacturing cell. In this case the computer monitors the entire process and downloads programs and information to the various cell elements as it is required. Invariably this master or host computer is a mini or mainframe whilst the computers fitted to the robots are mini or micro.

Integrating the Computer into the Factory

If all of the elements within a company are independent then quality and control is only as good as the worst element. If however we organize the elements such that they are linked by both a physical arrangement of material communication and a computer network, then the efficiency and productivity of the company as a whole will be increased.

In the majority of companies within manufacturing industry, there is a hierarchy of communication and responsibility. For instance, the packers in the despatch department take their instructions from a foreman who works in

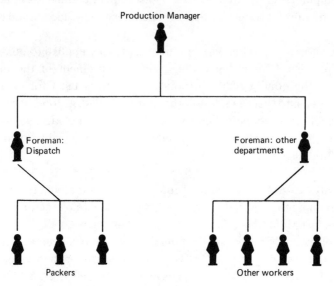

Fig 8.14   A typical hierarchy in industry

the same department. In turn the foreman receives instructions from the production manager, who similarly receives instructions from superiors.

The organization indicated in figure 8.14 is very important in that it ensures that each individual knows what has to be done and what is expected. Furthermore, in the case of a problem there is always someone else in the structure to whom it can be addressed.

Computers in an automated factory are also arranged in a similar hierarchy. This is done specifically to make the programming of the computers easier by rigidly defining the task and responsibility of each computer without unnecessary overlap of functions between them. Unless the hierarchy is well structured, the use of computers becomes confused and inefficient.

Computer Hierarchy

Earlier we said that computers were used for data logging, quality control through inspection and machine control. Figure 8.15 shows a typical **computer hierarchy** of a manufacturing process in which these activities are placed at the bottom of the structure.

The inspection of process quality is performed at the next hierarchical level above the data logger. The reason is that in a computerized system, information must flow vertically up or down the hierarchy and not across it. The inspection computer must therefore receive information from the data logger and respond to the supervisor.

Figure 8.16 shows a schematic layout of a computerized inspection cell for automated printed circuit board (PCB) population (that is, inserting components into blank circuit boards). The cell contains a conveyor belt that

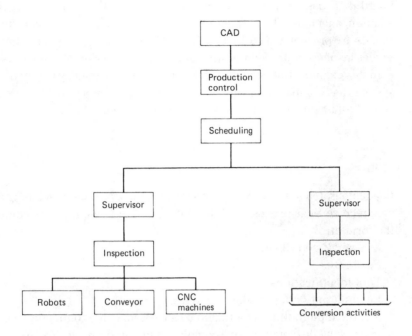

Fig 8.15   Computer hierarchy for a manufacturing process

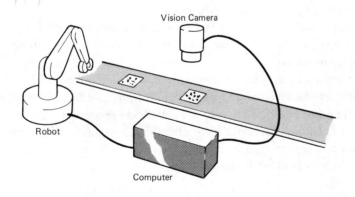

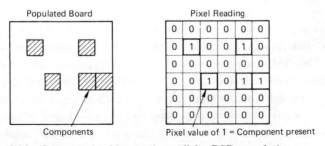

Fig 8.16   Computerised inspection cell for PCB population

moves naked circuit boards to an assembly robot. The robot inserts the correct integrated circuit (IC) chip into the correct position on the PCB. The populated board then passes through an inspection station prior to entering the flow soldering machine. The purpose of the inspection station is to check that all of the ICs are present and correctly inserted. The ICs themselves pass through an earlier inspection procedure prior to entering the assembly cell.

In this example the assembly process will be inspected by means of a vision system that compares information stored in its memory with the image presented to it as each processed board passes beneath the camera.

Machine Control

In an integrated system, machines such as lathes, presses, machining centres, etc., receive their processing information from the supervisory computer in the form of:

X, Y and Z coordinates

Feed rates

Tool identifications

Input/output data for other machines.

It is the input/output data that allows each machine to function as a stand-alone unit, while being part of a complete integrated system. For instance, only when the press has opened is it safe for the robot to advance its gripper and pick up the processed item. If this *interlock* does not exist then the robot might collide with the press or be crushed by it.

Although a robot is simply a flexible machine, its method of programming differs considerably from that used with traditional computer-controlled machines. Since a robot is used to perform a variety of different tasks, we will find that a number of routines that we use are common to many of the tasks. These routines, such as motions from a home position to a machine, opening or closing a gripper, or performing a palletizing operation, can be stored as *subroutines* within the robot's own computer. This means that the supervisory computer has only to deal with a number of statements that link and initiate the subroutines held by the individual robots.

Automated Material Storage

Every manufacturing process involves adding value to raw material. If we consider batch manufacturing, then the material is moved between a storage area and machines several times during its progression through the factory. In order that the integrated system will function efficiently, the supervising computer must know the whereabouts of each piece of material, component or sub-assembly and what work is being performed on it. When value-added work is being performed, the computer is informed as to what activities are occurring and what the result of those activities is. The computerisation of material storage allows total control to be maintained from the time that the raw material enters the factory until the finished products leave.

New stocks of raw material or purchased components are inspected upon arrival at the factory and if acceptable are then booked into the stores. Depending on physical size or value, the material is stored either as discrete items or in containers holding a certain quantity of items. If we can visualise a storage system in which each stored object has its own identification number and in which the storage area is divided into pigeonholes, again with individual code numbers, then we have some idea of the complexity of the computer map that describes the computerised stores. The material is directed by computer to specific pigeonholes, where it remains until required. As the raw material is converted into value-added goods, it is checked out of the stores and taken to the various machines for processing. When those activities are complete, the items are allocated new identification numbers – since they have changed both their shape and value – and are booked again into the stores. This procedure continues until the products are fully assembled and dispatched to satisfy orders. Through computerised storage of material, we have knowledge about what material is in stock, what is being processed and through production control we are able to determine the need, contents and delivery of new raw material for the stores in order to keep the system functioning.

Material Movement

The one aspect of manufacturing that links machines together is the material being processed. Therefore it is logical to computerise the movement of material through the system. The transportation system usually has its own computer and is linked to the machines via the network controlled through the supervisory computer.

Automated computerised material transportation can be done by several means, including conveyor belts, carousels, rotary tables and mobile vehicles. The conveyor/carousel/table option has disadvantages: it is fixed in position and therefore blocks access to machines, it can only be used for the machines to which it is connected, and, as it is not flexible, it cannot be easily reconfigured. These disadvantages are overcome by the the **automated guided vehicle** (AGV). A typical unit is shown in figure 8.17. AGVs are self-contained trucks, guided around the factory by a number of alternative means:

1 The AGV can follow wires laid beneath the floor. These wires create a magnetic field that is detected by the steering system of the AGV. The routes can be simple or complex, with junctions, crossovers and marshalling areas. As the vehicle approaches a "decision point" in its route, the supervisory computer tells it which branch to take.
2 An alternative guidance system uses white lines painted on the surface of the floor. These lines are detected by sensors that measure the light

reflected from them. This option is not always satisfactory since the painted track can become dirty, or damaged in other ways.

3 Paths can be marked out with infra-red or visible light beams. Obviously here the problems are in traversing tortuous paths or the beam being distorted by objects accidentally in its way.

4 Finally we can use free-ranging AGVs that contain their own onboard guidance system which reacts with radio and visual beacons. The supervisory computer can track it and then advise it where to go.

AGVs are battery-driven and therefore their batteries need recharging from time to time. Most AGV circuits have automatic plug-in recharging points to which the AGV can be sent whilst waiting for further instructions from the supervisory computer.

Whatever the means of guidance, the AGVs onboard computer receives instructions from the supervisory computer. It then collects the material from one point in its route and transfers it to another. AGVs can move high payloads of material around. Loose components, jigs and tools and major assemblies such as automobile engines can all be carried. Special transfer devices allow them to directly transfer their cargo onto the spur conveyors that extend from the various work stations. Alternatively, the vehicles can approach a loading dock alongside a machining centre and the supervisory computer will then instruct a robot fitted to the dock to transfer the material from the AGV to the machining centre.

Fig 8.17   An automatic guided vehicle (AGV) (Courtesy: Babcock Fata Ltd.)

The Supervisory Computer

To indicate the power and function of the **supervisory computer** we will take the example of the manufacture of gear wheels. This scheme is shown in figure 8.18. Let us suppose that the gear wheel is moulded from metal powders and is then sintered (heated so that the powder fuses into a solid) in a furnace. Also let us suppose previous orders for this product have been processed under control of the supervisory computer. The computer then has the following information:

(*a*) The amount of powder required to manufacture the desired number of gear wheels.

(*b*) The length of press stroke to produce the required thickness of gear wheel.

(*c*) The amount of pressure to ensure that the powder compaction is sufficient for the desired physical properties of the gear wheel.

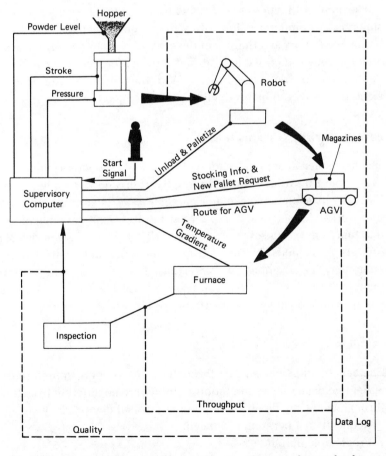

Fig 8.18 The operations involved in the manufacture of gearwheels

(d)   The pickup points of the formed gear wheels from the press and their loading matrix on the storage trays.

(e)   The route of the AGV when the storage trays are full.

(f)   The temperatures for the kiln in which the gear wheels will be sintered.

(g)   Inspection data to check the sintered gearwheels

Before the process can begin, we must ensure that the correct moulds are fitted into the press. This is a manual task, as is filling the hopper with powder. The supervisory computer is loaded with the instructions stored on disc and, when the manual tasks are complete, production of the required number of gear wheels can begin. Obviously, we keep the furnace on continuously from batch to batch and the only changes required by the computer are slight variations of the temperature for each product.

The process is initiated manually. This is a safety feature which ensures that the person supervising the system is aware that the process has started. The system will then, subject to continuous supplies of powder, make the number of gear wheels specified by the computer from its record of the order. The system has a full safety system, such that if anything starts to go wrong then the system is automatically shut down.

The number of types of product whose manufacture can be overseen by the supervisory computer is limited by the technical capability of the machines within the factory and the size of the computer's database. If we want to make a new product, then we have to put information about the product and the process into the database. Provided that the machines are free and the tools exist, the items can be produced.

Flexible Manufacturing Systems (FMS)

The final stage in our exploration of the use of computers in manufacturing is that of the **Flexible Manufacturing System**, known throughout industry as FMS. We have already seen, in Chapter 7, that the arrangement of machines into work cells is a logical step forward from a number of machines arranged into functional groups. We can consider FMS to be simply a series of machines or work cells linked by the transfer of material and controlled by a master computer. The advantage of FMS is that the system as a whole can be used to manufacture a wide range of products through simple reprogramming, whereas an individual cell is virtually product or process dependent.

The Benefits of Using FMS

The benefits that we can gain through the use of FMS, in preference to using either manual or hard automation methods, are no different from those gained through using any flexible computer controlled device. They are:

Reduced cost per item produced.

Predictable output.

Improved consistency of quality.

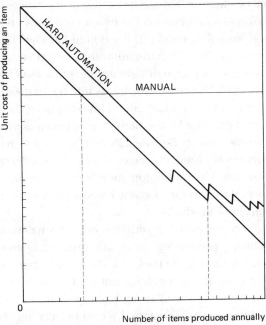

Fig 8.19   Cost versus demand for three different methods of production

Figure 8.19 shows a graph of how the unit cost of producing an item (vertical axis) varies according to the number of items produced annually (horizontal axis). Three lines are shown: manual processing, hard automation and flexible automation.

Manual processing is usually a fixed cost and does not vary with quantity. The benefits that we can expect are a minimal expenditure on capital equipment and the adaptability of the person to accommodate variable quality material, yet still yield an end product of acceptable quality. The problems with manual processing are those of variable quality, unpredictable output rate, and relative high cost per unit produced.

Our second option from figure 8.19 is that of **hard automation**, which, as mentioned earlier, is machinery designed specifically to perform a series of tasks on a very narrow range of products – usually only one. Examples of hard automation are a can-making plant, a milk-bottling plant, or a cigarette-making machine. The benefit of this option is one of short cycle times, or high output rates per shift. The problems are that high volumes are required in order to be cost effective.

The third option that we have is that of **flexible automation**, and the prime example of this is the robot. This option again has the problem of needing very precise components as does hard automation but does not need such a high volume in order to be cost effective. In terms of expenditure on capital equipment, hard automation is more expensive than flexible automation, though provided that the high demand levels can be generated, the unit cost that we can expect from hard automation is by far the lowest.

The range of annual production that can be economically processed by FMS is shown on the horizontal axis between the two dotted lines on figure 8.19. Annual production figures falling outside these dotted lines can be seen from the graphs to cost more by flexible automation than by other processes. In spite of this fact, batches of one type of item are nevertheless claimed to be ideal for processing by FMS. The reason for this is that the unit assembly cost in figure 8.19 is calculated by taking the capital investment of the equipment and cost of material and dividing by the number of items manufactured per unit time. However, in the case of flexible automation it is not necessary to invest in new equipment every time it is required to make a different item. By contrast, the equipment used in hard automation is by definition limited to a single type of product. We therefore cannot consider it for manufacturing single quantities of different products.

Bearing in mind the above, we are left with the comparison between manual processing, semi-automatic processing, automatic processing and FMS. The comparison must be made directly on the basis of cost of manufacture and/or throughput time. Semi-automatic or fully automatic processing usually involves material transfer between different machines laid out in functional groups. Since the machines are not integrated, a cost penalty may be incurred through time wasted in the non-productive activities of waiting and transportation. This can dramatically increase the cost per item. In addition, significant delays mean more time between receiving the order and receiving payment on delivery. This incurs storage costs as well as cash-flow problems.

Why then should we use FMS, if it does not seem to have anything special to offer? The answer is one of scale and integration. A cell can only be so big before it collapses under its own inefficiency. We can perhaps think of human society in which small units can perform tasks up to a certain magnitude, after which they flounder. This is so because as the groups need to increase in size, their control structure cannot cope with the additional responsibility and burden. A small group has a hierarchy with very few levels. This is ideal for dealing with the small detail necessary for its viability, but useless on a global level. Major products therefore require a multi-hierarchical system, in which the desired result is reached through the concept of divide and conquer, with the hierarchical integration of objectives and tasks.

FMS can also progress an item through a large number of different machines and processes with minimal delay between operations. The item is scheduled into the FMS by the master computer, which then sends programs to each of the machines or processes involved in the value-adding operations on that item. Its progression through the FMS is pre-arranged by the computer such that it is automatically transported to those machines that are free and equipped to perform the necessary tasks.

In common with the manufacturing cell, the local and supervisory computers have large databases in which are stored information on all of the relevant items that have been or could be processed. If we have a new item to be processed, the machines can be programmed offline and, once proven, the data can be entered into the database. Often the new item is a variant of an existing item, in which case modification to the data base is relatively simple.

FMS is presently more of a concept than a reality, since like the variation in definitions of a robot, FMS means different things to different people. While we have successful FMSs such as the SCAMP project at the 600 Group in Colchester (see figure 8.20), we also have companies claiming that a single machine-centred cell is also FMS.

Set-up Costs Determine Viability

The set-up time of any machine is time consuming and is often many times greater than the processing time of the components to be manufactured. It is therefore not surprising that many sectors of the manufacturing industry prefer to process items in batches which are larger than necessary to satisfy existing orders. The exact number produced depends upon many factors including set-up time, cutting time, storage costs, machine utilisation, etc. The effect of batch size on the cost of an item is illustrated by the following simplified example.

If the set-up time is 32 man-hours at a rate of £10.00 per man-hour then the set-up cost is £320.00.

For a batch size of 10 items at a direct and material cost of £100.00 each, the processing cost is £1000.00. The total processing cost is therefore:

$$[320 + (100 \times 10)]/10 = £132.00 \text{ per item}$$

If 100 items are made, then the cost is:

$$[320 + (100 \times 100)]/100 = £103.20 \text{ per item}$$

Now suppose that of these 100 items only 20 could be sold immediately, the remainder incurring a storage cost at a rate of £30.00 per item per annum. If the remaining 80 were sold steadily during the following year, this would result in an average storage cost of

$$[80 \times 30]/2 = £1200$$

This figure spread over the 100 items means an average increase of £12 per item, bringing the cost per item to £115.20. If the stored items could not be sold during the one year period then the increased cost to the company would be higher, at

$$80 \times 30 = £2400$$

This would raise the average cost per item by £24 to £133.20.

Therefore, unless we can be sure of a quick sale, there are cost penalties that should not be overlooked if we manufacture for stock.

Using FMS the cost per item can be reduced. With the exception of major changes, the set-up of machines and processes within FMS is carried out via the supervisory computer with only minor hardware changes being performed manually. Assuming this resulted in a reduced set-up time of 8 man-hours, the set-up cost for items evaluated above would be reduced from £320 to £80. The cost of producing 10 items would then become

$$[80 + (100 \times 10)]/10 = £108.00 \text{ per item}$$

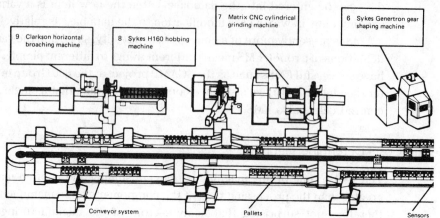

Fig 8.20 The SCAMP project at the 600 Group in Colchester (Courtesy: IFS (Publications) Ltd.)

Autotool Changing and Monitoring

The machines within FMS are often general in nature. In order that these machines can process a number of different items, they have to be provided with the correct tools and a means of ensuring that they are available for use. The majority of these machines are fitted with tooling drums containing over 100 different tools. When a new tool is required, the drum is indexed automatically to a loading position near a pick-and-place device. The pick-and-place device then changes the new tool for the old one, which is then placed in its correct position within the drum. The process then continues until a different tool is required.

FMSs are designed to operate continuously through two and perhaps three shifts. Since tools wear and break, the system needs to be sure that faulty tools can be detected and changed before they damage or scrap the items being processed. Computer technology now allows us to monitor tool wear through sensors fitted to the machine spindles that "listen" for a variation in the sound of the cutting process that will indicate a worn or broken tool (see figure 8.21). Alternatively the power on the cutting spindle can be monitored for abnormalities that indicate faulty tooling.

Working Practices Using FMS

FMS systems are having and will continue to have a profound effect upon the working practices commonly assumed within the manufacturing industry. The basic features of FMS are:
- Small to medium batches, with a minimum batch size of one.
- Maximising the use of software to achieve changes in product capability.
- Minimising the need for human intervention
- Maximising the use of computer-based technology for control, monitoring and metal removal.

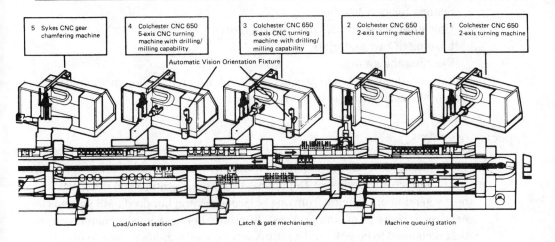

5 Sykes CNC gear
   chamfering machine

4 Colchester CNC 650
   5-axis CNC turning
   machine with drilling/
   milling capability

3 Colchester CNC 650
   5-axis CNC turning
   machine with drilling/
   milling capability

2 Colchester CNC 650
   2-axis turning machine

1 Colchester CNC 650
   2-axis turning machine

Automatic Vision Orientation Fixture

Load/unload station

Latch & gate mechanisms

Machine queuing station

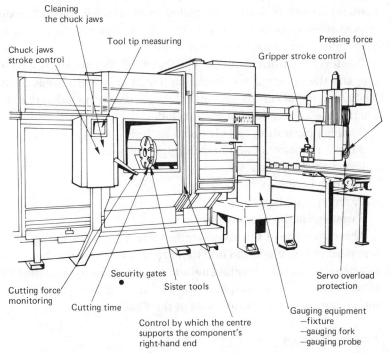

Cleaning
the chuck jaws

Tool tip measuring

Pressing force

Chuck jaws
stroke control

Gripper stroke control

Security gates

Sister tools

Servo overload
protection

Cutting force
monitoring

Cutting time

Control by which the centre
supports the component's
right-hand end

Gauging equipment
—fixture
—gauging fork
—gauging probe

Fig 8.21   Auto tool monitoring (Courtesy: SMT Machine Co. Ltd.)

FMS systems are designed to operate twenty-four hours a day, seven days a week whereas people naturally prefer to work the hours that best suit them socially. Further, the majority of people function best in the traditional shift from 0800 hours to 1700 hours and so it should ideally be this shift in which all of the human activities associated with the FMS are conducted. This leaves the remaining two shifts for the FMS to function unhindered. The human activities include:

Maintenance and repair.

Programming for new items.

Set-ups for new batches.

Unloading finished part from buffer stores.

Loading of raw materials.

Cleaning the system.

Administrative routines of procurement and dispatch (although computerisation of these activities is in the very near future).

Applications of FMS

FMS systems that currently exist are totally within the metal cutting sectors of the manufacturing industry. Depending on which literature you read, you will be given numbers ranging from one or two to several hundred FMS systems in existence. There is, of course, a vast difference between an automated system that is claimed to be FMS and a fully computerised manufacturing system that contains robots, computer-controlled work stations, fully integrated internal transportation systems, automated storage and retrieval systems, and that has been fully operational for several years.

Whatever the truth about the existing FMS systems, the principle is a good one and the potential for their adoption is very high. Areas away from the traditional metal cutting sector of the manufacturing industry that are investigating the applications of FMS include:

Sample preparation and chemical analysis

Sample preparation and metallurgical analysis

Biomedical analysis

Food preparation

Clothing manufacture

Farming, via the use of AGVs.

Although some of the above applications may seem strange uses for FMS, you must not be blinkered into thinking of the systems as being massive and restricted to the metal cutting industries. The philosophy of the FMS is one of total control over a complete process, through computer supervision and interaction at all structural levels of the FMS hierarchy.

Further Reading

1. *Fundamentals of Interactive Computer Graphics* by J. D. Foley and A. Van Dam, published by Addison Wesley
2. *Computer Aided Design and Manufacture* by C. B. Besant, published by Ellis Horwood Ltd
3. *Computer Aided Design – Fundamentals and System Architectures* by J. Encarnacao and E. G. Schlechtendahl, published by Springer-Verlag

9 Robots and Economics

Industrial robots are increasingly being used in the manufacturing industry, and although the installed base of robots in the UK for example is currently small, there are many forecasts of substantial growth in the use of robots. The reasons given by firms for introducing robots are often economic in nature. In this chapter we will look at what the economics of the firm are, and at some of the objectives and constraints under which firms operate. We shall begin with the production process, as this is the area in which robots have the most direct impact.

The Production Process

The production process (that is, actually making the goods) in manufacturing industry is of key importance, but it does not work in isolation, and is closely dependent upon other functions in the organization. Other functions which are important are:

The Marketing Function – to identify suitable markets, and ensure the supply of goods to those markets.

The Design and Development Function – to enable new and improved products to come to the market.

The Finance Function – to ensure that adequate funds are available for the short and longer term needs of the business.

The Personnel Function – to recruit suitable personnel, to assist with good working relations (for example, union negotiations, working conditions, etc) within the firm.

So much for the production process in relation to the other parts of the organization. Let us now look at what the process comprises.

One way of looking at this area, commonly used by economists, is to categorize production into three factors: labour, material and capital. These are sometimes called *inputs*. By examining production in this way, it is possible to look at the *balance*, or *production mix* as it is sometimes called, between these factors. We will now examine what each of the factors are.

Labour   There are many kinds of labour input in terms of human effort, varying from the physical labour of a road builder to the intellectual labour of a research scientist. However, when used in theoretical economic discussion, labour is the collective name given to all these different kinds of human productive services. The costs of labour inputs are the sum of all the costs of remuneration of the employees in the organization (that is, wages, salaries, bonuses, etc.).

Production labour costs (as opposed to, say, administrative staff costs) are the costs most relevant to robotization and robot suppliers are keen to pitch the costs of running a robot against those of using human labour. Production labour costs vary tremendously in different organizations depending upon the type of manufacturing activity, for example the numbers of production employees required. In some industries such as those producing hand-made goods, the process can be said to be labour-intensive, whereas in a highly automated industry such as car production, the process is not labour intensive. Production labour costs are also related to the skill levels required to carry out the operations ranging from unskilled (and therefore cheaper) labour on assembly line operations, to highly skilled craftsmen in machining shops. A further factor influencing labour costs is the amount of shift working required within the organization.

Materials   This factor of production is used to describe the material inputs of a manufacturing enterprise. The material "inputs" are converted by the production process to become the "output" of goods from the enterprise. These materials are not necessarily raw materials for conversion. Many manufacturing organizations use materials that are already processed in some way, such as sheet metal car components.

Capital   This term is widely used in business and by economists. It has however a wide range of meanings and there is no universally agreed definition of the term. Capital inputs for the production process are generally considered to be "fixed" capital consisting of durable goods such as plant and machinery. If a production process uses very expensive plant it can be said to be capital-intensive.

The term capital can also be used to refer to work-in-progress capital which includes the value of raw materials, components and made-up stock held by the firm.

Types of Production

Before examining the "mix" in production factors, we shall look at the three main types of production as these are closely connected to the factors of production. These are:

  Custom production
  Mass production
  Batch production

The type of production appropriate to a particular firm is dependent upon the variety of products the firm produces, and the number or volume of each product required.

1 Custom Production As the name implies, jobs in this type of production are carried out individually to the specific order of a customer. Ship building, bridge building and craft products are common examples of custom production. This type of production does not normally lend itself to mechanization or automation since the work tasks vary considerably between different jobs. It therefore tends to be labour intensive, often involving the use of highly skilled labour.

2 Mass Production Mass production is the opposite of custom production and is suitable where large numbers of identical parts are manufactured. As the work tasks are constant and repeatable, highly automated specialist machinery is used and the labour content is comparatively small in relation to the high level of capital investment in the machine.

3 Batch Production Batch production lies between mass and custom production methods in that it involves repeated but not continuous production. Firms involved in batch production tend to make a number of similar items but not in sufficient quantity to justify continuous manufacture. In batch production a batch of products of one design is made, and then a batch of another design, and so on. Batch sizes vary tremendously according to the product or industry sector; interestingly, 40% of all engineering products produced in the UK are made in batches of 50 units or less.

Traditionally, batch manufacture uses proportionately more labour and less machinery than does mass production. This is because machinery has to be more versatile (or flexible) to be efficient in batch manufacture. Again, due to the variety of work involved, the skill requirements of batch production tend to be greater than those required in mass manufacture. The flexibility requirement of batch production is of key importance. Robot technology is, in theory, very appropriate in this type of manufacture.

Financial and Management Issues

In the manufacturing industry in the UK almost all processes are becoming more capital intensive. Production processes are using comparatively more capital relative to the quantities of other production inputs (labour and materials).

Economies-of-Scale Theories of the Firm

The changing mix in production inputs is closely tied to another economic maxim – that of "economies of scale". This is a phrase used to explain the advantages that can be gained by making more of a product with less costs per unit. An economy of scale can therefore be said to exist when expansion of production capacity increases output with proportionately less production costs.

Economies of scale vary from industry to industry and not all products necessarily benefit from large-scale production. The explanation for these variations lies partly with the technology of the production process. Owing to technical constraints, large plants can produce goods such as steel more efficiently, whereas in the textile industry large plants are often a disadvantage.

In many UK manufacturing sectors, however, large-scale mass production has been favoured in order to meet the competitive pressures of the inter-national market. It is difficult for example for UK manufacturers to compete against mass-produced Japanese television sets or Italian fridges if production methods cannot offer the same economies of scale (that is, reduced manufac-turing cost per unit.) To achieve such economies of scale, significant increases in capital investment are required. Investments in advanced manufacturing technology are part of this trend away from labour inputs in favour of capital inputs.

Historical Development of Ownership

It is a commonly stated view that the main objective of a company is to "maximize profits". This view asserts that all other considerations are second-ary to this maximization of profits. It therefore follows from this view that the purpose of a manufacturing business is to produce goods that can be sold at the maximum profit (subject to demand and cost considerations). Achieving this aim involves finding an appropriate mix in the factors of production.

Profit maximization is the traditional economic theory used to explain the objectives and hence the behaviour of firms. It is a theory which is rooted in the historical development and ownership patterns of the firm. Since the latter part of the nineteenth century, businesses have increased in size and the relationship of the owner of the company to the day-to-day operations has changed radically. Before the advent of larger more complex companies the relationship was quite straightforward: the owner of the company provided the financial resources to enable the business to exist, *and* managed the business. The owner could therefore set objectives, control policy, and distribute resources in order to reach these objectives. The link between ownership and objectives was very clear and direct.

Since the latter part of the nineteenth century, there has been a marked trend towards companies becoming larger, and ownership structures have changed accordingly. This has led to a position where the true owners of companies (namely shareholders) are generally not involved in the company's management. There has therefore evolved a division between ownership, management and labour.

The modern shareholder in a joint stock company, be he or she an individual investor or an institution (such as a pension fund), no longer exerts very much influence on the management of the company. The investor is mainly interested in the financial returns the investment will bring, relying on other people (salaried managers) to manage and direct the company. It is now generally the purpose of management to formulate and pursue the objectives and policies of the firm. This is not, however, to say that managements act as totally independent agents; they have by law to take into account the financial expectations of the shareholders and protect their interests.

Does this mean that the purpose of the firm is merely to maximize the financial benefits of its shareholders?

The Profit Concept – Behaviouralist Theories of the Firm

As we have already stated, the idea of profit maximization is at the core of the economic theory of the firm. However, profit is a concept which is defined and used in a number of ways. We shall briefly examine how profit is qualified in accountancy terms. Accountants are responsible for drawing up annual Profit and Loss accounts. These accounts give a picture of the financial status of a firm at the end of each year's trading. There are two major kinds of accounting profit: gross profit and net profit.

Gross profit refers to the difference between the total sales revenue of the firm and the direct costs the firm has incurred, for example, labour, materials and fuel.

Net profit is calculated on the gross profit once other factors have been deducted such as interest on loans, tax, depreciation, etc. Net profit is therefore what is left for distribution to the firm's owners (that is, dividends to shareholders) and to fund new investment.

The theory that the objectives of firms are to maximize profits is therefore very simple in that it allows certain predictions to be made about their likely behaviour. Many decisions made in firms are based on the relative profitability of the proposed alternatives. However, the notion that profit is the objective of the firm has been increasingly questioned. During the recent economic recession, many companies with good order books and which have been profitable on paper have, in fact, gone to the wall due to poor cash-flow management. This has highlighted the inadequacy of profit as a measure of success. As we mentioned previously, profit is a paper measure which provides a picture of the company at the end of the trading year. Cash flow can be a much more telling indicator of the firm in that, without an adequate cash-flow situation (that is, without getting its money in from creditors), a company can easily become insolvent despite overall "paper profitability".

In moving away from the classical economic theory of the firm, some theories try to predict and explain the behaviour of firms by analyzing the behaviour and motivation of managers – sometimes called managerial theories of the firm. Such theorists argue that, due to the divorce of management from ownership, managers are *not* solely interested in maximizing profits, but are motivated by other maximization factors. So, for example, it was argued by Baumol in 1959 that since the status of a manager is judged by the *size* of the firm rather than by its profits, a manager will consequently seek to maximize sales revenue. Managers will try to achieve what gives them personal satisfaction, and will manage the firm accordingly.

We have now looked at some economic theories of the firm, and some behavioural theories of the firm. Do you think any of these theories really explain why firms operate as they do? Do they operate just for the benefit of shareholders? Are they driven by the status aspirations of managers?

In response to such questions and issues, behavioural scientists have developed some broader theories of the firm. These theories take into account a wider range of parties involved in the formulation of a firm's objectives, based on a belief that objectives are not established purely in the interests of managers or shareholders. These theories take into account other groups such as workers, the local community, suppliers and customers. All parties involved are defined as *stakeholders* in that they are all affected by the activities of the firm and must all therefore be taken into consideration. This theory is known as the stakeholder theory.

The essence of the theory is that the objectives of firms are influenced by a broad range of both *social and economic factors*, and the firm's obligations are not only to the owners, but also to the employees, its customers and the community as a whole.

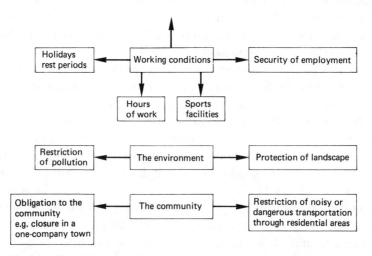

Fig 9.1   Social factors influencing economics of the firm

Figure 9.1 shows some of the social factors that might be taken into account.

It is therefore clear that management is often faced with conflicting social and economic responsibilites such as those of:

Owner

Employee

Society

The way in which management sets objectives and policies is clearly influenced by a wide range of factors; economic theory alone cannot explain the behaviour of firms, and the constraints under which they operate.

At this point, we shall leave the theories and adopt a more practical approach, looking at what economic benefits are claimed for robots and how firms go about measuring or justifying such benefits. This practical approach will, however, use concepts and ideas that have been explained above.

The yardsticks used by management to measure the economic worth of investments in production machinery such as robots are commonly referred to as *financial appraisal* or *investment appraisal techniques*. Robots, although often considered to be different and new, are nevertheless to be regarded like any other capital expenditure. An analysis has to be made of the prospective costs and predicted benefits of the investment in order to evaluate the desirability of committing company resources. The most commonly used and simplest appraisal method is called pay-back appraisal.

Pay-back Appraisal   Pay-back appraisal involves fairly crude calculations in which the time taken to recover the capital outlay is measured and the results are expressed as a period of time. Pay-back methods therefore answer two basic questions about an investment.

1   How much is it going to cost?
2   How soon shall we cover the cost of the investment?

Pay-back appraisals take into account a limited range of costs and benefits and are easy to calculate. The time scales involved in pay-back calculations are normally short and include economic factors such as interest rates, inflation, etc.

Robot suppliers have commonly adopted pay-back calculations to justify robot purchases. These normally demonstrate short pay-back periods and are therefore considered to be a good selling tool, with slogans such as "Pays for itself in under two years!"

A survey by the Machine Tools Trades Association (MTTA) in the UK has shown that purchasers also favour pay-back methods. They found that over 80% of firms still use pay-back to assess investments in production machinery.

So, why not use pay-back? If used as the main appraisal method to measure the economic viability of investment in robots, pay-back has a number of major limitations, which may result in discouraging the adoption of robots. This is because payback calculations cannot measure many of the effects a robot can have on the economics of the firm. The limitations of pay-back are that

a) It concentrates on a limited number of variables (such as purchase costs and labour savings) and ignores many other factors.

b) It focuses on the very short-term and ignores longer-term benefits after the pay-back period.

c) It emphasizes cost savings rather than broader issues of profitability.

To examine why these limitations are important, one needs a broader understanding of the sort of impact a robot can have on the economics of a firm's operation. So, before discussing alternative appraisal techniques, we shall examine some effects of robots on a firm's operations. From this we should be able to develop a clearer picture of what sorts of factors these financial yardsticks should measure.

The Economic Benefits of Robot Installations

Tangible Benefits

To examine the savings we need to adopt the perspective of "before" and "after", and look at the major factors of production discussed previously:

1 Labour Savings In a survey carried out in the UK amongst UK robot users, labour saving was listed as the most important factor in the decision to introduce robots. Although some work and tasks are created by the introduction of robots, the overall tendency is nevertheless towards displacement. In theory, therefore, robots appear to be shifting the factors of production away from labour inputs in favour of capital inputs.

The cost of employing a person is high compared to the cost of employing a robot because, generally speaking, wages are not directly linked to attendance. A firm has to pay wages regardless of whether an employee is at work, on vacation, ill, or absent. Furthermore, since the quality from a manual process is not consistent, it is necessary to employ additional people to inspect the work.

Not surprisingly, the capital investment required for a process to be performed robotically is higher than for the same process to be performed manually. However, if the cost of installing robots is amortised over several years, then the per hour cost will be shown to be lower than that for employing a person. The comparison of costs is shown in figure 9.2 and most importantly we can observe how the relative hourly costs diverge rapidly in favour of robots as time goes on.

Notice that figure 9.2 assumes a long useful life for the robot. While you would be correct in saying that the robot itself could quickly become out of date, its flexibility ensures a long life span because it can be programmed and re-programmed to deal with new processes.

A further benefit of robots is realised in the reduced cost of training. People have to be trained and supervised to ensure that their work is performed correctly. Additionally every change in task means more retraining and further disruption to output. When a person is transferred from one task to another, the skills learned and acquired with the original task deteriorate quickly through lack of use. Consequently, if that person is returned to the original task, the task will be performed at a lower output level and with a lower quality until the person has relearned the necessary skills.

Whenever we teach a task to a robot, the information is stored in memory and unless that memory is erased the information need never be "forgotten". The result is that the robot will always perform that task to the same quality level no matter what the time interval is between usage. For the firm, this

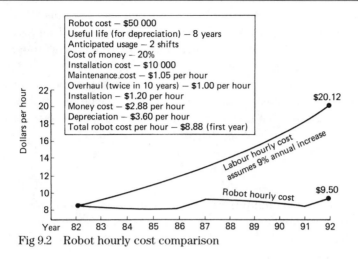

Fig 9.2 Robot hourly cost comparison

means that each task need only be taught once. Subsequently the program can be run at any time on that robot, without fear of error due to lack of practice.

2 Improved Product Quality Among robot users, improved product quality was mentioned as a significant contributory factor in introducing robots. If a product is manufactured with variable quality, then the company will have to absorb the costs of repair, the wasted expenditure of material in processing scrap products, and the lost revenue from the lower rate of acceptable quality products.

In many applications the robot is programmed to reproduce the activities of humans and can then repeat these activities indefinitely. This is the case in paint spraying and welding. Here, the robot's performance is very consistent and imitates the best performance of the human operator. Note, however, that consistent performance by itself does not necessarily mean a higher quality. It simply means consistency about the level of quality that is programmed into the robot. If a robot is incorrectly programmed, it could produce 100 percent scrap items – the quality level will be consistent although not acceptable.

3 Reduced Material Cost In addition to the benefits of reduced scrap levels mentioned above, there may be savings made in process materials.

A typical example of the savings made by using robots is in the underseal application process at a Rover Group plant. Here, a robot achieves considerable savings in the quantity of underseal that is required per car, since it follows the optimum path and does not have to go over or "patch up" its work. People doing a similar job tend to use more material than necessary, or throw away nearly empty containers of material.

Further, we all know that material is cheaper in large containers than in small containers. If we make use of the robot's control systems and large payload capacity, then we can often use consumable materials such as glue, paint and screws, directly from larger containers, or use rolls of welding wire instead of welding rods. This gives us three economic advantages. The first advantage is that the amount of material to be used is programmed into the robot. Usage rates are therefore known, helping stock control and preventing overstocking or stock-outs. The second advantage is that the purchase of large containers of material can lead to economies of scale resulting in lower per unit material cost. The third advantage is that the percentage waste from a large container is lower than that from a small container, assuming that the shelf life of the material (paints, sealants etc.) exceeds the time taken to use the material.

4   Increased Throughput   In many installations robots can increase the output of a product. Examples of how this is achieved include:

(*a*) More products per hour getting through quality checks due to better and more consistent quality.

(*b*) Higher volume of production.

Although the speed of operation of a robot is typically slower than that of a person, the throughput per shift is actually greater. The reason is that a robot does not take washroom or coffee breaks nor does its output rate vary through fatigue. It should be noted however that in a number of factory operations robots are programmed to work at the speed or output of human operators performing other activities.

Apart from the variation in performance of people, we must also consider and cater for uncertain attendance patterns. We know that people take vacations, change jobs, or do not go to work if they feel ill. A production schedule must therefore take into account this unreliability of people as production elements. Robots on the other hand are reliable, they are always at work and if they break down they can often be repaired quickly. Further, if necessary, a robot can be used 24 hours a day, 7 days a week; whereas if it were required to run a manual process in the same manner there would be problems in attendance reliability and variation in operating costs because of different payments for different shifts.

Intangible Benefits

The common features of the four categories of savings outlined so far are all quite "tangible" in nature, in that they can be separated from other costs, and calculated. There are, however, other less visible economic benefits which robots can bring which do not fall so neatly into tangible categories for analysis.

These intangible benefits are very significant, but are rarely included in investment appraisal calculations. It may be true to say that investments in robots present new challenges to our methods of appraising capital investment and this is because they offer new kinds of benefit, which are more difficult to assess in economic terms.

To understand these issues we need to look back to the heart of the matter – the nature of robot technology. Although robots are a class of automation, they have characteristics which make them fundamentally different from other kinds of automation equipment. These characteristics are based on their flexibility, that is their ability to be *reprogrammed.*

Other automation machinery, such as transfer lines, is *dedicated* to manufacturing one kind of product such as light bulbs, bottles or car components. The equipment is designed specifically to manufacture one product or component and, due to the high cost of design and development such, dedicated or special-purpose automation equipment is normally only economically appropriate in mass or large batch manufacturing environments.

Robots, however, enable a different kind of automation as they are not dedicated in the same sense as traditional forms of automation. They can be reprogrammed to perform their process (for example; handling, welding, spraying, etc.) on a wide range of parts or products. Robots therefore provide **flexible automation**, and this flexibility is a very important economic factor. For example, when a product line changes, a robot can be redeployed on the next product line, whereas dedicated automation equipment is not capable of being easily redeployed without immense cost. This considerably increases the effective working life of the equipment.

Robot flexibility is at the core of the new benefits we have referred to, so let's go on to look at the implications of this flexibility and examine some of the new benefits.

1   *Robotic automation can make a company more responsive to market demands, and enable a firm to offer a better service to its customers.*
The equipment is not dedicated to one product or part, and can be reprogrammed to cope with new or changing parts as demanded by the marketplace.

Example 1   *The Cosmetic Industry*   This industry operates in a very volatile marketplace. It is subject to fashions and fads which demand frequent changes in products and in the presentation and packaging of these products. Robotic handling devices are used by some major companies in the United States to package cosmetic goods. These robotic devices are used in some cases in place of dedicated machinery (dedicated to packaging one shape) and, in others cases, in place of human workers. The robots are reprogrammed easily and cheaply to grip and pack the redesigned pots, boxes, lipstickholders, etc. It is therefore easier and cheaper for the cosmetics company to change product packaging in response to changing market conditions.

Example 2   *The Car Industry*   The car industry is also strongly influenced by a volatile marketplace in which model changes and improvements are an important competitive factor. On robot spot welding lines, for example, the robots can be reprogrammed to cope with slight changes in shape due to model updating and indeed can cope with entirely new models once the new programs are written. In addition, the firm can easily adjust the balance of production between existing models – coupé, hatchback, saloon etc. – in response to market demands. As long as the robot knows which model is coming down the line, it can apply the correct stored program to the job.

2   *Robots can make small batch production more economically attractive and reduce work-in-progress inventories.*

Earlier, we discussed the three major kinds of manufacturing production: mass, batch, and custom. Flexible automation (such as robots and FMS) can bring the same economies of scale traditionally only possible in mass or large batch automation through its ability to be easily reprogrammed.

Example 3   *Machining Shop: Robots Working within a Flexible Manufacturing System (FMS)*   In FMS, computerized numerical control (CNC) machine tool and robot part programs can be stored and recalled when certain parts are needed. Prior to flexible automation, the time and effort required to set up machines to make different parts was considerable and parts were generally made up in large batches for storage. This has traditionally led to large work-in-progress inventories, that is a lot of capital has been locked up in parts made up and stored. Flexible automation makes it more economically feasible for parts to be made up more or less on demand in small batches, thereby reducing work-in-progress inventories.

3   *Robots can bring a firm an improved "image" in the marketplace. This is brought about through goods being produced with more consistent quality resulting in fewer customer complaints, etc.*

In addition, it is interesting to note that some companies (notably Fiat) have emphasized in their advertising campaigns the improved quality achieved by robotic production ("Built by Robots").

4   *Robots can help to bring new products to the market with shorter lead times.*

This benefit is particularly appropriate where robots are operating in widely automated production environments incorporating CAD facilities. This is because information about a part (weight, geometry, etc.) produced in the design phase can be used to produce robot programs. This direct link into the design data can considerably reduce the time taken to bring a part to the market (the lead time).

There are, therefore, both tangible and intangible benefits resulting from the adoption of robots into the manufacturing process. These are summarised in Table 9.1

Table 9.1.

ECONOMIC BENEFITS OF ROBOT INSTALLATION	
Tangible	*Intangible*
Labour savings	Better response to market demands
Improved quality	Reduce work-in-progress
Reduced material cost	Improved company image
Increased throughput	Shorter lead times

Other Methods of Appraisal

As we have already seen, pay-back fails to take into account the long-term and the less-tangible benefits offered by robots and in many senses is an inadequate and inappropriate technique to measure the economic effects of flexible automation such as robots. There are, however, more sophisticated and longer-term investment appraisal techniques including, for example, discounted cash flow (DCF) and life cycle costing techniques. These techniques are far more complex and take into account a wider range of economic factors. Nevertheless, they have not gained wide acceptance and pay-back continues to dominate investment decisions in production machinery.

As we discussed earlier, appraisal techniques are an aid to management to enable them to take some kind decision on a rational course of action. In practice, however, the choice of technique appears to be more subjective in nature in that an appraisal technique is selected on the basis of which is considered easiest or the most easily communicated. This choice is influenced by "people issues", and investment decisions and appraisal techniques are not as rational and objective as they appear.

The effects of this are:

1 A tendency towards seeking and emphasizing short-term tangible benefits.

2 An inherent conservatism towards taking the perceived risks of investing in new manufacturing technology.

These conservative traits have influenced UK investment in production technology and UK firms have generally been slow to adopt new manufacturing techniques such as robots. If one examines, for example, the pattern of robot adoption in the UK, it is clear that small robot installations (that is 1 or 2 robots) have been favoured. This contrasts sharply with the more full-scale commitment to robots shown in other major industrial nations such as West Germany, the United States and Japan.

The choice of poor appraisal techniques is therefore one example of management attitudes influencing investment levels in automation. Financial procedures however can only go so far: they are a means to provide some sort of measurement and to reduce the areas of uncertainty in investment decisions, but managerial judgement must continue from that point. This brings us to the conclusion that investment decisions are in many senses highly subjective and investment in automation equipment may be an "act of faith" in the long-term future of the firm. Due to the many and far-reaching economic benefits that flexible automation can bring to large-scale investment, such automation is an act of commitment to the future of the firm and its ability (and determination) to survive in the evolving and competitive international marketplace.

10 Current and Future Developments

The field of robotics and computerised automation is a dynamic one with developments proceeding at an extremely fast pace. In this chapter we will be looking at the underlying trends of this development and examining some of the products.

As you will be aware from having studied the earlier chapters of this book, the field of robotics encompases a wide range of separate disciplines. These include computing, mechanical engineering and electronics. All these individual areas are rich in research and development programmes and many of the products of this research will ultimately be of benefit to robotics as well as to other fields which depend on these technologies.

Of more immediate relevance to robotics, however, are the developments taking place in what we might call "applied technology". This type of research, usually funded from industrial sources, aims to find solutions to industrial problems based upon existing technology. Examples of this are software improvements to provide new algorithms for robot control, the development of higher-resolution vision systems, improving sensor capabilities, and the development of communication protocols to aid the integration of computer-controlled factory equipment. Sometimes, of course, these developments are held up because the appropriate technology is not yet available; very often, however, it is possible to make use of existing technology to solve an identified problem.

An example of an original solution using existing technology is provided by a requirement which arose for an assembly robot. The robot was required to be "compliant" horizontally to allow for variations in the components being assembled, but rigid in the vertical plane to enable components to be positively inserted where required.

The conventional robots available at the time did not fulfill the need (see figure 5.1): all the compliance of most robots is in the vertical plane and is caused by the backlash on the rotating joints. The horizontal compliance available due to backlash in the base rotation could not really be efficiently transmitted to the end effector. The solution adopted was simple and effective and required no technological breakthrough. Simply, the robot was effectively rotated through 90 degrees and the SCARA robot was born (see figure 5.1e and also Chapter 5). With this new configuration all the backlash is now in the horizontal plane whilst the robot remains rigid in the vertical plane.

During the remainder of this chapter we will examine other areas where the needs of industry have dictated developments in the field of robotics and we will look at some of these developments in greater detail.

Areas of Research

The table of figure 10.1 shows, across the top, some of the major application areas where robots are employed in industry. Down the side of the table are listed some of the features of robotic systems considered, by users, to be of importance.

The actual entries in the table show which features are considered to be in need of development for particular application areas. The table is included here as a rough guide only and is intended to give you a "feel" for how the demands of users are the motivating force behind the development of new or improved features of robotic systems.

	Palletizing	Machine Loading	Spot Welding	Arc Welding	Surface Coating	Grinding/Deburring	Assembly	Inspection
CAPABILITIES								
Vision Systems	■			■	■	■	■	■
Programmability	■	■		■	■	■	■	■
Gripper Dexterity	■	■	■			■	■	■
Flexibility		■				■	■	
Size, Weight		■			■		■	
Control System				■	■	■	■	■
PERFORMANCE								
Speed	■	■	■		■		■	
Positioning Accuracy		■	■	■	■	■	■	■
Repeatability		■	■	■	■	■	■	■
Reliability		■	■	■	■	■	■	■
OTHER FEATURES								
Costs	■	■	■	■	■	■	■	■
Communications	■	■		■	■		■	
Safety		■		■	■	■	■	

Fig 10.1

Vision Systems

State of the Art

In Chapter 6 we looked at why vision systems are considered to be so essential in the area of robotics and we examined the basic principles of their operation.

Vision systems for industrial applications have four major components:

Data capture   The camera with its lens system and electronics which provide the image.

Image processing   The electronic circuits and the associated software which digitise and manipulate the image.

Data presentation   The VDU which displays the image to the operators and supervisors.

Data communication   The subsystem responsible for passing the processed data to other parts of the robotic system.

All the individual areas benefit from the general advance of technological development because they are linked with more general applications. The technology for data capture and data presentation, for example, is already very advanced since cameras and VDUs are already produced for a very active television and computer market. The fourth area, that of data communications, is also bound up with general developments in computer technology.

The developments taking place specifically in the industrial application of vision are in the software and system design associated with image processing. One of the problems facing users is that where a vision system is required to have high resolution (more pixels) or higher definition (more information about each pixel) then the demands on the processing subsystem become more acute. More pixels or more data means that either the processor must become more powerful and hence more expensive, or else the processing has to be slowed down. Image processing time which is in excess of 10 percent of the total cycle time for a robotic activity is, in general, considered unacceptable.

Two examples from the real world will serve to demonstrate how the problems are dealt with.

The first example comes from the world of microchip fabrication where vision systems are used extensively. In one stage of the process, however, they are experiencing difficulties. This is the stage where the connecting wires from the outside of the package are bonded to the semiconductor substrate itself and the results of this activity need to be inspected.

With a currently available high-power high-speed vision system a device of size 0.04 inches by 0.04 inches can be analysed for defects in about 1 second, and this is perfectly satisfactory. A device measuring 0.2 inches by 0.2 inches, however, would require 25 seconds and this length of time is unacceptable to semiconductor manufacturers. The only solution currently available is for the inspection to be carried out by well-trained human operators who can complete the inspection in a fraction of the time. It is anticipated that developments in grey-scale image analysis techniques will enable this task to be automated within the next few years, but for the time being vision systems do not offer a solution.

Another approach to dealing with the limitations of current systems has been taken by a group of researchers at the University of Hull. Their problem was to automate the manufacture of power diodes using a PUMA robot. The power diodes are made of an assembly of seven components each one picked up in turn from feeders by the robot and transferred to the assembly point. The imperfections in the components are such that unless there is some form of visual feedback it will be impossible to consistently align the assembly.

The assembly cell is fitted with a high resolution vision system to monitor the entire assembly area and to provide positional information on all the objects in that area. This information is used to guide the robot. As each component is presented for assembly, it is required to be inspected. This is carried out by a second camera mounted on the robot's gripper. Significant savings are achieved by using a low resolution system for this task. It is possible to use low resolution in this case because of the close proximity of the camera to the part being inspected.

The same processor is used for both high and low resolution processing, switching being under the control of software and a real-time clock. In this way the use of the available processing power has been optimised and costs have been kept in check.

Future Developments

In image processing, the fundamental problem has always been to separate the object of interest from its background. For a 256×256 pixel frame with 8 bits of grey level information the amount of computing power required for image processing is tremendous and, until recently, industrial vision applications have concentrated on reducing the data to be processed in an effort to overcome this.

The new generation of image processing systems uses grey scale techniques which are *edge-oriented* in operation. In this system each pixel and its neighbouring pixels are subjected to an arithmetic filtering operation known as "convolution" that enhances edge features of the image. Several types of convolution can be used to enhance various types of features. This type of edge detection is not affected by general illumination intensity on the part or colouration of the part as long as there is some contrast between edges. Using these methods, complex images can be processed in real-time without seriously affecting the cycle time.

Before leaving the subject of vision it is worth looking at a more lateral development proposed by Dean Wilson in the USA. His suggestion is to reduce the dependence on what he calls "passive mode technology" whereby vision systems have to deal with components and parts which have been designed without the vision system in mind. Instead, he proposes that, when parts are designed, the requirements of vision systems should be actively taken into account. Such parts are known as "self-referenced parts" and are designed to the following criteria:

to improve image sensing
to simplify fixturing
to simplify optics
to make the part self-calibrating
to provide orientation
to simplify mechanical handling.

The methods he suggests include:

Change of profile: by adding a notch or making a component non-symmetrical in order to aid orientation.

Non-profile changes: this includes attaching labels or the spraying of dot or colour codes on to the part. Furthermore, the design of the label itself could aid orientation, reference being made to the label rather than the part.

Temporary references: here the reference is made to the part carrier which may or may not be discarded during assembly.

Programmability

If you were asked to name the most significant technology employed in the modern factory environment, you would probably answer that it was the technology of the computer that has had the most far-reaching effects on recent industrial development. In this book you have had the opportunity to read about how the computer, at the heart of the control system, is able to provide a measure of "intelligence" to the automatic operation of machinery.

The immense benefits associated with the use of computers accrue for three main reasons:

● They allow the systems to be *programmed* and reprogrammed to carry out a desired set of tasks thereby creating *flexible* systems.
● They provide the capability of on-line moment-by-moment *optimization* of the equipment and its use.
● They are able to organize factory data to enable resources to be used in the most efficient way.

All these applications require, of course, that the computer or computers be properly programmed to carry out these tasks. The developments taking place are in response to a demand to make this programming task *simpler* and more *universal*. One such development is the CAM-I graphic programming system.

CAM-I stands for Computer Aided Manufacturing International and is an organization formed to further the cooperative research and development efforts of companies involved in CAD/CAM. The programming system being developed by this group aims to provide four powerful modules:

Off-line programming of a complete work cell.
Simulation and animation facilities.
A full database containing geometric, sensor and kinematic information.
Artificial intelligence based software for on-line operation.

The four modules interface with each other to provide a universal programming system. Individually they work as follows:

1 *Off-line Programming*   In Chapter 2 we discussed off-line programming at length and analysed its requirements. In the CAM-I system the off-line programming is universal, having data structures that relate to all aspects of robot cell programming and to all types of robots, sensors and ancilliary devices.

2 *Simulation and Animation*   Associated with off-line programming is the off-line testing of programs. The CAM-I system contains software to display on the VDU screen a 3D simulation of the work cell being programmed. The software also provides for animation of the image so that a programmed sequence can be "run" and debugged before even being tried out on the real cell.

3 *Database*   The software is split into *generic* software which applies to all systems, and a database of *specific* software which contains elements relating to those components which are included in the work cell being programmed. The database will provide geometric information about the cell; kinematic information relating to the load/speed characteristics of the moving parts of the cell; information relating to the controller; sensor information and information relating to the ancilliary actuators connected to the cell. The generic software would work together with the database and would provide post-processed information that can be used to drive the actual cell or the simulation.

4 *On-line Software*   The virtues of using a computer to control a mechanical system include the fact that it can respond quickly to changes in on-line conditions. Thus if a part jams or is presented in the wrong orientation the computer can cause appropriate action to be taken. Using traditional methods of programming, these evasive actions are pre-programmed in the computer and when a particular condition is encountered, one of these actions will be selected from the total number available. The CAM-I system uses an artificial intelligence based *expert system* to make these decisions on the basis of a constant stream of information received from the system's sensors.

The initial thrust of the development programme is to produce what is known as a Robot Planner which is to be a complete graphics-based off-line programming system. As the project develops, the on-line interface will be made available. An interesting by-product is that, when the cell is actually operating, the graphics software will also be available to display on a VDU an animated image of the operation of the real cell.

Gripper Dexterity

Robotics is a synthesis of mechanical and electronic engineering. Many of the areas of development that have been or will be discussed in this chapter are in electronic and associated computer science fields. However, much research and development is taking place on the mechanical side of robotics and gripper development is included in this.

Currently, end effector design is usually carried out using a "horses for courses" approach, whereby a gripper will be designed for a particular operation. Thus, in an application for the insertion of electronic components into printed circuit boards, grippers will be built to suit each component being handled.

This approach appears to be at odds with the ideal of making a robot into a flexible type of transfer device and some attention is being paid to overcoming this. One approach, certainly, is to attempt to design a universal end effector, but more commonly the solution is for dexterity to be achieved by *automatically* changing grippers to accommodate parts being held.

The "Quick Change" System   One such development is being carried out by the United States National Bureau of Standards and is known as the "Quick Change" system. In this system, a set of interchangeable end effectors has been developed each of which is fitted with a standard termination – the B-Plate – which mates with a matching termination – the A-Plate – permanently mounted at the end of the robot arm.

The end effectors are stored within the robot's work envelope, in a set of specially designed "holsters". When it is required to change the end effector, the following sequence is carried out:

Move to holster

Place current end effector in holster

Disconnect end effector

Move to new holster

Connect new end effector

Move to work position

Carry out task

The mating system not only ensures a reliable mechanical connection between the arm and the end effector, but also it is designed to allow the following connections across the A/B interface:

38 electronic/fibre optic channels

9 hydraulic/pneumatic channels.

The provision of these services allows a wide range of end effectors to be connected including those which incorporate multiple sensing elements.

There are a number of aspects of the design of this system worthy of note.

Locking/Unlocking Mechanism   The A and B plates are connected by a form of bayonet connector which requires the B plate to be inserted into the A plate and twisted until it locks into position (rather like inserting a light bulb into its holder). The locking is achieved by a pin in the A plate moving in a tapered slot in the B plate.

In the Quick Change system the twisting action is accomplished by applying a burst of compressed air through a specially designed mechanism in the A plate. The kinetic energy of this pulse of air is harnessed to provide a controlled force to overcome the friction and the "sticktion" forces and to ensure reliable unlocking and firm locking. The status of the locking mechanism is monitored at each gripper change by two infra-red sensors mounted in the A plate. These are focussed on to a reflective surface on the B plates.

Holsters   The holster system is designed in the following way. The B plate of each gripper is fitted with a pair of "ears". On each holster are two "shoes" which catch the ears as the end effector is placed in the holster. The shoes hold the ears firmly as the making/unmating sequence is carried out.

A feature of the design is that the holster is not fabricated as a rigid system, but instead, it is made compliant in the X,Y and Z directions. This compliance is necessary for the following reasons:

1   As explained earlier the A and B plates are joined by rotating them relative to each other, and this rotation takes place within the holster. If the holster were rigid then any inadvertent excess force could cause the locking mechanism to stick. By making the holster compliant, excess twisting force is absorbed by the compliance and the locking mechanism is protected.

2   When the robot is being programmed, it tends not to move smoothly but in discrete steps, sometimes of the order of 1/16 inch. Without compliance, excessive overshoot can cause very large forces to build up on the locking mechanism as the end effector is held in the holster. Once again the compliance protects the locking mechanism.

3   A compliant system allows the easy correction of minor misalignments. This permits easier programming which does not now have to rely on components being presented in precisely the right position and orientation. This also allows the holsters to be stored in parts of the working envelope where the robot performs with less accuracy and repeatability allowing the remainder of the envelope to be used for more demanding tasks.

Size/Weight

The question of the size and weight of robots is one that has been addressed by a number of development teams. The less massive a robot is, the less inertia it has and the easier it is to control at high speed. On the other hand, if it is to handle heavy loads then it needs to be strong enough to do so. Clearly the ideal is the minimum mass contingent with the loads that it has to carry.

Sometimes, however, robots have to be more massive than they would otherwise be because of the weight of the motors which power their joints. If a requirement for a particularly lightweight robot exists, then often one will be selected that is driven by compressed air (pneumatics). However, the penalty here is that fine control of pneumatic actuators is harder to achieve (see Chapter 5) and we are usually limited to simply moving the actuator between fixed end stops. In the past this has meant that pneumatic robots have been restricted to pick-and-place applications, but a group of researchers at the University of Montreal are developing a method for the complete control of a pneumatic robot.

The unique feature of this research project is the braking system. The system works as follows. Each pneumatically-powered joint has associated with it a pneumatically activated brake which is normally on. The compressed air supply to both actuator and brake is controlled by solenoid-operated valves electrically connected to the controlling computer. When the robot is to be activated, the appropriate joint is energised and its brake released.

To stop the motion at a predetermined point, the brake is applied. However, the motion of such a system is not linear, but varies in a way similar to that shown in figure 10.2. There is a period of acceleration followed by a period of uniform velocity and finally a period of decceleration once the brake has been applied.   In order to stop the robot at a precise location, the brake needs to be applied shortly before it reaches the target. It is the calculation of this stopping distance that is the major activity of the research team. It has been found that the major factor in determining when the brake is to be applied is the instantaneous velocity of the joint and this, of course, depends on the load.

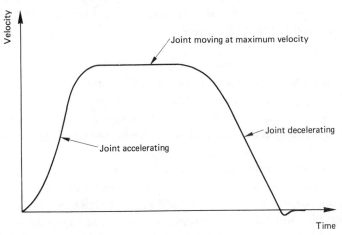

Fig 10.2   Motion of a pneumatically powered joint by a robot

At the time of writing, this research programme is still under way with the goal of achieving true on-line control of a pneumatic actuator. To achieve this, positional feedback is supplied to the controlling computer via a position transducer and an analog-to-digital converter. This data can then be used to calculate the velocity (by differentiation) and the distance from the target, thereby allowing the brakes to be applied at precisely the correct time in the cycle.

Flexibility

It was explained in Chapter 8 how the choice of production method depends to a large extent on the size of batches being produced. For very large runs, "hard" automation will probably be required; for extremely short runs, it may make more sense to produce the goods manually; robotics and "soft" automation come into their own when considering medium-sized batches.

The manufacturer who produces medium-sized batches also usually has another requirement: for the same production machinery to be available very quickly for the manufacture of different items in the range. The manufacturer wants the equipment to be *flexible*.

The change from one product to another will normally involve two functions:

Program change (software)

Tooling change (hardware)

It is usually a straightforward matter to select the appropriate software; it is often more difficult to incorporate flexibility into the hardware. In the section on gripper dexterity we discussed one method of tool changing to achieve some degree of flexibility, but clearly this is not the whole story. How, for example does the robot decide which of the tools to select?

A research group at the Fraunhofer Institute for Manufacturing Engineering and Automation in Germany is looking at the problem of flexibility by examining the role of sensors in the automation environment. They have found it useful to identify three categories.

1 *Sensor Aided Automation (SAA)*

In this group are sensors which have been developed for *one special task* such as palletizing, jet cutting or welding. Here the system's sensors provide on-line information relating to the task being carried out, and the controlling computer takes this data into account when driving the robot. This is probably the most common use of sensors.

2 *Sensor Based Automation (SBA)*

In this group, sensors provide essential information for carrying out the task but do not participate in the task itself. Examples of this type are sensors for part identification (bar code readers) or those supplying geometric data about the part. In this case, the information from the sensor will indicate to the system what course of action to take but will have no part to play in that action. It provides a form of open-loop control.

3 *Sensor Controlled Automation (SCA)*

This area is the one of greatest interest to the German researchers who suggest that it can provide a framework for the development of flexible systems. Sensors in this category are provided with a great degree of intelligence and can make decisions on the basis of information which they collect.

In the traditional approach (SAA and SBA), the robot controller interrogates the system sensors and takes the appropriate action, based on the information received. In the SCA approach, some of the intelligence is devolved to the sensor which can *specify* which action to take. Thus for example in the case of the tool-changing system, the sensor will detect an object of type A and will signal to the controller which is the appropriate tool to use.

What the German group is suggeting is no more than an *approach* to development, but nevertheless it is worthy of note because it is an approach which lends itself to the principles of Artificial Intelligence methods where the actual sequence of operations is not predetermined at system programming time, but depends on the situation pertaining at run time.

Control

Probably the most widely researched area of the whole field of robotics is that of control. Teams at many research institutes are seeking to develop methods of control of robots and other machinery that will fully harness the power of the computers that drive them.

The Step-by-Step Environment   Today's computer-controlled machines operate in a step-by-step mode. In this environment, the tasks which the machine has to carry out are carefully analysed *in advance* and broken down into discrete steps. The job of the programmer is to take these steps and code them in such a way that the computer-controlled machine can replay them at a later stage.

This approach is **prescriptive**, that is every possible eventuality has to be foreseen and programmed for. The machine is incapable of reacting to a situation that has not been specified and for which it does not have an algorithm. This approach requires that the work environment is structured and ordered and imposes a demand for accurate positioning of jigs and fixtures so that the robot will always be able to locate the parts it is working on.

Goal-seeking Robots   The thrust of today's research is to remove the restrictions of prescriptive programming and to enable computer-controlled machines to react to changes in their environment which may not have been predicted. This is **adaptive control** and here the ultimate aim is to be able to give robots tasks which they can then carry out without further instructions. They become goal-seeking machines operating independently of the environment in which they are situated.

To carry out this aim, developments are required in sensor technology and in software design. Sensor design may well be based on the SCA model described earlier, but what of the software?

The software for goal-seeking behaviour will be of the type, such as the Prolog or Lisp languages, which are able to build up a knowledge base. A machine operating with this system will take its decisions based on its perception of the current situation – derived from its sensors – coupled with its own experience which it obtains from its knowledge base. To carry this out, it will have been programmed with a number of problem-solving algorithms from which it will select the best one for each case.

A worked example Imagine a two-dimensional plane where a machine is operating under the supervision of a vision system, as in the diagram of figure 10.3. This example only holds for a step-by-step environment, and whilst its essential elements would carry over into other environments, the argument does not generalise.

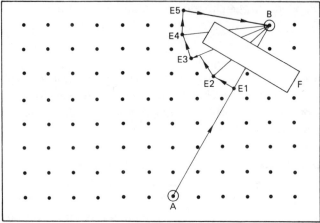

Fig 10.3

The system is represented by a circle, and the circle can move to any point on this plane. The sensitivity of the vision system is assumed to be of one unit length. The machine is ordered to move from point A to point B. An obstacle F, in the shape of a rectangle, is placed in its path after the robot has started to move. Before F was added, the robot started by activating the movement algorithm and this told the robot to move along the straight line from A to B.

When one unit of length away from F, the vision system detects the obstacle. This happens happens at E1. The first reaction of the program is to stop the robot in order to avoid a collision. To reach point B, the robot now invokes its problem solving algorithm. One simple option would be a trial-and-error approach. For instance, such an approach would be to turn 90 degrees anti-clockwise, take another step forward and look again in the direction it is aiming for. Using such an algorithm, the robot will come to point E2 and look in the direction of B.

At this point it will again sense obstacle F and, therefore, should activate the same algorithm once again. Repeating this the robot will reach point E5. There, for the first time, it will receive the information that the path E5B is free and it will start moving along that path to point B.

Needless to say, improvements could be made whereby the vision system could sense the obstacle at an earlier stage and find the best path from A to B through a simulation process. It could also contain some means of memorising and mapping the environment for future reference.

Actual Experience   Two groups working in the USA have revently reported experimental work in this field. The first group work at the Centre for Engineering Systems Advanced Research (CESAR) at Oak Ridge, Tennessee. They are building a device called HERMIES-1 (Hostile Environment Robotic Machine Intelligence Experiment: Series 1) which will ultimately be able to operate in hostile environments related to energy production. A characteristic of this type of environment is that it is for the most part unstructured, and many events happen simultaneously, at high speeds and in unpredictable sequence.

The robot is expected to operate efficiently while dealing with resource constraints (including time), imprecise information, multiple and sometimes conflicting goals, emergency interrupts, parallel actions and learning.

The device built by the group has the following characteristics:

(*a*) It is mobile.

(*b*) It is equipped with two sonar transducers, a 256×256 pixel vision system and an infra-red communications link. One of the sonars is used to provide auto-focus for the vision system. The camera and sonar are mounted on a head which can rotate through 350 degrees and tilt 45 degrees above and below the horizontal.

(*c*) It has three modes of operation:

autonomous

remote control

remote control plus sensor override.

(*d*) It has two processors on board, an 8088 master and a Z-8671 slave which communicate via 2K of common memory

(*e*) Position sensing is by two optical encoders on the drive shafts.

HERMIES-1 is programmed in Lisp and the method is to provide a "world model" by means of a *property list* which is stored in the memory of the 8088. This model is adjusted in real-time by means of a set of rules, also stored in memory, which stipulate how external changes affect the property list. Data for this is, of course, obtained from the system's sensors.

Initial experiments with HERMIES-1 have shown that that the system is capable of generating plans of action to suit various circumstances and to carry them out. Further research will enable problems of increasing complexity to be solved.

A far less complex experiment has been carried out by a group at the University of Central Florida. This group have been comparing the actions of a robot when provided with *a*) ALPHA intelligence and *b*) BETA intelligence.

The robot was a computer-controlled mobile unit fitted with three types of sensor:

Ultrasonic sensor (sonar)

Tactile sensors (bumpers)

Light sensor (photodiode)

Its task was to successfully traverse the space between two points negotiating randomly placed obstacles on the way.

In both cases, the robot is provided with a set of fixed responses to be executed when a change in the environment is sensed. A robot exhibiting ALPHA intelligence selects its response on a purely random basis. Trial and error determines whether a response is appropriate in a particular set of circumstances. BETA robots exhibit alpha behaviour at first, but they store successful responses in memory. When faced with the same environmental situation again, a BETA robot retrieves its successful past response from memory and employs it.

It was found, as expected, that because of their ability to learn, BETA robots demonstrated a gradual improvement in performance over time. The programming language used in this experiment was a dialect of Basic and interested students can carry out similar experiments at low cost using devices such as the BBC Buggy.

Communications

So far in this review of developments in robotics we have covered the items under the heading of "Capabilities" in the diagram of figure 10.1. The final part of this chapter will now concentrate on the question of developments in Communications.

The importance of efficient communication between computer-controlled machines has greatly increased as CIM (Computerised Integrated Manufacture) begins to become a reality. In this environment, products are manufactured according to designs developed using the techniques of Computer Aided Design (CAD) as discussed in Chapter 8. The output of the CAD process is a *database* of information relating to the product from which the manufacturing department is able to plan and execute the actual fabrication of the product.

It is obviously useful if the data produced by CAD is in a form that can be read by the CAM (Computer Aided Manufacture) equipment. However, until very recently, this has been more of a dream than a reality. Another problem is that manufacturing is rarely carried out by a single machine, but rather by a group of machines working together. Once again, if these machines are computer-controlled, then it is obviously advantageous if they can communicate with each other.

One of the problems experienced by users is that different machines are made by different manufacturers and they each may use a different *protocol* for communication. In such a case communication between different machines in the same factory is often extremely difficult if not impossible.

In order to overcome these problems, one of the largest manufacturers in the USA, General Motors, has taken the initiative to specify a universal protocol to be adopted by all CAM suppliers. This protocol is known as **MAP** (*Manufacturing Automation Protocol*) and, because of the backing it is getting from important users like GM, it is gradually gaining acceptance in the manufacturing community.

The MAP protocol deals with all aspects of machine communication from control of an individual cell to communication between cells. For example, at the cell control level one needs

Fast communications, able to deal with many short messages

Immunity from electrical noise

Fast acknowledgement of messages affecting safety

Recovery from errors

The different areas of communication are dealt with in a series of seven layers to conform with another existing standard, namely the ISO (International Standards Organisation) model for open systems interconnection (OSI).

In order to implement the protocol, equipment manufacturers will need to include specialised electronics into their systems, and MAP chips are currently available from Intel, DEC and Motorola. Other suppliers are making complete boards available. All MAP products have to be tested for *conformance*, that is the ability to communicate with similar products from other manufacturers, before they can gain official approval.

In the UK, Leeds University is recognised as the leading authority on MAP implementation, and are likely to be reponsible for the conformance testing of UK products. Manufacturers wishing to use MAP are receiving encouragement from the Department of Trade and Industry.

Appendix I

Optical Shaft Encoders

Optical shaft encoders come in two basic types: *incremental* and *absolute*; both types work on the same principle. Incremental encoders are relatively less expensive and offer high angular resolution (that is, they can detect even a very small amount of rotation). Absolute encoders have the important advantage of highly reliable data transmission – especially useful when powerful electrical equipment is liable to cause interference.

Absolute Optical Shaft Encoders   The principle of an absolute encoder is shown in figure A1.1 and the disc shown in detail in figure A1.2. Notice that the disc shown in the figure has 16 sectors (numbered 0 to 15 inclusive) and that each sector has 4 rows. As the disc rotates, the four pairs of optical sensors and detectors produce a unique code of 1s and 0s as each of the 16 sectors passes between them. The signals from the detectors are fed to a computer or some other digital electronic device which can then use the information to determine the position of the shaft – to within one sixteenth of a revolution if there are sixteen sectors. The disc shown in figure A1.2 is coded in binary code. Assuming that transparent segments of the disc are counted as binary 0s and that opaque segments are counted as binary 1s, then you can see that sector 0 will produce the code "0000", sector 1 "0001", sector 2 "0010", and so on. Each

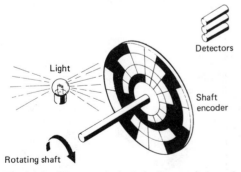

Fig A1.1   How an optical shaft encoder works

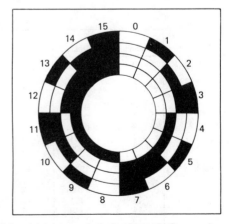

Fig A1.2   A binary coded absolute shaft encoder

sector produces a binary number in the range 0 (bin 0000) to 16 (bin 1111). Since no two sectors have the same code, the computer can use the information to determine not only how much a joint has rotated but also the absolute position of the joint.

At first sight the binary code seems to be the most sensible way of coding the sectors on the disc. In practice, however, binary code is found not to be the best and a more sophisticated code, known as Gray code, is used instead.

Binary Code and Gray Code   The disadvantage of binary coded discs can be seen if you imagine what happens as the disc is rotating. At the point where the boundary between two sectors passes across the detectors, the signals from the detectors will change. Now, in practice, not all four detectors change at *exactly* the same instant in time. Therefore if the computer happens to read the signals at the instant the detectors are changing, the result could be meaningless. The worst case occurs in passing from sector 7 (bin. 0111) to sector 8 (bin. 1000) when all four detectors change state – the 0 changes to 1 and the three 1s change to 0s. The most widely used method of overcoming this problem is to use a cleverly devised code known as Gray code. Figure A1.3a shows a disc marked in Gray code next to a binary coded disc so that you can

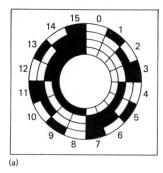 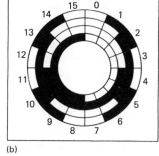

(a)   (b)

Fig A1.3   (a) Disc marked in binary code
(b) Disc marked in Gray code

Decimal	Binary	Decimal	Gray Code
0	0000	0	0000
1	0001	1	0001
2	0010	2	0011
3	0011	3	0010
4	0100	4	0110
5	0101	5	0111
6	0110	6	0101
7	0111	7	0100
8	1000	8	1100
9	1001	9	1101
10	1010	10	1111
11	1011	11	1110
12	1100	12	1010
13	1101	13	1011
14	1110	14	1001
15	1111	15	1000

Fig A1.4   The Gray code

compare the two. The point about Gray code is that in passing from one sector to the next, only *one* of the four detectors changes state. You should check this point for yourself before reading on – make use of the table in figure A1.4. Absolute shaft encoders using Gray code effectively eliminate false readings since at the very worst the error can only be one count.

Incremental Shaft Encoders   The disadvantage of absolute shaft encoders is that they tend to be expensive. As we have just seen, a disc having 16 sectors will require four detectors and the resolution produced will be only 22.5 degrees (that is 360/16) which for many purposes is not good enough. Even using eight detectors would only allow 256 sectors to be encoded, giving a resolution of 1.4 degrees (360/256).

Incremental shaft encoders offer a solution to the problem of obtaining high resolution cheaply, although they have some disadvantages as we shall see. A typical incremental encoder disc is shown in figure A1.5. Notice that it has only one row of markings but that these are smaller and more closely spaced than those on the absolute encoder.

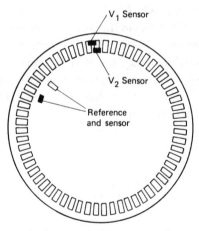

Fig A1.5   A typical incremental encoder disc

The principle of the incremental shaft encoder is that as each mark passes the sensor, a signal is sent to the computer – the more marks there are, the greater the resolution. Looking at figure A1.5 again you will notice that there are three sensors altogether. The two sensors V_1 and V_2 are slightly offset from each other in order that the computer can determine whether the disc is turning clockwise (V_1 is triggered before V_2) or anticlockwise (V_1 is triggered after V_2).

The third sensor is used to keep track of the position of the disc. A pulse from this sensor is sent each time the reference mark passes and this is used to trigger a counter which counts either up or down depending on the direction of rotation.

The Linear Variable Differential Transformer (LVDT)

Don't be put off by the long name. The LVDT is a simple and reliable transducer for producing a voltage from a linear movement (that is, motion in a straight line).

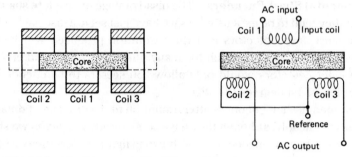

Fig A1.6   The linear variable differential transformer (LVDT)

Figure A1.6 shows the construction, which is based on the principle of the transformer. The core of the transformer is in the form of a long rod which is able to move backwards and forwards inside the coils. The output voltage from coils 2 and 3 depends upon the position of the core. With the core in the centre, the output is zero because the equal voltages induced in coils 2 and 3 cancel each other exactly. When the core is moved, in either direction, the voltage at the output increases in proportion to the movement.

Appendix II

Binary Numbers

In the decimal or base-ten number system we are all familiar with, any number, however big, can be written using a combination of ten different symbols:

0, 1, 2, 3, 4, 5, 6, 7, 8, 9

In the binary (base two) system, only two symbols, 0 and 1, are used.

If you see the number 327 in base 10, you immediately recognize it as meaning "three hundred and twenty seven". If on the other hand you see 723, you would know it is "seven hundred and twenty three". You know this from the positions of the digits. Starting from the *right*, the first digit is "ONEs", the second digit is "TENs" and the third digit is "HUNDREDs" and so on. We can write it like this:

100's   10's   1's
  3   2   7

When you read the number, you know that there are 3 hundreds, 2 tens, and 7 ones. In other words:

$(3 \times 100) + (2 \times 10) + (7 \times 1)$

We can use a similar rule to this one to read binary numbers. Since binary numbers use only 0s and 1s, an example could be 1001 (this may be written 1001_2 or bin. 1001 to distinguish it from a base ten number). Starting from the *right* each digit increases by two times, so that the rightmost digit is ONEs, the next digit is TWOs, then FOURs, EIGHTs, SIXTEENs and so on. We can write it like this:

8's   4's   2's   1's
 1   0   0   1

From this you can see that the binary number 1001 is equal to:

$(1 \times 8) + (0 \times 4) + (0 \times 2) + (1 \times 1)$

Which if you do the multiplications, gives

$8 + 0 + 0 + 1$

Which is a total of 9. So, the binary number 1001 is another way of writing 9 in base ten.

Changing Base Ten Numbers to Binary   Very small numbers can often be converted into binary by a combination of experience and trial and error (mathematicians call this "by inspection"). For longer numbers there is a formal method.

```
2 into 29 = 14 remainder 1
2 into 14 =  7 remainder 0
2 into  7 =  3 remainder 1
2 into  3 =  1 remainder 1
2 into  1 =  0 remainder 1
```

Fig A2.1   The steps involved in converting the number 29 in base ten to a number in binary

The method consists of repeatedly dividing the number by 2 and each time writing down the remainder, which is always either 0 or 1. Figure A2.1 shows all the steps involved in converting the number 29 into binary. By the last step, there is nothing left to divide into and you are left with a list of 1s and 0s which are the remainders, and these represent the required binary number. You must remember that the last digit in this list of remainders is the *leftmost* digit in the binary number. Figure A2.2 will help you to remember this. Drawing the arrows in this way will prevent the mistake of writing down the digits starting from the wrong end.

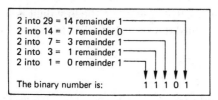

Fig A2.2   The arrows help you to remember the correct order for writing down the binary number

Hexadecimal Numbers

The hexadecimal system has 16 as its base.

A group of four digits in a binary number can be written using only a single digit in hexadecimal notation. Since the conversion of hexadecimal to binary (and vice versa) can be done simply (with a little practice it can be done in the head) the notation provides a compact way of representing long strings of 1s and 0s.

As an example of converting binary to hexadecimal, we shall take the binary number 1001001 (73 in base ten). Since this number only has seven digits, and since we shall need to split it into groups of four, we make it up to eight digits by adding a zero on the left to give 01001001 (we cannot add a zero on the right because that would make it a different number). Now split the number into groups of four digits:

0100   1001

Beginning with the first group, 0100, convert it to base ten and write down the answer:

    0100   is $(0\times8) + (1\times4) + (0\times2) + (0\times1) = 4$

So far you have this:

    0100   1001

      4

Now do exactly the same with the next group of four digits, 0011.

    1001   is $(1\times8) + (0\times4) + (0\times2) + (1\times1) = 9$.

Now you have

    0100   1001

      4   9

The number 49 is now in hexadecimal and is written 49_{16}. It is read as "hex four nine" and not as "forty nine."

Hexadecimal notation also uses the letters A to F of the alphabet. So, A is 10, B is 11, C is 12 and so on. The full set of hexadecimal "digits" is therefore:

    0, 1, 2, 3, 4, 5, 6, 7, 8, 9, A, B, C, D, E, F

The letters are used to avoid having to write down two-digit numbers such as 10, 11, 12, etc. For example, binary 1011 is equal to 11 in base ten and this group of four digits is therefore represented by B. The letter F represents 15, and you never need higher than this because the largest four digit binary number is 1111 (which is 15 in base ten).

You can now convert, say, binary 01101100 into hexadecimal. First of all, separate it into groups of four digits.

    0110   1100

The first group, 0110, is 6 and the second group, 1100, is 12 which is given the symbol C.

The binary number 01101100 is then hex 6C.

Converting Hex to Binary Converting hexadecimal to binary is quite simple. Take the number hex 83 for example. Change the 3 back to a four-digit binary number, and you get 0011. Change the 8 back to a four-digit binary number, and you get 1000. Put these two binary numbers together and you have

    hex 83   is   bin 10000011

Since you are only ever dealing with four binary digits at a time, the conversion can easily be done in the head.

Converting Hex to Base Ten Converting hexadecimal numbers to base ten is also straightforward. Since a hexadecimal number is a number in base sixteen, the method for changing hexadecimal back to base ten is therefore very similar to the method used for changing binary to base ten. The difference is that instead of the digits being worth ONE, TWO, FOUR, EIGHT, etc., they are worth ONE, SIXTEEN, TWO HUNDRED AND FIFTY SIX, and so on.

Take the number hex 83 for example. This is $(8\times16) + (3\times1)$ which is $128 + 3$ and this gives 131.

Boolean Algebra

Boolean algebra is an important subject in the study of computers and automation because it deals with the laws through which a digital computer can make decisions or perform arithmetic. These laws are expressed in terms of two conditions, TRUE and FALSE and they are useful to us because digital signals are also concerned with two conditions, ON and OFF. By replacing TRUE and FALSE by 1 and 0, the rules of Boolean algebra can also be applied to binary arithmetic.

For the purpose of illustrating the principles of Boolean algebra, we will look at an example of a decision which can be made by combining symbols representing only two items of information: to decide whether a creature is an octopus we have to ask whether the following two statements are TRUE or FALSE:

(a) It has eight legs

(b) It lives in the sea

Only if *both* these statements are true, can we conclude that it is an octopus.

In Boolean algebra, statements such as these are represented by letters of the alphabet (just as in ordinary algebra, numbers are represented by letters of the alphabet). We can use letters as follows:

A represents "it has eight legs".

B represents "it lives in the sea".

For the conclusion, we shall use the letter f, so f represents "it is an octopus". We now write

$$A.B = f$$

which is read: "if A is true AND B is true, then f is true." It may look like multiplication but it's not! The . sign is the Boolean symbol for AND (sometimes a $\times$ is used instead). Going back to the octopus, we need a symbol to say that "it is NOT true that it has eight legs" or "it is NOT true that it lives in the sea" and so on. This is done by writing a line above the letter, so for example, $\bar{A}$ means "A is not true" ($\bar{A}$ is read "A not"). Now, if we write in Boolean algebra

$$\bar{A}.B = \bar{f}$$

What we mean in words is

"It is *not* true that it has eight legs AND it is true that it lives in the sea; therefore, it is *not* an octopus"

There are of course other possibilities. Perhaps it has got eight legs but does not live in the sea (that would make it a spider), or maybe it does not have eight legs and does not live in the sea either (that would make it almost anything). You can write all of these possibilities using Boolean algebra as follows:

(i) $\quad \bar{A}.\bar{B} = \bar{f}$

(ii) $\quad \bar{A}.B = \bar{f}$

(iii) $\quad A.\bar{B} = \bar{f}$

(iv) $\quad A.B = f$

Check for yourself that all four make sense.

The four Boolean expressions that we have just written are, of course, not just limited to octopuses. They can be used to represent any logical decision in the form: something (f) is only true when two other things (A and B) are both true. The logical operation that we have performed is called the AND operation and we can summarize it by writing down all of the possibilities in a table, as shown in figure A2.3. Tables such as this are called **truth tables** and are very useful, especially for looking at complicated decisions.

A	B	f
False	False	False
False	True	False
True	False	False
True	True	True

Fig A2.3   Truth table for the Boolean AND

Not all decisions are like the one we have just looked at. Sometimes, the conclusion is true when one condition is true OR another is true. Think about this example:

"If it rains OR it snows, then I'll wear my hat".

We will use:

A to represent "it rains".

B to represent "it snows".

f to represent the conclusion "I will wear my hat".

To write down all of the possibilities in Boolean algebra we shall need a symbol to represent OR. The Boolean symbol for OR is the + sign. Be careful not to think of it as a "plus". Now we can write all the possibilities as follows:

(i) $\bar{A}+\bar{B} = \bar{f}$

(ii) $\bar{A}.B = f$

(iii) $A.\bar{B} = f$

(iv) $A.B = f$

The truth table for the OR operation is shown in figure A2.4. If you examine this table you will notice that there is an important difference between the Boolean

A	B	f
False	False	False
False	True	True
True	False	True
True	True	True

Fig A2.4   Truth table for the Boolean OR

OR and the way that the word "or" is used in everyday language. The Boolean OR *includes* the possibility that *both* A and B are true, whereas in everyday language we normally mean either A or B but not both. This type of Boolean operation is therefore called the INCLUSIVE-OR.

Unless specifically stated, it is usually assumed that an OR operation is the INCLUSIVE type. The alternative to this is the EXCLUSIVE-OR (abbreviated to XOR or EOR) which has its own special symbol $\oplus$ and is as follows:

(i) $\bar{A} \oplus \bar{B} = \bar{f}$

(ii) $\bar{A} \oplus B = f$

(iii) $A \oplus \bar{B} = f$

(iv) $A \oplus B = \bar{f}$

A	B	f
False	False	False
False	True	True
True	False	True
True	True	False

Fig A2.5   Truth table for the Boolean EXCLUSIVE-OR

The truth table is shown in figure A2.5. Note that here the possibility of both A and B being true is excluded.

To complete the set of Boolean operations, we have to add one more. There are a lot of logical decisions based simply on something NOT being true. For example, "if it does NOT rain, then it will be dry". If

> A represents "it rains"
>
> f represents the conclusion "it will be dry",

then all of the possibilities written in Boolean algebra are:

(i) $A = \bar{f}$

(ii) $\bar{A} = f$

That is, "if it does rain, then it will not be dry" and "if it does NOT rain, then it will be dry". Simple enough. The truth table is just as simple, and is shown in figure A2.6.

f	A
False	True
True	False

Fig A2.6   Truth table for the Boolean NOT

Another way of looking at this is to say that

> if A is TRUE, then $\bar{A}$ is FALSE
>
> and if A is FALSE, then $\bar{A}$ is TRUE.

Some Relationships in Boolean Algebra

Boolean algebra would not have become so important if all you could do with it was to write down simple decisions like those we have been looking at. The real power of Boolean algebra comes from the rules for combining ANDs, ORs and NOTs and simplifying the results.

Here is an interesting relationship to begin with. It says:

$$\overline{A.B} = \bar{A} + \bar{B}$$

This is a simple form of a theorem called De Morgan's Theorem. Another relationship, also part of De Morgan's theorem, says that:

$$\bar{A}.\bar{B} = \overline{A+B}$$

Boolean algebra need not be confined to decisions based on just two statements, A and B. It can be applied to three, four or any number. For example,

$$A.B.C = f$$

says that f is true only if A AND B AND C are true. The complete truth table, in figure A2.7, shows all of the possible combinations of A, B, C – there are eight of these. Notice that the conclusion is only true when all three, A, B, and C, are true.

A	B	C	A.B.C
F	F	F	F
F	F	T	F
F	T	F	F
F	T	T	F
T	F	F	F
T	F	T	F
T	T	F	F
T	T	T	T

Fig A2.7

A	B	C	A+B+C
F	F	F	F
F	F	T	T
F	T	F	T
F	T	T	T
T	F	F	T
T	F	T	T
T	T	F	T
T	T	T	T

Fig A2.8

The OR truth table for A, B, and C is shown in figure A2.8. Again, there are eight possible combinations of A, B and C and the conclusion is always true unless all A, B and C are false.

De Morgan's Theorem can also be extended to deal with more than two statements. For example, it is possible to show that

$$\overline{A.B.C} = \bar{A} + \bar{B} + \bar{C}$$

and that

$$\bar{A}.\bar{B}.\bar{C} = \overline{A + B + C}$$

Being able to change ANDs and ORs and vice versa enables engineers to design complicated electronic circuits which can perform arithmetic and make logical decisions. This is the reason that Boolean algebra has become so important since the introduction of computers.

Logic Gates

Logic gates are the electronic circuits which are able to implement the rules of Boolean algebra. Their circuitry is built onto silicon chips and they form the basis of both computer memories and microprocessors. There are three basic types of logic gate:

AND gates

OR gates (two forms, INCLUSIVE-OR and EXCLUSIVE-OR)

NOT gates

By combining the functions of these logic gates, two more types can be made:

NAND (NOT-AND) gates

NOR (NOT-OR) gates

All electronic logic circuits are constructed from combinations of these five logic gates. The NAND gate is of particular importance since it can be used for all the electronic circuits of the central processing unit of a digital computer.

In electrical circuit diagrams, logic gates are represented by symbols. Figure A2.9 shows the symbols for all of the logic gates mentioned above. These are the American symbols, used in all manufacturers' data sheets and many textbooks. Convention dictates that the power supply connections to the logic gate are not normally represented.

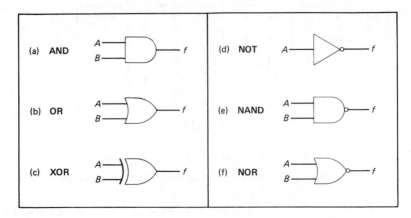

Fig A2.9   Logic gate symbols

The AND Gate   The AND gate shown in figure A2.9a has two inputs, labelled A and B, and an output labelled f. The conditions that determine whether or not a pulse shall appear at the output are as follows:

      If there is a pulse at A
    AND
      if there is a pulse at B
    THEN
      a pulse will appear at f

Any conditions other than this will result in no pulse being output at f.

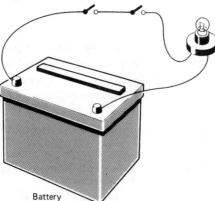

Battery

Fig A2.10   Operation of an AND gate

The operation of the AND gate can be likened to the simple electric circuit shown in figure A2.10 comprising a battery, a bulb and two switches. The bulb will only light when both switches are in the ON position.

It can be seen that the AND gate performs the Boolean AND operation

$$A.B = f$$

and we can summarise this in a truth table, using 1 to represent the presence of a pulse and 0 to represent the absence of a pulse, as shown in figure A2.11. Note

A	B	f
0	0	0
0	1	0
1	0	0
1	1	1

Fig A2.11   Truth table for AND gate

that the figures 0 and 1 used in the truth table are not being used in this instance as numbers but as *symbols*. They represent the ON and OFF conditions of the input and output signals.

The OR Gate   The symbols for the OR gate are shown in figure A2.9*b*, and figure A2.12 shows the truth table.

A	B	f
0	0	0
0	1	1
1	0	1
1	1	1

Fig A2.12   Truth table for OR gate

An output appears at *f* if one or other, or *both* the inputs are ON. This type of OR gate performs the Boolean INCLUSIVE-OR operation

$$A + B = f$$

and is called an INCLUSIVE-OR gate. Its operation can be likened to the electric circuit shown in figure A2.13 in which the lamp will light if one or both the switches are ON.

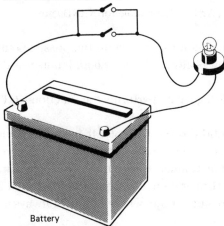

Battery

Fig A2.13   Operation of an OR gate

The EXCLUSIVE-OR (XOR or EOR) logic gate produces an output only when one input or the other but not *both* is ON. That is, it performs the Boolean EXCLUSIVE-OR operation

$$A \oplus B = \bar{f}$$

The symbols for the EXCLUSIVE OR gate are shown in figure A2.9*c* and the truth table is shown in figure A2.14.

A	B	A⊕B
0	0	0
0	1	1
1	0	1
1	1	0

Fig A2.14   Truth table for EXCLUSIVE-OR gate

The NOT Gate The NOT GATE, also called an **inverter**, performs the Boolean NOT operation

$$A = \bar{f}$$

changing 1 to 0 and 0 to 1. Normally it is shown attached either to the inputs or to the outputs of the other types of gate, as discussed below. When used alone

A	f
0	1
1	0

Fig A2.15   The inverter and its truth table

the symbol shown in figure A2.9d is combined with the triangular symbol for an amplifier as in figure A2.15. The truth table, shown next to it, is this time very simple.

The NAND Gate The NAND logic gate performs the function NOT AND:

$$A.B = \bar{f}$$

which is the opposite function to the AND gate. It is shown in diagrams by adding the NOT symbol to the output of the AND symbol as in figure A2.9e. The truth table, shown in figure A2.16, is easily derived from the AND gate truth

A	B	$f=\overline{A.B}$
0	0	1
0	1	1
1	0	1
1	1	0

Fig A2.16   Truth table for NAND gate

table by performing a NOT operation on each of the possible outputs f. The result is a gate whose output is always 1 unless *both* inputs are 1.

The NOR Gate The NOR logic gate performs the function NOT OR:

$$A + B = \bar{f}$$

which is the opposite function to the OR gate. It is shown in diagrams by adding the NOT symbol to the ouput of the OR symbol as in figure A2.9f. The truth table is easily derived in a similar way to the NAND gate truth table, but this time performing the NOT operation on the outputs f of the OR gate. This is shown in figure A2.17. The result is a gate whose output is always 0 unless *both* inputs are 0.

A	B	$f=\overline{A+B}$
0	0	1
0	1	0
1	0	0
1	1	0

Fig A2.17   Truth table for NOR gate

In explaining the different types of gate we have only looked at 2-input gates. In fact, all of the gates discussed can have two, three, or any number of inputs. The corresponding truth tables for multiple input gates are shown in the examples of figures A2.7 and A2.8.

New Gates for Old   It was pointed out at the beginning of this section that the NAND gate can be used to build all the logic circuits of the central processing unit of a computer. We will now show how this can be done.

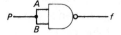   Fig A2.18   NAND gate connected to function as NOT gate

The NOT gate is easily made from a single NAND gate by connecting together the two inputs as shown in figure A2.18. Doing this ensures that both inputs, A and B, are *always* the same as the input P. Therefore, when P is 1, then f is 0 (since A and B are both 1). Similarly, when P is 0, the f is 1 (since A and B are both 0). Check this for yourself from the truth table.

Two NAND gates can be used to build an AND gate. This follows since a NAND gate is really a NOT AND gate – that is, an AND gate with a NOT on its output. The NOT can be cancelled out by simply connecting it to another NOT as shown in figure A2.19.

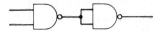   Fig A2.19   AND gate made from two NAND gates

The fact that an OR gate can also be made from NAND gates is a good opportunity to demonstrate the use of De Morgan's Theorem in Boolean algebra. Recall that

$$\overline{A + B} = \bar{A}.\bar{B} \tag{1}$$

If we perform a NOT operation on both sides of this equation (which we are allowed to do) we get

$$\overline{\overline{A + B}} = \overline{\bar{A}.\bar{B}} \tag{2}$$

Now, two NOTs cancel each other, so the left-hand side can be simply written $A+B$, that is

$$A + B = \overline{\bar{A}.\bar{B}} \tag{3}$$

The left-hand side of equation (3) is the OR function and the right-hand side tells us that we can obtain it by generating $\bar{A}$ and $\bar{B}$ and putting them through a NAND gate. This is shown in figure A2.20.

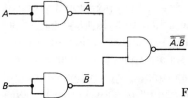

Fig A2.20   OR gate made from three NAND gates

Practical Uses of Logic Gates

1 As we have seen in Chapter 3, at the heart of a microprocessor is a unit called the ALU (the arithmetic-logical unit). This unit performs both the arithmetical operations and the logical (decision-making) operations of the microprocessor. It relies entirely on the use of logic gates.

Remembering that a computer works with binary numbers in which all the digits are either 0 or 1, we can see that the fundamental arithmetic operation of addition is easily accomplished using logic gates. The basic rules for addition of two binary digits are

   (i)   0 plus 0 = 0

   (ii) 0 plus 1 = 1

   (iii) 1 plus 0 = 1

   (iv) 1 plus 1 = 0 and carry 1

Compare this with the truth tables of the logic gates we have so far dealt with. It will be noticed that these rules are the results of the EXCLUSIVE-OR operation, with the important exception that some additional mechanism must be devised in order to produce a *carry*. This additional mechanism is in fact simply provided by an AND gate to detect when both inputs are 1. The resulting combination is shown in figure A2.21 and is called a **half-adder**. It is called half-adder (rather than a full adder) because although it is capable of generating a carry, it does not itself make use of a carry that may have been generated by a previous operation. A full adder can be built by connecting together two half-adders.

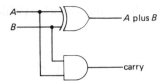

Fig A2.21   The half-adder

Computer arithmetic is not a subject we deal with in this book, except to say that *all* arithmetic operations can be carried out through the basic operation of addition: subtraction is the addition of negative numbers; multiplication is repeated addition (for example, 3 times 2 is in fact 2+2+2); and finally, division is repeated subtraction (6÷2 = 3, means that is 2 is repeatedly subtracted from 6, it can be done 3 times). A further point to note is that, in the decimal number system, shifting a row of digits one place to the *left* has the effect of multiplying by 10, and shifting one place to the *right* has the effect of dividing by 10. The equivalent operation on binary numbers produces multiplication or division by 2. *Shifting* is another operation that can be carried out by logic gates. It will be appreciated, then, that the logic gates discussed can in principle be configured to perform *any* mathematical operation. Even more complicated operations such as square roots and logarithms can be broken down into procedures (called algorithms) which involve only the repeated application of addition, subtraction, multiplication and division.

2 Apart from the ALU which deals with the arithmetic and logical decisions of the microprocessor, the other essential requirement is **memory** to store the binary digits which make up the program, the data and in fact all the information that the microprocessor deals with.

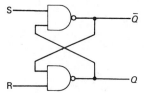 Fig A2.22   The S-R flip-flop

A circuit able to hold a 1 or 0 can be made by connecting together two NAND gates in the way shown in figure A2.22. The arrangement is called an **S-R** (Set-Reset) **bistable** or **flip-flop**, and forms the basic element of memory. The two NAND gates are connected so that the output of each gate is fed back to the input of the other gate. The effect of the circuit is to be able to set Q to 1 or to reset it to 0 by pulsing S or R. The action of the circuit is as follows.

Initially, with each of the inputs S and R set to 1, there are *two* equally likely possibilities for the value of Q:

either $Q=1$ (and $\bar{Q}=0$)

or $Q=0$ (and $\bar{Q}=1$)

(Check this for yourself by referring to the NAND gate truth table.) There is a fifty-fifty chance that it will take up either of these two output configurations – but whichever one it happens to be, it will remain in it as a stable condition.

Assume initially that $Q=1$ (and $\bar{Q}=0$). If the reset terminal R is *momentarily* put to 0, then this will result in Q changing to 1 and, this being fed to the other gate, will also result in $\bar{Q}$ changing to 0. Now, when R is restored to 1, the input to the lower gate in figure A.22 will be 1 AND 0, and so a new stable state will be established in which $Q=0$ (and $\bar{Q}=1$). Note that if this condition existed initially then a 0 applied to R would have had no effect.

By a similar argument, if initially $Q=0$, then a momentary 0 applied to S will change the state to $Q=1$. Likewise this would have no effect if $Q=1$ initially.

To summarize:

(*a*)   Applying a momentary 0 to S will result in $Q=1$ (with no change if this condition already exists).

(*b*)   Applying a momentary 0 to R will result in $Q=0$ (with no change if this condition already exists).

The flip-flop therefore behaves as a memory in which Q can be set to store a binary digit of either 1 or 0 by sending a momentary pulse of 0 to either S or R.

Note that S and R must not both be made 0 simultaneously as this would imply the impossible condition of $Q=1$ and $\bar{Q}=1$.

Appendix III

Robot Specification Sheets

In this appendix we will examine a number of extracts from robot specification sheets. For ease of comparison and discussion we will concentrate only on the information that is given in "block" form. By this we mean that many robot specifications are several pages long and contain a blocked summary, usually on the back page. If we were to read every word of the multipage document, look at all of the illustrations and discuss the robot with a salesperson, then we would get more information than just using the blocked data. However, if we are trying to narrow down the choice, we should be able to use these summaries to perform this first pass selection.

(1)   **Unimate PUMA 761/2 Series**   The block data for this robot is not very extensive. Straight-line velocity is given directly in units of m/sec and for a quick assessment this can be more useful than angular velocity. However, detailed information on the velocity of each axis (not included in this data) is still useful to have.

Physical dimensions of the equipment have been included in this data sheet and this is useful when planning a work cell layout.

Program capacity is given, but this is in kilobytes of memory. More useful would be an indication of the number of points that can be stored and whether several programs can be held in the memory.

UNIMATE®
PUMA™ 761/2 SERIES
SPECIFICATIONS

PERFORMANCE

Repeatability	± 0.2mm	
Load Capacity		
761 Series	10 kg	
762 Series	20 kg	
Straight Line Velocity	1m/sec	
Environmental Requirements	10-50°C	

PHYSICAL CHARACTERISTICS

Arm Weight		
761 Series	600 kg	
762 Series	590 kg	
Controller Size 1160 × 800 × 600		
Controller Weight	182 kg	
Controller Cable length	5 metres	

STANDARD SPECIFICATION

Configuration	6 Revolute Axis
Drive	Electric DC Servo
Controller	System Computer (LSI-II)
Teach Method	Teach Pendant and/or Visual Display Terminal
Program Language	VAL II
Program Capacity	(24K Cmos non-vol user)
External Program Storage	Double sided Double Density Disc Drive
External I/O	32 + 32 I/O AC or DC Selectable
End Effector Control	4 Way pneumatic solenoid
Power Requirement	240/380/415/440/480 3 PH 50/60 Hz 4500W peak
Standard Accessories	Visual Display Terminal Disc Drive Unit Teach Pendant. I/O module CX module
Options	Refer to Unimation for separate option list

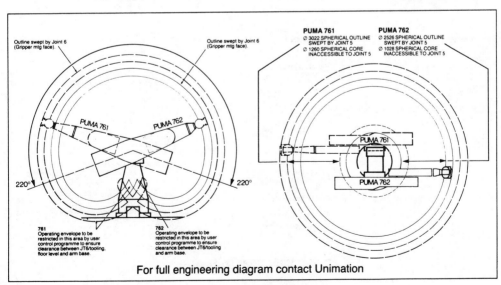

PUMA 761
Ø 3022 SPHERICAL OUTLINE SWEPT BY JOINT 5
Ø 1260 SPHERICAL CORE INACCESSIBLE TO JOINT 5

PUMA 762
Ø 2526 SPHERICAL OUTLINE SWEPT BY JOINT 5
Ø 1028 SPHERICAL CORE INACCESSIBLE TO JOINT 5

Outline swept by Joint 6 (Gripper mtg face).

761
Operating envelope to be restricted in this area by user control programme to ensure clearance between JT6/tooling, floor level and arm base.

762
Operating envelope to be restricted in this area by user control programme to ensure clearance between JT6/tooling and arm base.

For full engineering diagram contact Unimation

(2)   **Thorn EMI Team-Mate L3 Robot Arm**   This is a more detailed specification sheet and drawings of the work envelope are clear and easily understood. Details of speed and range are presented for each axis but a calculation would be needed in order to determine the maximum linear velocity of the end effector. Note that position repeatability appears to be better than for the PUMA. However, it would be wise to make more detailed enquiries as to how this figure is arrived at and under what circumstances it applies. Information on the memory capacity gives the number of points that can be held but, again, no mention of whether more than one program can be held. A particularly useful feature of this robot is the facility for co-ordinate transformations (see Chapter 5). This allows the programmer to enter co-ordinates in either cylindrical or X-Y-Z form.

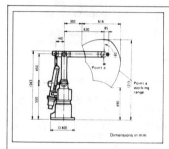

Dimensions in mm

Dimensions in mm

TEAM-MATE™ L3 Robot Arm

Number of axes:
5 standard revolute axes, plus optional linear axis – all electric DC servo motors

Motion range and maximum speed:
S-axis 240°,   120°/sec
L-axis 80°,   110°/sec
U-axis 60°,   110°/sec
T-axis 360°,   225°/sec
B-axis 180°,   150°/sec
C-axis 800mm, 440mm/sec (optional axis)

Mounting:
Floor mounted or wall mounted (motion range on S-axis is 90° for wall mounted option).

Position repeatability:
±0.1mm

Handling payload:
3Kg including gripper or tooling

Weight:
93Kg including base plate

Finish colour:
Blue BS 18E51

TEAM-MATE™ Control Unit

(a) Physical Features

Construction:
Totally enclosed cabinet with indirect air cooling system.

Ambient temperature:
0° to 45°C max, no condensation

External dimensions:
700(W) × 1140(H) × 580(D)mm

Power supply:
AC415Vm 3-phase, 50Hz, 2kVA (max)

Control panel:
Integral panel or optional separate mounting panel up to 24m from main unit.

Teach pendant cable:
8m standard, up to 12m optional.

Weight:
200Kg

Colour:
Blue

(b) Control Features

Axis control:
Simultaneous, incremental digital positioning control on 5 axes using high reliability pulse-width-modulation servo drive units.

Memory capacity:
32K bytes RAM (with battery back-up) equivalent to 2200 points plus 1200 instructions, with optional memory equivalent to 5000 points plus 2500 instructions.

Input/Output:
48 input ports, 24 output ports, plus additional dedicated ports.

Panel display:
VDU with 228mm (9 inch) green CRT display, full alphanumeric set on 32 characters × 16 lines. Continuous display of PROGRAM, JOB, STEP and INSTRUCTION numbers plus a menu of requested displays including:
  Alarm code and description
  Error code and description
  Self-diagnostic messages
  Parameter settings
  Position data
  Current and command position in cartesian or machine co-ordinates.

Bulk memory:
External auxiliary memory interface for cassette data storage.

Programming method:
Direct entry via control panel keyboard or by using teach pendant.

Computer Interface:
RS232C or RS422 (choice of either)

Speed control:
During teaching it is possible to inch the gripper forward to bring it to the required position safely and accurately. The operating speed may be set in one of two ways: either by absolute speed, in 1mm/sec units; or by travel time between points, in 0.01 sec units.

Acceleration/deceleration control:
Velocity ramp control is automatic.

Program editing:
Full facilities are available to insert, delete or correct points in existing programs. The random search facility makes editing very quick and easy.

Continuous path motion:
Linear and circular interpolation provides continuous path control on 5 axes in 3-dimensional space.

Tool point control:
The tool point may be held stationary and the wrist axes moved to provide the correct angle of approach for the gripper.

Co-ordinate transformation:
For ease of teaching, the programmer may switch between cartesian co-ordinate and cylindrical co-ordinate systems.

Dry run:
A number of features assist dry run operation, for example reduced speed for safety checking, step back and step forward for trajectory checking, and machine lock to check signals to and from ancillary equipment with the robot stationary.

Transformations:
Transformations for mirror imaging, scaling and 3-dimensional workpiece shifting.

(c) Safety Features

Monitoring and self-diagnosis functions:
Motor terminal voltage
Pulse generator faults
Servo motor overload
Power fuse
Control cabinet temperature
Control unit faults
Battery voltage
Power leak detection
Door interlock switch

Other safety measures:
Emergency stop buttons on control panel and teach pendant.
'Teach-lock' mode
Software limitation on teaching speed
Shielded start button
Software limits to prevent overtravel in addition to hard-wired limit switches
'POWER ON' lamp on robot arm
Exclusive cabinet door key

■ **THORN EMI Robotics**

Knighton Heath Estate, Ringwood Road, Bournemouth BH11 8NE
Telephone: 0202 570811   Telex 417261

(3) **IBM 7545 Manipulator** This is a SCARA type robot and used a great deal for the assembly of electronic printed circuit boards. For this work, high repeatability is essential and this robot has a repeatability 4 times better than the PUMA.

A great deal of information is given on the speed of each axis. This is done because the robot can run with different maximum speeds selected by the operator using either hardware or software.

[*Note*: a new model, the IBM 7546, has been introduced to replace the 7545, and this has considerably improved specification.]

Note that physical dimensions do not appear in the specification.

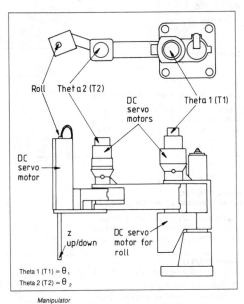

Manipulator

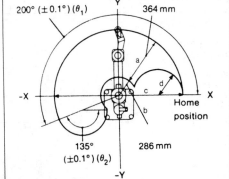

Work space

IBM 7545 Manipulator Specifications

Degrees of freedom	4
Maximum payload	10 kg (22 lb) (includes end-of-arm tooling)
Repeatability based on a constant temperature, load and speed	± 0.05 mm (± 0.002 in.)
Weight	107 kg (237 lb)
Operating Conditions Temperature	10° C to 40.5° C (50° F to 105° F)
Humidity (see repeatability specification)	8% to 80%

T1 Axis	Swivel movement	
Range	0° − 200° ± 1°	
Switch setting	Maximum tool tip speed for axis per setting	Maximum load
Low	700 mm/sec (28 in./sec)	10 kg (22 lb)
Medium	1100 mm/sec (43 in./sec)	6 kg (13.2 lb)
High	1450 mm/sec (57 in./sec)	1 kg (2.2 lb)

T2 Axis	Swivel movement	
Range	0° − 135° ± 0.10°	
Switch setting	Maximum tool tip speed for axis per setting	Maximum load
Low	530 mm/sec (21 in./sec)	10 kg (22 lb)
Medium	850 mm/sec (33 in./sec)	6 kg (13.2 lb)
High	1050 mm/sec (41 in./sec)	1 kg (2.2 lb)

Z-Axis (up/down)	Maximum tool tip speed for axis per setting	Maximum load
Range	250 mm ± 1.0 mm (9.8 in.)	
Low	140 mm/sec (5.5 in./sec)	10 kg (22 lb)
Medium	220 mm/sec (8.6 in./sec)	6 kg (13.2 lb)
High	280 mm/sec (11.0 in./sec)	1 kg (2.2 lb)

Roll Axis (rotation)	
Range	± 180° (± 0.5°)
Maximum load centred	10 kg (22 lb)
Speed:	
Low	240°/sec
Medium	370°/sec
High	480°/sec
Rotating torque	70 kg − cm

IBM 7545 Controller Specifications

Positioning control system		Point-to-point
Storage System		Battery backed-up integrated circuits
Storage retention time with power off		Up to 80 days
memory capacity		24 Kbytes maximum
Number of programs stored		Up to 5
Number of controlled axes	4	(4 servoed)
Point teaching method		separate programming unit
External input signals (DI)		16 Expandable to 64
External output signals (DO)		16 Expandable to 64
7545 Controller Electrical Power		220 Vac ± 10% 50 ± ± 3.0 Hz, 0.75 kVA, 3.4 AMP
Operating conditions	Temperature	10° C to 40.5° C (50° F to 105° F)
	Humidity	8% to 80%
Weight		182 kg (400 lb)
Communications		RS 422 RS 232

Note: Specification is subject to change.

Index

Absolute shaft encoder 245
Actuator 74
Accuracy 162
Address 40
Address bus 41, 54
Address bus, external 45
Advanced computers 62
ALU see Arithmetic logical unit
AND, Boolean 252
   logic gate 256
   truth table 253
Anthropomorphic geometry 66, 69, 161
Architecture 41, 47
Arithmetic logical unit 41, 260
ASEA robot 72
Assembler 51
Assembly language 51
Availability 175
Axes of motion 65, 160
Axis conversion 98

Backlash 96, 103, 229
Bang-bang control 13
Batch production 216
Bath tub curve 177
BCD 44
Beaded cable 102
Belt drive 101
Bevel gear 98
Bimetallic strip 128
Bin-picking 139
Binary code 246
Binary numbers 249
Binary code 29, 31, 246
Binary image 141
Bistable 261
Bit 29, 40
Bit mapped 186
Boolean algebra 29, 252
Boundary tracking 145
Buses 41, 54

Byte 29, 40

CAD 25, 179, 226, 233
CAE 194
CAM 233
Capital 216
Car industry 225
Cash flow 219
Carry flag 44
Cartesian geometry 66, 69, 161
Camera 140
CCD 140
Central processing unit 47
CESAR 241
Chain drive 103
Charge coupled device 140
CIM 194
Circular spline 99
Clock 28, 45
Closed loop control 7
CNC machine 195
COM 189
Commissioning 168
Communications 242
Commutator 86
Compiler 53
Computer aided design see CAD
Computer hierarchy 202
Computer, coordination of 55
Computer, supervisory 207
Condition code register 43
Configuration, 65ff, 159
Connectivity analysis 145
Continuous path control 17, 21, 105,
   163
Contouring 24
Control, of machines 204
Control 7, 239
Control bus 41, 55
Control unit (microprocessor) 41
Control system 163
Controlled system 8
Controller 8
Coordinates, robot 74
Coordinate transformation 74

Cosmetic industry 225
Cost comparison 223
Cost, set-up 211
CP see Continuous path control
CPU 47
Critical gain 17
Crown wheel 98
Cursor control 184
Curve adaptivity 23
Curve fitting 192
Custom production 216
Customised chip 37
Cycle time 151
Cylindrical geometry 66, 70, 161

DAC see Digital-to-analog
   convertor
Data bus 41, 45, 54
Data bus, external 45
Data bus, internal 46
Data direction register 59
Data input 184
Data logging 196
Data output 186
DCF 227
Degrees of freedom 65, 160
Design considerations 180
De Morgans theorem 259
Derivative control 15
Design process 179ff
Design, traditional 182
Detection (vision) 137
Differential amplifier 10
Digital circuit 29
Digital-to-analog convertor 11, 31
Digital signal 27ff
Digitization 141
Digitizer pad 184
Discounted cash flow 227
Discrimination 148
Display software 192
Double acting cylinder 77
Draughting 183
Drive system 162
Drive through 163

Economics 215ff
Economies of scale 217
Electric motors 82ff
   bell 88
   compound-wound 90
   DC 86
   disc 88
   permanent magnet 89
   series-wound 89
   stepper 91
   universal 89
End effector 104ff
Error 7
Exclusive-OR 253
External sensors 122

Failure 177
Feedback elements 8
FEM 190
Field of vision 140
File handling 195
Finite element method 190
Flag register 43
Flexible automation 209
Flexible manufacturing system see
   FMS
Flexspline 99
Flip-flop 261
FMS 208ff, 226
FMS, applications 214
Frequency response, sensor 124
Functional layout 149

General-purpose registers 44
Geometry, robot 65ff
Geometry transformation 52
Gears 92ff
   bevel 98
   crown wheel 98
   helical 97
   reduction 95
   skew 98
   spur 97
Gear ratio 94
Goal-seeking 239

Graphics, computer 184
Graphics tablet 184
Gray code 246
Grey scale 143
Grippers 104ff
Grippers, compressed air 113
   dexterity 234
   dual 108
   magnetic 114
   pads 106
   suction 110
Group technology 150

Half adder 260
Half-carry flag 44
Handshaking 60
Hard automation 209
Hard copy 187
Hardware stop 18
Hardwired 25
Hardwired logic 37
Harmonic drive 99
HERMIES-1 241
Hexadecimal 250
Hidden line removal 192
Hierarchy, computer 202, 210
   of automation 9
High-level language 50
Hydraulic actuator 74ff
Hydraulic accumulator 79
Hydraulic systems, advantages 80
Hydraulic transfer valve 77
Hysteresis 17

IBM-7545 robot 265
IC see Integrated circuit
Inclusive-OR 253
Incremental encoder 245
Identification (vision) 137
Inertia 17
Injury 169
Input/output management 56
Input/output ports 56ff
Input/output register 59
Installation, robot 168

Intangible benefits 224
Integral control 14
Integrated circuit 33
   advantages 33
   applications 36
   cost 35
   reliability 35
   size 34
   speed 36
Interface 40
Interface, programmable 58
Interpolation 164
Interpreter 53
Interrupt 60
I/O see Input/output
Isolated I/O addressing 56

Joystick 184

Kondratieff 2

Labour 215
Labour savings 222
Ladder logic 50
Latch 58
LDR 126
Lead-through 21, 163
Lifo 45
Light-dependent resistor 126
Light pen 184
Linear programming 199
Linear sensor 127
Linear variable differential
   transformer (LVDT) 248
Linearity, sensor 123
Logic circuit 29, 255
Logic gates 37, 255ff
   combination of 259
Logical view of microprocessor 39
Loop, control 8
Low-level language 50
LSI 34
LVDT 248

Machine code 50

Machine interface 52
Machine control 201
Machine control
Machine Tools Trades Association 221
Macro 183
Magnetic grippers 114
Maintenance 171
Maintenance 176ff
Mainframe computer 47ff
Manual processing 209
MAP 242
Maskable interrupt 60
Mass production 216
Materials, in production mix 216
Mean time to failure (MTTF) 171
Mean time to repair (MTTR) 175
Memory 261
Memory 40
Memory-mapped I/O addressing 56
Microcomputer 39, 47
Microfilm 189
Microprocessor 39ff
Microprocessor, architecture 41
Microprogram 43
Minicomputer 47ff
Modelling 183
Modelling software 190
MSI 34
MTTA 221
MTTF 171
MTTR 175
Multiplexing 46

NAND gate 258
NC machine 25, 195
Negative flag 44
Noise 32
Non-maskable interrupt 60
Non-servo controlled robot 18
NOR gate 258
NOT, Boolean 252
   logic gate 259
Numerically controlled machine 25, 195

Object code 53

Off-line programming 25
On-line software 234
On-off control 13
Opcode 42
Open loop control 7, 8
Optical shaft encoder 12, 245
Optimal response 16
OR, Boolean 252
   logic gate 257
   truth table 253, 257
Orientation (vision) 137
Oscillatory response 16
Overflow flag 44
Overshoot 16

Parallel processing 63
Parallel system, failure in 174
Parallel transmission 28
Pascal's law 74
Pay-back appraisal 221
Payload 167
PC 43
PCD 93
PD 15
PDI 15
Peripheral 48
Persistence 186
Perspective 193
Photodiode 127
Phototransistor 127
Physical view 39, 45
PI 15
PIA 58
Piezoresistive sensor 130
PIO 58
Pitch circle diameter 93
Pixel 141
PLC see Programmable logic
   controller
Plotters 187
Pnuematic actuator 80, 237
Pnuematic systems, advantages 80
Pneumatic sensor 131
Point adaptivity 23

Point-to-point control 17, 21, 104, 163
Polar geometry 66, 70, 161
Port 41
Portability 25
POP 45
Position servo 10
Power 82
Price 167
Prismatic joint 67, 160
Product-related data 194
Production control 198
Production costs 200
Production mix 215
Profit concept of firms 219
Program, computer 42
Program counter 43
Program status register 43
Programmability 233
Programmable I/O port 58
Programmmable interface 58
Programmable logic controller 20, 49ff
Programmed end effector change 120, 235
Programming, robot 163
Project management 168
PROM 50
Proportional control 14
Prototype 181
PTP see Point-to-point control
PUMA robot 159, 263
PUSH 45

Quality 178, 200, 223

Rack and pinion 98
RAM 40
Random access memory 40
Raster display 186
Rate control 15
Recognition (vision) 137
Recognition time 139
Reference input 8
Register 42
Refresh display 186
Relative stability 17
Reliability and maintenance 171

Repeatability 162
Research areas 230
Resolution 136, 143
Revolute joint 66, 160
Robot, choosing 151, 155
Robot geometry 65ff
Robot, specifying 158
Robot vision see Vision
ROM 40
R/W line 55

SAA 238
Safety 169
SBA 238
SCA 238
SCAMP 212
SCARA geometry 66, 70, 161, 229
Scheduling 199
Semi-custom chip 37
Sensors 121ff, 238
    acoustic 131
    binary 130
    gas 133
    heat 128
    matrix 130
    optical 126
    piezoresistive 130
    pneumatic, 131
    point contact 130
    proximity 134
    sensitivity 124
    tactile 129
Sensor interface 52
Sequential processing 63
Serial I/O port 56
Serial system, failure in 174
Serial transmission 28
Servo amplifier 10
Servo-controlled robot 20
Servomechanism 10
Set-up costs 211
Shading 193
Shaft encoder 12, 245
Sign flag 44
Signal 27

Simulation 183
Size and weight 236
Skew gear 98
SLSI 34
Software, on-line 234
Software stop 20
Source code 53
Specifications, robot 262
Speed 84
Spool valve 77
Spring return piston 76
Spur gear 97
SR flip-flop 261
SSI 34
Stack 45
Stack pointer 44
Stability 16
Steady state error 14
Steady state response 15
Step-by-step environment 239
Step change 15
Storage display 186
Suction grippers 110
Summing point 8
Supervisory computer 207
System boundary 9
System start-up 170

Tachogenerator 11
Tachometer 11
Talon V robot 71
Task analysis 151ff
Teach arm 165
Teach-pendant 21, 166
Team-Mate L3 robot 264
Template matching 146
Thermistor 129
Thermocouple 129
Three-bus system 54
Three-dimensional display 192
Throughput 224
Throughput time 151
Timer 61
Tools (end effector) 104, 116ff
   welding 116

paintspraying 118
Toothed belt 102
Torque 83
Torque conversion 96
Tracker ball 184
Training and preparation 168
Transducer 125
Transformation, coordinate 15, 74
Transient response 15
Transputer 64
Truth table 253

UART 57
Unstable response 16

Vacuum grippers 110
Variable transformer 13
VDU 186
Vector display 186
Velocity, arm 167
Velocity control 24
Venturi 110
VIA 58
Vision 135ff, 230
VLSI 34
Von Neumann architecture 47

Walk-through 21, 163
Wave generator 99
Weight 236
Window (vision) 140
Wire-frame drawing 192
Word length 42, 48
Work cell 149
Work envelope 70
Worm-wheel gear 98
Wrist 68
WRITE 55

Zero flag 44